A PETITE PALLACE OF
PETTIE HIS PLEASURE

A PETITE PALLACE OF
PETTIE HIS PLEASURE

Edited by

HERBERT HARTMAN

OXFORD UNIVERSITY PRESS

LONDON NEW YORK TORONTO

1938

Printed in the United States of America

TO
K.H.B.

Preface

THE *need for a new edition of Pettie's* PETITE PALLACE
OF PLEASURE *requires but little explanation. In first re-
printing this 'direct precursor of Lyly's Euphuism' Gollancz furnished, in* 1908, *a version which was patently
'modernized, but not aggressively so,' along with a scanty
Preface and variant readings which, we know today, took
no cognizance of two of the six extant texts. Moreover, during the last quarter century, while its resources were being
extended Tudor scholarship has become more exacting. In
several notable studies the texture and origins of euphuism
have been re-examined, the 'identification' of proverbs has
become increasingly easy, and the equipment and methods
of bibliography have been far advanced. It is with a view to
supplying these benefits and providing a faithful text that
the* PETITE PALLACE *in all its 'comely colours' is newly set
forth.*

*In preparing the edition I have had far more than my due
of courtesies. The text is reproduced from the perfect former Britwell copy, generously made available by its present owner, Mr. Carl H. Pforzheimer; the unique copy of
the second issue was, in the same spirit, made accessible for
collation by Dr. A.S.W. Rosenbach. In certain vexing bibliographical matters Dr.R.B.McKerrow and Mr.F.S.Fer-
guson gave expert counsel. From numerous errors of igno-
rance, judgement, and taste I have been saved by the sugges-
tions, emendations, and revisions of Professors John M.
Berdan, Douglas Bush, Stanley P. Chase, Albert Feuillerat, and Morris P. Tilley, all of whom were gracious*

*enough to read the manuscript. Mr. William A. Jackson,
who first suggested the edition, supplied most of the
bibliographical data. Generous grants from the American
Council of Learned Societies, for which I am duly grateful,
made the undertaking possible. Finally, but for the pains-
taking services of my niece and certain other gentle gentlewomen readers, errors of transcription and reference might
have been numerous. After such various kindnesses, of
course, it is I alone who—like the printer Watkins—must
crave pardon of all friendly readers 'for the oversightes
whatsoever herein committeed.'*

H.H.

Bowdoin College

Introduction

It was Anthony à Wood, Pettie's own grand-nephew, who first consigned *A Petite Pallace of Pettie his Pleasure* to its particular limbo. Noting, with some condescension, that its author 'became excellent for his passionate penning of amorous Stories' in a 'neat style,' the Oxford antiquary concludes, of his copy of the book,[1] that 'for the respect I bear to the name of the Author (he having been Uncle to my Mother *Maria la Petite*) I will keep it; but 'tis so far now from being excellent or fine, that it is more fit to be read by a Schoolboy, or rustical amoratto, than by a Gent. of mode or language.'

Autres temps, autres moeurs. Wood can scarcely be expected to have foreseen the time when, for several good reasons, scholars would exhume the *Petite Pallace.* For the book is a valuable index to certain once-fashionable mid-Elizabethan tastes, and its blend of ingenuous matter with a rococo manner has for the modern reader a quaintness all its own. Moreover, it has an indisputable place, not merely among *curiosa,* in the evolution of English prose. 'No one reading the *Petite Pleasure,*' wrote a student of Lyly thirty years ago,[2] 'can doubt that Pettie was the real creator of euphuism in its fullest development, and that Lyly was only an imitator.' Pet-

---

1 Now in the Bodleian (Wood C.33), 1608 ed. It has but one short passage scored and a few rhymes and word-plays underlined—possibly by other owners, a John Crofts and a Phillidelpha Cary.

2 John Dover Wilson, *John Lyly* (1905). A more cautious estimate of Pettie's historical position is to be found in Professor Wilson's later remark, that in Pettie 'we find a complete euphuist before *Euphues.*'

tie's claims as inventor or innovator may easily be over-
stated, but the facts remain unchallenged: that his book
antedates *Euphues* by several years; that at least six editions by 1613 attest its popularity; and that if he did not
actually play the sedulous ape, Lyly found the *Petite
Pallace* a 'schematic' prose pattern, encrusted with proverbs to be had for the pilfering.

By its popularity *Euphues* was to give its name—perhaps misleadingly—to the courtly fashion of mannered
writing which Pettie earlier exhibits in its full development. But neither Pettie nor Lyly, nor lesser euphuists
earlier than they, may be charged with the invention or
creation of the vogue. The specific mannerisms which in
sum comprise euphuism were present in subordinate
functions in many classical and medieval prototypes. It
was deliberate overemphasis upon them that induced the
fashionable, pseudo-aristocratic style. Yet euphuism in
its time was as inevitable as the exploits of Hawkins and
Drake. English prose was struggling for self-expression;
it required exercises and adventures in the sound and arrangement of words to shape the new instrument. The
results were laboured, baroque, and puerile. But without
such extravagances in its making, the medium of the
Authorized Version could not have been achieved.

Wood's biographical sketch of George Pettie may be supplemented with but a few details.[1] His grandfather, John
le Petite (*vel* Pety, *vel* Pettie), came of old Oxfordshire
stock, and married Alice 'sister to John Sparhauke,
Gent.' of Tetsworth parish. Pettie's father was the elder

---

1 Supplied from *Harleian Soc.Pub.*,V (1871),215;Rev.F.G.Lee, *History &c. of
the Prebendal Church of the Blessed Virgin Mary of Thame* (1883),216–18;
Andrew Clark, *Life and Times of Anthony Wood* (1891),i.32–6; *Miscellanea
Gen. et Her.*, 4th Series, V (1914),198; Harleian MS.1095,2b; Ibid.,1557,
fols.25b–26; Queen's Coll. MSS.,No.CXXIX,33.

of their two sons, John, to whom arms were granted by
Clarentius Cook.[1] Pettie's mother was Mary Charnell,
of Snareston, Leicestershire, who bore six children. The
eldest, John Pettie, of Stoke Talmach, who married
Elizabeth Snapp, of Fawler, Oxfordshire, died in 1589.[2]
The second son, Christopher (who was to become the
executor and chief beneficiary of George Pettie's will)
married a Lamborne, of Lambourne, Berkshire. A third
son, Robert, settled at Wiveold, near Reading. George
Pettie, born c.1548, was the fourth son. Of the fifth and
youngest son, Henry, nothing is known. A younger
sister, Frances, was twice married: to John Ray, of
Hagbourne, Oxfordshire; then to Leonard Lydcott, of
Checkendon, whose mother was a daughter of Sir Robert
Cheney, of Chesham Bois, Bucks. (Anthony à Wood's
mother—by Thomas Wood's second marriage, in 1621
—was Mary Pettie, or Maria la Petite, the daughter of
George's next oldest brother, Robert, who removed to
Wiveold. Her brother Charnel, George's nephew, was,
according to Wood, 'an old puritan, and an honest
and quiet man,' who became high sheriff of Oxfordshire,
with estates at Tetsworth and elsewhere (d.1660). Another brother, likewise George's nephew, was Maximil-
ian, whose daughter Elizabeth married Willam Burt,
later master of the Thame free-school.)

Thus George Pettie was the fourth son and child of 'a
gentile and ancient family' of Oxfordshire, whose members through several generations 'intermarried with
members of many of the most ancient houses in this part

1 Quarterly or and azure over all; on a bend vert, three martlets of the first.
   Crest: out of a ducal coronet or, an elephant's head argent, armed and eared
   gules.—Stowe MS.692, fol.78; *Ency.Her.*, ed. Berry; Lee's *Thame*, op.cit.,
   215–16.
2 Add.MS.32,490 EE,41 has a rubbing of the sepulchral brass at Stoke Tal-
   mage, with the Pettie-Snapp arms.

[Tetsworth and Stoke Talmage]'—market towns of small parishes within a dozen miles of the university.

Of Pettie's childhood nothing is recorded. He became in 1564 a scholar at Christ Church, where, along with a Richard Vere and Richard Rowlaund, he had for tutor Canon Thomas Barnard, former chaplain to Archbishop Cranmer, then Vicar of Pyrton. At Oxford, Wood testifies, Pettie formed a close friendship—although they were graduated seven years apart[1]—with William Gager, the Latin dramatist (remembered now for having publicly defended the thesis, in 1608, that it was lawful for husbands to beat their wives).

In the years following Oxford, Pettie 'travelled beyond the seas' as a soldier, his services carrying him to France,[2] 'Flaunders, Holland, Zeland, and most of the lowe countries.' Whatever the precise nature of his exploits—and we may judge from his contempt for the types that he was no 'fresh-water soldier' or 'carpet knight'—he had at twenty-eight a reputation for extemporaneous discourses whose 'wittie & pithie pleasantnes' beguiled 'his owne and certaine of his friends private occasions.' So that in 1576 a certain 'R.B.,' transgressing the bounds of friendship (unless, as is conceivable, he acted with Pettie's connivance), caused to be published for 'gentle Gentlewomen readers' those same youthful discourses as *A petite Pallace of Pettie his pleasure*, a title devised by 'R.B.,' who acknowledged his debt to Painter. Within the next five years Pettie, seemingly

---

1 Pettie, that is, received his B.A. on 29 March 1569/70; Gager entered Oxford in 1574. Wood is the sole authority for their relationship, speaking of Pettie's 'amorous Stories equal for poetical invention with his dear Friend *Will. Gager.*' In Gager's extant verses and epigrams (Add. MS. 22,583) Pettie, however, is nowhere mentioned.

2 In his *Guazzo* he remarks 'as with blushyng I have often behelde in Paris.'—*Civ. Con.*, ed. Sullivan, i. 10.

against his wishes, had 'already wonne such fame, as he which fyred the Temple of Dianae.'[1] And by 1613 the *Petite Pallace* was to reach its sixth—possibly its seventh —edition.

Meanwhile, in 1581 was issued Pettie's translation (principally through Chappuy's version, supplemented by Belleforest's) of Guazzo's *Civile Conversation*, Books I–III.[2] 'I thought,' wrote Pettie in his preface, after branding his *Petite Pallace* as a light, trifling work, 'it stoode mee uppon, to purchase to my selfe some better fame by some better woorke, and to countervayle my former Vanitie, with some formal gravitie.'

In the stories of the *Petite Pallace*, Pettie confessed, the author's own friends were 'darkely figured forth.' Is there, in the dedication of the *Civile Conversation* to Lady Norris, a possible clue to the type of society in which Pettie moved, at whose repasts his euphuistic tales, full of wise saws and modern instances, were welcome? Marjorie Williams, daughter of Baron Williams of Thame, Lord President of Wales, had married (?1545) Henry Norris, late sheriff of Oxfordshire and Berkshire. A gentleman of note, he entertained Queen Elizabeth (who called the handsome dark Marjorie her 'black

1 Ibid.,i.7. Greene's familiarity with the tales and proverbs is as demonstrable as Lyly's. Koeppel first revealed the allusions to Pettie's characters in the former's early euphuistic romances (*Studien zur Geschichte der italienischen Novelle*, 27 n.1). And a host of the proverbs, as indicated in the Notes, reappear in Greene, where they may readily be traced through Grosart's index.

Admetus and Alcest, Tereus and Progne, Scilla and Minos, appear as *exempla* in the *Carde of Fancie*; Amphiaraus, Eriphile, and Infortunio, in the *Tritameron of Love*; others in *Mamillia, Follie and Love*, etc. (cf. Grosart ed.,ii.34;iii.69,70,73;iv.39,147,219;ix.27).

2 The 2nd ed. (1586) included Bartholomew Young's translation of Book IV, at which Pettie had balked 'for that it contayneth muche triflyng matter in it.' (Wood's copy, in the Bodleian, has many notations and scorings, but in another's hand.)

crow'), was appointed her Ambassador to France 1566–70, and in 1572 was created Baron Norris of Ryecote, near Thame—the estate and manor-house which he had come into in 1559. All six of the Norris sons became in their time distinguished soldiers,[1] learned and 'worthy Captaines' of the very sort Pettie manifestly revered and emulated. His dedication, moreover, is no mere suit for patronage:

. . . much more must it make me duetifully affectioned to your Ladiship, who am neither stranger to you, nor unacquainted with your noble and vertuous disposition . . . neither can my pen possibly procure more honour to your name, then it hath alredie gotten, partly by your owne doinges . . . humbly requesting you to accept in good part this small proofe of my good will, and to assure your selfe of my redinesse to doe you service in greater matters when it shall please you to imploy mee.

In the Norris household had Pettie the occasional role of a neighbourly dinner-guest and welcome *raconteur*?[2] The tales of his *Petite Pallace* were designed not as stories for publication but as discourses for private pleasure, 'for that divers discourses touch neerely divers of my nere freindes . . . only they whom they touch, can understand whom they touch.'

All that is known of Pettie's subsequent career can be quickly told. He had become 'a Captain and a Man of note' by the time of his death, at forty-one, late in July 1589, at Plymouth. 'He was buried,' Wood concludes, 'as I have been told, in the great Church there [St. An-

---

1 Especially Edward (d.1603), lieutenant to Sidney in Holland, later governor of Ostend; John (d.1597), a captain under Essex in Ireland, then president of Munster; and Thomas (d.1599), also a captain of horse in Ireland, and John's successor at Munster. Edward and John, like Pettie himself, had seen service in the Low Countries.
2 Cf. 'as you h[e]ard at dinner . . . '—p.257.

drews].'[1] His will, preserved at Somerset House (78 Leicester) reads:

In the name of god amen. I George Pettie of Tetsworthe in the Countie of Oxford Captayne beinge wholl in mynde but sick in bodye make this my last will and testament: first I bequeathe my sowle into the handes of god and my bodye to be buried wheare I shall dye. Towchinge my worldly goodes I giue to my brother Christopher Pettie all that my free land in Kingeston and Aston Rowant to him and to his heiers for euer as I think that must by law fall to him by vertue of survivor. Then I giue to my neece Marie Pettie a bond of twoo hundrethe poundes whiche will growe to me from Mr Doyle of Cheslington. Then I giue to my coozen Edmund Pettie fortie poundes. And of this my last will I make my brother Christopher Pettie only and sole executor disannulinge and renouncinge all former wills whatsoeuer. In witnes whearof I haue sett my hand seale herevnto at Plymouthe the twentithe of Julye a thousand fiue hundrethe eightie nyne. George Pettie in the presence of thes vndernamed Henry Docwraye, William Heues, William Styleman.

(Proved at London before William Drury 25 October 1589 by Christopher Pettie.)

The bibliographical account of the *Petite Pallace* is in many respects as puzzling and obscure as Pettie's own career. From his lodging in Holborn on 12 July 1576 Pettie sent the manuscript of his twelve 'Tragicall trifles' to one 'R.B.,' who, after hearing them sundry times in sundry companies, had earnestly importuned the author for written copies. By 6 August the book entitled *A petite Pallace of Pettie his pleasure* was licensed to Richard Watkins; and, presumably within the same

---

1 The parish register, however, has no entry of the burial of George Pettie for July 1589, nor for any other date. The sole Pettie entry near that date is '12 Nov. 1589 Thomas Petty, Mariner, buried.'

year, the quarto appeared, undated, bearing the simple colophon 'Printed at London by R.W.'

Not Pettie but 'R.B.' had 'christened' the discourses after Painter's hundred and one eclectic tales of ten years before,[1] although Pettie of course knew the popular *Pallace of Pleasure* and drew upon it for a dozen allusions among his *exempla*. 'R.B.' also, it is clear, had run the risk of Pettie's avowed displeasure by committing the tales to a printer. And he it was who rather unctuously commended their 'wittie & pithie pleasantnes' to 'the gentle Gentlewomen Readers.' The printer Watkins, who received the manuscript from a 'special friend' intermediary between 'R.B.' and himself, discreetly excised certain offensive matter—with the hope that he had not 'gelded' too much—and supplied the summary Arguments, asking pardon of both Pettie and 'R.B.,' neither of whom he knew, for any oversights or errors. In this roundabout fashion the *Petite Pallace* came to be printed, the author protesting perhaps too much that his ornately devised tales were no more than oral discourses.

Among several possible identifications of the mysterious 'R.B.'[2] only one seems probable: the author of *A new tragicall comedie of Apius and Virginia*,[3] a rather

---

1 'I dare not compare this woorke,' writes 'R.B.,' 'with the former Pallaces of Pleasure, because comparisons are odious, and because they contain Histories, translated out of grave authors & learned writers: and this containeth discourses ... reported in a manner *ex tempore*.' Pettie's letter also alludes to Painter: 'there was then some *Pallas* in place which furthered my invention.'

2 The *S.T.C.* (1057–64) lists eight other works by unspecified 'R.B.'s' between 1570 and 1595; and Hazlitt's *Hand-Book* adds a printer 'R.B.' of five works in 1592. Of other authors during these years Roger Baynes and Richard Barnfield have no apparent claim to the identification. *Cetera desunt.*

3 W.How for R.Jhones, 1575; entered 1567/8. Reprinted *Tudor Facsimile Texts*, ed. Farmer, 1908; also Malone Society, ed. McKerrow and Greg, 1911.

nondescript classical interlude whose kinship of subject (originating in Livy) and style of casuistry alone urge some connexion. On the other hand, the tradition, begun by Hazlitt,[1] of regarding 'R.B.' as the reversed initials of Barnabe Rich is tantalizing: Rich was also a forthright euphuist and a captain who had served in the Low Countries, and his *Farewell to Militarie profession* (1581) is dedicated 'To the right courteous gentlewomen, bothe of Englande and Irelande.' In 1576, however, Rich was the author of but one book, a *Dialogue betwene Mercury and an English souldier*; and both *Greenes Newes* (1593)[2] and *The Irish Hubbub* (1617) bear his 'B.R.' not reversed. Other evidence is wanting. But whoever 'R.B.' may have been[3]—patron, friend, fellow-soldier, well-wisher, or pest—we owe it to his 'faithles enterprise' that Pettie's curious discourses finally found their way, through a 'special freind' of Watkins, into print.

1 *Hand-Book*, 1867; incorporated in Warton's *Hist.Eng.Poetry*, ed. Hazlitt, 1871,iv.336-7 (wanting in the 1824 ed.); also mentioned by Sidney Lee in his *D.N.B.* account of Pettie, and by Gollancz, I.xxv.

2 'Commended to the Presse by B.R.'—probably Rich (cf. McKerrow ed.).

3 The further possibility that 'R.B.' was merely a disguise or hoax meets with at least three objections: the substance and tone of his letter 'To the gentle Gentlewomen Readers' and the protestations of the author's own letter all argue the presence of an entrepreneur entrusted with these 'fruites of [Pettie's] former folly'; the printer Watkins' disclaimer of acquaintance with either the author or 'his freind that procured it to bee published' has the ring of truth; and, finally, the Preface to the Guazzo has Pettie's seemingly honest declaration that the 'trifling woorke . . . by reason of the lightnesse of it, or at least of the keeper of it, flewe abroade before I knewe of it.'

EDITIONS

A [1576]

4to. A–Ff⁴ (116 leaves). 'To the gentle Gentlewomen Readers,' A2. 'The Letter of G.P. to R.B.,' A3. 'The Printer to all Readers', [A4r]. *Text*: [A4v]–Ff4v; pp.[A4v]–1–224 (17 misnumbered *19*; 214,*215*; 215,*214*).
Title-page: title within lace ornament border. Motto: *Omne tulit punctum, /qui miscuit vtile dulci.* Printer's device, McKerrow No.188*a*. n.d. [entered *Sta. Reg.* 6 August 1576].
Colophon: Printed at London, by R[ichard]. VV[atkins].
Copies: British Museum, G.10,442 (Grenville).
        Morgan (Turner-Pope-Hoe).
        Pforzheimer (Bindley-Heber-Britwell-Clawson).
        [Cambridge University Library (Sanders): leaves 1–3 in facsimile].

B

4to. [A]², B–Y⁴, Aa–Bb⁴ (106 leaves). 'Letter of G.P. to R.B.,' [A2]. *Text*: B–Bb3; pp.1–182 (60 misnumbered *67*; 90,*94*; 91, 95; 94,*98*; 95,*99*; 110,*101*; 121,*120*; 143,*341*; 160,*193*; 163, *361*).
Title-page:[1] simple ornament, no compartment or device;

---

[1] The title-page of *B* is reproduced in *The Rowfant Books* (Dodd, Mead, 1906), 62. *A* is the frontispiece to the Gollancz edition.

    Note: Any approximate dates for *B*, *C*, and *D* would be conditioned by the following data: *B* antedates *C* on textual evidence cited later; the state of *C*'s title-page compartment appears somewhat later than the *Phisicke against fortune* (1579) and *D*'s later than Cortes' *Arte of nauigation* (1584)— but the evidence of a widening break in the block is untrustworthy; also an ornamental initial and a tailpiece in both *C* and *D* were once John Charle-

same wording of title as in *A*, with orthographic variants. Same motto. n.d.

Colophon: as in *A*.

Unique copy: Rosenbach (Osterley Park-Locker Lampson-White). *B* alone of the later editions retains the 'Letter of G.P. to R.B.' Although it has none of Watkins' devices or ornaments and lacks his prefatory note, *B* has two factotums belonging to Thomas Dawson and Richard Gardiner, trade-printers employed by Watkins, who used the same peculiar format for their Breton's *Workes of a young wyt* (1577). The variant readings also substantiate the fact that *B* is the second, and authorized—not pirated—edition, agreeing with *A* in literal lections but adding the long interpolations which *CDEF* follow.

C

4to. [—]², B–Z2⁴ (88 leaves). *Text*: pp.1–13, fol.13–92 (fol.69 misnumbered *68*).

Title-page: title within compartment, McKerrow & Ferguson No.141. Device as in *A*, here surmounted by six stars. Same motto. n.d.

Colophon: as in *A B*.

Copies: British Museum, C.27. b.16 (Garrick-Jolley).

Huntington (Steevens-Swainson-Huth).

D

4to. [—]², B–Z2⁴ (88 leaves). *Text*: pp.1–13 (order, on rectos, 1,2,5,4,9,11,13), fol.13–92 (misnumberings vary slightly).

Title-page: as in *C*, but with device excised (McKerrow No. 188 *B*) and no stars. Same motto. n.d.

Colophon: as in *A B C*.

Copies: British Museum, C.40. d.5 (Charlemont).

Folger (Sotheby's, 16 March 1903: lot 890).

wood's, whose widow in 1593 married James Roberts, then a partner of Watkins.

[Bodleian (Malone): with *C* title-page, and wanting 8 leaves].

E 1608

4to. A–Z⁴, &3 (95 leaves). *Text*: A3r–[Aa3v].
Title-page: title within compartment, McKerrow & Ferguson No.100*B*. Same motto. 'Imprinted at London, by G. Eld. 1608.'
No colophon.
Copies: British Museum, 12613. b.10 (Roxburghe-Sykes-Heber-Bliss).
    Bodleian (Wood).
    Folger (Heber-Corser-Christies, 18 January 1902).

F 1613

4to. A–Z⁴, Aa–[Aa3] (95 leaves). *Text*: A3r–[Aa3v].
Title-page: as in *E*, with change in date.
No colophon.
Copies: Bodleian (Douce).
    Boston Public Library (Barton).
    J. T. Kenrick, Esq., Birmingham (Wolferstan).

Wood's *Ath. Oxon.*, Bliss ed. (1813), i.552, lists 'one without date by Wolfe [*A,B,C*, or *D* with colophon misinterpreted?], a third in 1598 by James Roberts' [unidentified]. Hazlitt's *Hand-Book* also lists an edition, mentioned by Warton, *Hist. Eng. Poetry*, 1824, iv.29, as printed by Roberts in 1598; Hazlitt, however, was 'unable to refer to a copy.' Finally, the *Sta. Reg.* (Arber, iii.284) licensed Francis Burton on 11 March 1605 to print 'one impression onely'—'And agreying with master [John?] *norton* for suche numbers thereof as he hath vnsold of the former Impression or staying this ympres-

sion, till Master *norton* hath sold the same.' This last
was never issued.

(Lyly's and Greene's debts to the *Petite Pallace* are
discussed elsewhere. One curious example, however, of
Pettie's 'influence' has recently come to light in *The
Most Excellent Historie of Lysimachus and Varrona,
daughter to Syllanus, Duke of Hypata, in Thessalia* (By
I.H.R. London. Printed by Thomas Creed. 1604).[1] This
eclectic little volume, 'Wherein are contained the effects
of Fortune, the Wonders of affection, and the conquests
of incertaine Time,' brazenly appropriates (in Sigs.
H2–K3, K4^V–N, N2–N4) nearly all the 'Sinorix and
Camma' tale and two-thirds of 'Germanicus and Agrippina'—verbatim except for the characters' names.)

Within a decade the *Petite Pallace* ran into four edi-
tions, yet the book fails of mention in the standard
works of Elizabethan criticism; one looks in vain for
even damaging allusions to Pettie in the writings of
Lodge, Harvey, Webbe, Nashe, Sidney, Carew, and
Meres. Not until 1660, in *Le Prince d'Amour*, by 'the
Wits of the Age,'[2] is notice found of Pettie's tales; under
'Offences inquirable by the Jury' we find:

#14. If any man suspect his Mistris upon any kindness, by
kiss, dance, looks, or congy given to her friend, this is Jeal-
ousie finable.

#15. If any man deprave the books of *Ovid de Arte amandi,
Euphues* and his *England, Petite Pallace,* or other laudable

1 *S.T.C.,* 13510 (attributed to John Hind). The unique copy, formerly
  Bridgewater, is now in the Huntington Library (61507). For discovery and
  identification of the lifted passages, which embrace 12:25–33:1, 56:24–
  76:14, and 33:7–39 of the present edition, I am indebted to Mr. Frederick
  Hard and Mr. William Ringler.
2 A cavalier prose treatise signed 'B.R.'—Sir Benjamin Rudyerd. Hazlitt's
  Hand-Book first called attention to the Pettie allusion.

discourses of Love; this is loss of his Mistris favor for half a year.

After this reference, which inevitably prefigures the kinship of Pettie with Rambouillet and Mlle. de Scudéry, there follows only Wood's perfunctory notice of his great-uncle's 'neat Stile'—and the *Petite Pallace* drops from view until the eve of the twentieth century, when students of euphuism found reason to excavate.[1]

In its subject matter the *Petite Pallace*, unlike Painter's famous miscellany, is almost entirely humanistic. Of Pettie's twelve tales five derive ultimately from Ovid, two each from Livy and Hyginus, and one from Tacitus. Of the others, the first of the lot, 'Sinorix and Camma,' was available in Plutarch, Hoby's version of *The Courtier*, and Guevara's *Diall*; the last, 'Alexius,' was based upon a widely known medieval saint's legend. Pettie, however, designedly uses the classical framework as mere excuse for debates, soliloquies, colloquies, and tirades—all the pros and cons of love, courtship, marriage, and fidelity. His narration, his manipulation of

1 Studies of Pettie include:

Koeppel, Emil. *Studien zur Geschichte der italienischen Novelle in der Englischen Litteratur des sechzehnten Jahrhunderts* (Strassburg, 1892), 21–29.

Gollancz, I. Ed. Pettie's *Petite Pallace*. 2 vols. London, 1908.

Tilley, Morris Palmer. *Elizabethan Proverb Lore in Lyly's Euphues and in Pettie's Petite Pallace*. 1926.

Bush, Douglas. 'Pettie's Petty Pilfering from Poets,' *Phil. Quart.*,v (October 1926),325–9.

——. '*The Petite Pallace of Pettie his Pleasure*,' *J.E.G.Ph.*,xxvii,No.2 (April 1928),162–9.

——. *Mythology and the Renaissance Tradition in English Poetry* (University of Minnesota, 1932),36–9.

(Allusions and citations are also found in Bond, Feuillerat, Croll, etc.— *vide infra*, xxviii,n.)

'plot,' suffers accordingly, not so much from his want of skill as from his blithe unconcern. He has other fish to fry. Not the *dramatis personae* of Ovid or Livy, but his own friends are his loquacious puppets; not the fortunes of war or the whirligigs of time are his subject, but love casuistry—*questioni d'amore* in the Italian fashion, with —principally—classical *exempla* galore.

The narration and dramatic action of Pettie's 'Tragicall trifles' count for little. The tales themselves were familiar to school-boys; they served Pettie merely as *exempla* bearing the authority of the classics and capable of modern parallels. As such they were ready and ample carryalls for three staples of Renaissance literature, especially dear to English readers of mid-Elizabethan times: amatory debates (and Pettie could afford to dub Aristotle, on the subject of women, 'an Asse sotted with over mutch studdy'); *exempla* from 'authoritative' sources; and, finally, proverbs, apophthegms, *sententiae*, and the like.

In the first of these, the amatory debate, the Renaissance found one of its chief sources of diversion and instruction, and a pastime rivalled, in prolixity at least, only in the *salons* of seventeenth century France. Pettie's 'problems,' that is, are one and all the *questioni d'amore* of Boccaccio, Bembo, Castiglione, Parabosco, Straparola—the list seems inexhaustible.[1] Under various guises the *Petite Pallace* reiterates the stock problems: wit versus beauty in women, the relative constancy of male and female, laws of love as opposed to laws of man and marriage, lust and cruelty set over against mischief

1 Violet M. Jeffery's *John Lyly and the Italian Renaissance* (Paris, 1929) is a careful, well documented treatise on the *Trattati d'amore*. Miss Jeffery's study of the antecedents of *Euphues* makes plain at nearly every turn the Italianate influences upon Elizabethan literature in the 1570's and 1580's.

and murder, the evils of vanity and covetousness, the rewards of chastity, the free choice of a mate, the fruits of jealousy—these and their kind in Scudérian plenty.

Therefore, Gentlewomen, I leave it to your judgments to give sentence, whether be more worthy reprehension, he or she . . .
I shall not neede here (gentlewoman) to exhort you to take the death of your husbandes when you shalbe married . . .
I am here, gentlewomen, to admonish you not to suffer yourselves to be caryed away with covetousness. . . .
Now I would heare your judgementes to whom you thinke this lamentable end of these lovers ought to be imputed . . .

—for each tale its concluding formula, its postulates for argument, or its pointed moral. And the gentle gentlewomen, one must conclude, who indulged in this postprandial pastime were but learning in the approved Italianate fashion (their own being as yet only a crude aristocracy) how to become—gentle gentlewomen. Not until Shakespeare was this surfeit of casuistry and the 'taffeta phrases, silken terms precise' which it engendered marked for doom, leaving *Euphues*, as designed, to be shut in milady's casket, and the *Petite Pallace* for its 'rustical amorattos.'

Exempla, on the other hand, were a sort of ubiquitous pollen of humanism. 'He that mindeth to perswade,' wrote Wilson in his *Arte of Rhetorique*, 'must needes be well stored with examples. . . . And therefore much are they to be commended, which searche Chronicles of all ages, and compare the state of our Elders with this present time. . . . If there be any olde tale or straunge historie, well and wittely applied to some man living, all men love to heare it of life.' The rhetorician's precepts found a ready exemplar in Pettie, whose tales are riddled with old favourites, and some new ones as well: from Homer, Virgil, Ovid, and Plutarch; from Solomon, the Vulgate, and English Biblical lore; from Painter's assortment of tales; from courtesy books and *novelle*—from whatever was grist for his mill. How mock-heroic they sound to modern ears!—

Did *Alcyone* seeynge the dead carkas of her husbande *Ceix* cast on shore, willingly cast her selfe into the Sea to accompany his death? And shall I see my sweet *Synnatus* slayne, and not drinke of the same cuppe? Did true *Thisbe* goare her gorgious body with the same sworde, wherwith princely *Piramus* had prickt him selfe to the hart: and are not my handes stronge inough to do the like? Did *Julietta* die upon the corps of her *Romeo*, and shall my body remayne on earth, *Synnatus* beyng buried? No gentle death come with thy direfull dart, and peirce my paynefull harte . . .

The authority of the ancients, it would seem, appeared more formidable when invoked *ad nauseam*.

Along with the *exempla* Pettie ornamented his tales with some two hundred proverbs, maxims, and their like. Once more it is the rhetorician's precept, that of 'amplification' with 'such sentences as are commonly spoken.' And Wilson furnishes the clue to Pettie's chief source: 'But what neede I heape all these together,' he asks, 'seeing Heywooddes Proverbes are in Print, where plenty are to be had: whose paines in that behalf, are worthie immortal praise.' Indeed, to Heywood's early collection[1]

---

1 Heywood's *Dialogue conteynyng the number of the effectuall prouerbes in the Englische tounge* and his *Three hundred Epigrammes* appeared in his *Woorkes*, 1562 (ed. Farmer, Early Eng. Drama Soc., 1906). The *Dialogue* was first printed by Berthelet in 1546; afterwards in 1547,1549,1556; revised ed. 1561. Heywood's euphuism is plain in a passage like the following (*Prov.* II.vii):

But had I not been witched, my wedding to flee,
The terms that long to wedding had warned me.

may be traced directly a host of Pettie's pithy sayings—
to Heywood, and to Erasmus, through whose *Adagia*
and *Similia* so much of the wisdom of the ancients was
decanted for the Renaissance.[1] Add to these the names
of Ovid, Cicero, and Horace; Publilius Syrus; Guazzo
(whom he may have begun translating, in French versions, before 1576); the Vulgate, as well as an early English (Geneva?) Bible, especially Paul's Epistles—and
the 'sources' of Pettie's sapience are well accounted for.
In an age when plagiarism was not yet a word, much less
a term of reproach, Pettie, like his contemporaries, incorporated and adapted as he chose, with perhaps an
enchiridion for the purpose. 'I protest for my part,' says
Magnocavalli in the *Civile Conversation* (Pettie's version), '(as occasion shall serve) to let you heare Proverbes, which verie Artificers have in their mouth, and
comptes, which are used to be told by the fireside, both
for that I naturally live by suche foode, and also to give
you occasion to doe the like.' Pettie not merely seized
occasions; he frequently created them, leaving the *Petite Pallace* a labyrinth of proverbial lore whose mazes
Lyly was the first to thread for his own advantage.

In substance the *Petite Pallace* is manifestly a blend
of familiar themes with conventional devices and rhetorical adornments.[2] Not his matter but his manner

First, wooing for woeing; banna for banning;
The banns for my bane; and then this, thus scanning—
Marrying marring. . . .
'Most of our hodiernal instinctive palavers,' Christopher Morley reminds
us, 'were already old when Heywood collected them in 1546.'—Preface to
Bartlett's *Familiar Quotations* (1937 ed.).
1 Erasmus' *Adagia* were first published in 1500, the *Varia Epigrammata* in
1506. New and enlarged editions, some pirated, soon followed. Aldus
printed the famous *Chiliades adagiorum* (3260 proverbs) first in 1508.
Taverner 'Englished' selections in 1539.
2 For example, in his *Rhetorique* Wilson, speaking of allegory, writes, 'The

gives Pettie his distinction today, and that manner begins with the title itself. 'And shal I so much debase the
height of my estate, as to match in mariage *with* so
meane a mate?'; '. . . hee reaped the right reward of
his doatinge desire, for there only grafts of greife must
needes grow, where sutch raw conceite doth set, and
sutch rashe consent dooth sowe'—in passage after passage, line after line, the 'comely colours' of the first re-
lentless euphuist are displayed. 'Seeing wee allowe,'
Pettie pleaded with 'R.B.,' 'of new fashions in cutting
of beardes, in long wasted doublets, in little short hose,
in great cappes, in low hattes, and almost in al things, it
is as mutch reason we should allow of new fashions in
phrases and wordes.' As much reason indeed, and for
precisely the same would-be fashionable purposes during the decade and more of the fashion's survival.

'Young Euphues,' wrote Gabriel Harvey, 'hatched
the egges that his elder freendes laide.' And it becomes
increasingly plain with each new study that euphuism
has no specific 'source,' that the prose mannerisms, the
raffinements, whose sum constitutes the formula popu-
larized by Lyly were present in kind, if not in degree,
in widely scattered antecedents. 'But Master *John
Lilly*,' as Webbe wrote in his *Discourse* (1586), 'hath deserved moste high commendations, as he which hath stept
one steppe further therein then any either before or since
he first began the wyttie discourse of his Euphues.'
It was of course that 'one step further' by Pettie
and Lyly especially that carried English prose seven
leagues distant from decency and common sense. But

English Proverbes gathered by John Heywood, helpe well in this behalfe,
the which commonly are nothing els but Allegories, and darke devised
sentences.' And again: 'Any one may gather a similitude, and enlarge it
at pleasure. The Proverbes of Hewood helpe wonderfull well for this purpose.'

there seems to be no limit to the diversity of earlier patterns proposed;[1] successive studies point tellingly to Cicero and Isocrates, Guevara's *Diall* and North's translation, Berners' Froissart (1524), Anglo-Saxon and early English literature, the Bible and liturgical and homiletic literature, Ascham's *Scholemaster*; classic oratory, *alto estilo*, complimentary addresses, the Queen's own mannerisms— one and all show the symptoms of euphuism. The inheritance may easily be traced from Greece and Rome through the medieval Latin of the Church fathers, from the sophists through the rhetoricians, with but one conclusion: the presence in nearly all tongues, for various purposes and in various stages of development, of somewhat the same vogue. And the voice of the turtle is still heard in the land.

Euphuism, then, is more than a style based merely upon antithesis and alliteration (which latter device Mrs. Battle called as pitiful an ambition in authorship—and as much a solecism—as flushes at cards); it is a demonstrable system of syllabic, verbal, phrasal, and clausal balance and correspondence, a system of *schemata* in which the medieval rhetoricians and their early six-

---

1 The principal studies of euphuism include:

Morley, John. *Quart.Rev.*,cix (April 1861), 350–83.

Weymouth, R.F. 'On Euphuism,' *Phil.Soc.Trans.*, 1870–2.

Landmann, F. 'Der Euphuismus,' *New Shakespeare Soc.Trans.*, 1881, pp. 241–76.

Schwan, Eduard. *Eng.Stud.*,vi (1883),94–111.

Child, C.G. *John Lyly and Euphuism*. Münchener Beiträge, 1894.

Norden, E. *Die antike kunstprosa* . . . Leipzig, 1898 (ii.773–809).

Bond, R. Warwick. Ed. Lyly's *Complete Works* (Oxford, 1902),i.119–75.

Wendelstein, Ludwig. *Beitrag zur vorgeschichte des euphuismus*. Halle, 1902.

Wilson, John Dover. *John Lyly*. Cambridge, 1905.

Feuillerat, Albert. *John Lyly* (1910),444–75.

Croll and Clemens. Ed. *Euphues* (1916), Introd.,xv–lxiv.

Whipple, T. K. *Mod.Lang.Rev.*,xi.No.1 (1916),15–27; Ibid.,No.2,129–35.

Jeffery, Violet M. *John Lyly &c*. Paris, 1929, pp.117–32.

teenth-century followers gave instruction, from Donatus and Priscian through Susenbrotus, Talaeus, Wilson, and Rainolde (Richard Sherrye's *Treatise of Schemes and Tropes*, for example, was issued in 1555). Thus the medium of Pettie and Lyly—Harvey first used the term *euphuism* in 1592 during its slow demise—was but the apotheosis of word- and sentence-designs long familiar in subordinate functions to past literatures. '*C'est lui* [Pettie] *qui employa d'une manière continuelle et exagérée les procédés dont les écrivains antérieurs n'avaient fait qu'un usage modéré.*'[1] The elements, whether medieval or classical,[2] are *schemata verborum*, sentence patterns, and special ornaments, which have been carefully analysed and exemplified by Lyly's editors. Pettie lends himself quite readily to the same sort of clinical examination, which may here be serviceable:

I. SCHEMATA VERBORUM

Alliteration (various sorts: initial, final, combined (*homoioteleuton*), transverse, cumulative (*polyptoton*), &c.

'seeing the sight of your sweete face hath fast fettered my fancy in links of love'

'What care of theyr instruction? What fear of their distruction?'

'you poore soules must bide behinde to abide the brunt and bitter blastes of this wretched world'

'in great favour began greatly to feare'

'Away impe of impiety!'

1 Feuillerat, op.cit.,470.

2 'It may be argued therefore, with some appearance of truth, that on the one hand it makes little difference whether we call the Euphuistic rhetoric classical or mediaeval, since whatever its immediate source may be its ultimate source is the school of Gorgias, and on the other hand that the problem is insoluble after all, since we have no instruments of precision delicate enough to mark the distinction between classical and mediaeval influences.'—Croll, op.cit.,xxxiv.

Anagram: 'loth to bee tied to one diet'

Paronomasia: 'hee had, to wit, a witles wenche to his wife'
   'if shee chaunced to present her selfe to his presence, his
   heart was presently lightned'

Antithesis (*parison*) of various sorts:

Annomination: 'man purposeth and God disposeth'

Assonance: 'ripest fruit are rifest rotten'

Consonance: 'The gods guide us to goodnesse'
   'I will bee bound in what bond she will'

Assonance-Consonance:
   'I doubt you would neither beleeve the cause, neither
   releeve my case'

Repetition (direct, indirect, and transverse):
   'vengeance asketh vengeance, & bloud bloud'
   'notwithstanding his wary watch and watchful warenesse'
   'Did I poure out pensive prayers for his safe returne from
      the *Turkes*, and doth his returne returne my good wil
      with sutch dispight?'
   'your fancy is fixed on a prince, you shew your princely
      minde in lyking your like'

Rhyme (single and double):
   'The good ever is to bee used, and the ill refused'
   'like as streames the more ye stop them the higher they
      flow: and trees the more yee lop them the greater they
      growe'

II. SENTENCE STRUCTURE (*isocolon*)

Of various types: balanced phrases and clauses; as/so construction; by how much the more/by so much the less (*quanto/
tanto*); etc.
   'O love without law, O rage without reason, O will without
      wit, O fansy fraught full of fury and frensy'
   'as sharpe sauce gives a good taste to sweete meate, so trou-
      ble and adversity makes quiet and prosperity far more
      pleasant'

'by how mutch more a man hazardeth him selfe for his misteris sake, by so mutch the more hee manifesteth the
constancy of his love, and meriteth meede at her handes
the more woorthily'

III. ORNAMENTS[1]

Anecdotes and Allusions:
'I will make you sutch answere as was made to *Craterus* the
Emperour by *Diogenes* . . .'
'the Erle of *Pancalier* may serve for testimony who when
ye duchesse of *Savoy* would not yeeld to his lascivious
lust, wrought sutch wyles, that she was condemned for
adultry' (from Painter)
Foreign words and phrases:
congé, beso los manos, vi et armis, Senes fornecatores, etc.
Mythology: '*Phaedra* made sute to *Hippolitus*: *Oenone*
pleaded her right with *Paris*: *Dido* dyd *Aeneas* to understande how deeply she desired him: *Bryses* besought the
goodwill of *Achilles* . . . infinit lyke examples I could
alleage'
Proverbs, Sententiae, etc.:
'the sea hath fish for every man'
'two wittes are better then one'
'all is not golde which glistereth'—etc. (cf.Notes)
Rhetorical questions:
'But what perpetuitie is to bee looked for in mortall pretences? What constancy is to bee hoped for in kytes of
Cressids kinde? may one gather Grapes of thornes, suger
of Thistels, or constancy of women?'
Recondite knowledge:
'[True freinds] are rather like the stoane of *Scilicia*, which
the more it is beaten the harder it is'[2]

1 Under this category, of course, are grouped a number of items not specifically
euphuistic. All, however, are devices upon which Pettie, Lyly, and the later
euphuists lean heavily for decorative effects.
2 This sort of unnatural-natural history, so familiar in Lyly, is most rare in

'as the herbe *Camamile* the more it is trodden downe the
more it spreadeth abroad'
Vernacular words and phrases:
'the Mouse mumpeth,' 'freshe water souldiour,' 'dolefull
dumpes,' 'swearing swash buckler,' etc.

—These, severally and collectively, often in combina-
tions, are the 'comely colours' of Pettie's euphuism.[1]
Perhaps no single passage better illustrates the strenu-
ous designs of his latticed prose than the following, from
'Amphiaraus and Eriphile':

In this mean while came the other wooer againe to renew
his sute afreshe, and seeinge this younge Gentleman, as hee
thought in great favour, began greatly to feare his owne part,
and thought the grasse had bene cut from under his feete:
and as a conning Pilot seeing the seas rough and the winde
contrary to his course, casteth ancker least his ship bee driven
against the rockes, or into some coast contrary to his minde:
so this Gentleman fearinge least wilfull waves in y̆e gentlewoman, should set her fast in the sands of slipper subtelty,
and dash his sute against the rockes of repulse, hauld in the
maine shete of her minde, and by the anckers of advise so
stayed her course, that no wynde which my wilfull youthe
could blow, could cause her any thinge to bow or waver: and
by assuringe her to a large joynter hee was chosen to rule
her sterne, wher the other was kept stil under the hatches.

In the mutations of English prose style the excesses
of euphuism were at the time inescapable. Equivalents
of the fashion occurred in other literatures, French, German, Italian, and Spanish; and its counterparts may be
seen in other aspects of mid-Elizabethan life and man-

the *Petite Pallace*; Pettie's similes are drawn not from Pliny but from hunting, hawking, etc.
1 For material for a more detailed diagnosis (through Peacham) cf.
William G. Crane, *Wit and Rhetoric in the Renaissance* (1937), 237–40.
Cf. also 189–91.

ners. During its vogue there were no sumptuary laws to govern prose style, just as, in poetry, there seemed no curb for Petrarchism. Moreover, like the false Arcadianism which supplanted it, euphuism was a deliberate, self-conscious effort to loose the bonds of the mother tongue. Its audience—'whom by my will,' wrote Pettie's sponsor, 'I woulde have onely Gentlewomen'—was still a crude, ambitious aristocracy of the parvenu among nations, given to Italianate posturings; yet behind the verbal exploits of the euphuists was the ready subsidy of nationalistic pride. And modern prose—whether critical cant labels it *nervous, crisp,* or *kinaesthetic*—owes the antique courtly schematic fashion a debt for its lessons in excess as well as for certain of its cadences and sonorities.

In the chronology of euphuism Pettie's place is secure. But in addition to that primacy his *Petite Pallace* has its peculiar little claim to passing notice in any survey of the development of the English short story. For Pettie confessedly refurbished classical tales as allegories cloaking contemporary friends; their identities cannot be unmasked, but it was a new use to which such extempore Ovidian discourses were being put. As stories, of course, the dozen tales are woefully below the standards set by the *novelle* and their translators. As a narrator Pettie lacks every qualification of his craft: in intricacy of plot, suspense, singleness of aim, bold characterization, focus, 'local colour,' irony—in the essentials of a good story well told the *Petite Pallace* simply misses the mark. Yet this remains to be said—that among the ethical disputes, *questioni d'amore*, exhortations, proverbs, and *exempla* which make up his 'pretie histories' the figure of Pettie moves not without occasional grace. With all its stale casuistry, self-propagating maxims, and plethora of 'comely colours' the *Petite Pallace* has passages of sage

reflection, some memorable aphorisms, a certain salti-
ness in native phrasing, and its quota, however deriva-
tive, of amatory counsel and worldly prudence. Not all
his proverbs are traceable to Heywood and Erasmus;
not all his cogitations are characteristically neo-Platonic
or Ovidian.

The first complete euphuist, then, was an Oxford-bred
soldier—'suche as I am (whose profession should chiefe-
lie bee armes)'—who at the age of twenty-eight had
made a reputation of a novel kind, as a re-teller of tales
investing his friends with classic guise, with practices en-
dorsed by heroes and heroines of the golden age. Tragical trifles Pettie called them, to entertain fashionable
gentlewomen[1]—in a decade when love casuistry was not
merely an Italianate courtly vogue but a grave national
pastime, fostered by the possibilities of Elizabeth's
marriage and an heir to the throne. That the tales appeared in print was, apparently, no fault of the author's,
but through 'R.B.'s' faithless—perhaps mercenary—
enterprise.[2] Pettie regarded the *Petite Pallace* as a trifling work, 'some fruites of my former folly,' which
brought him unwanted and unbecoming acclaim. These
may be the accents of false modesty; yet in turning to
his translation of Guazzo he hoped, so he declared in the
Preface, 'to countervayle [his] former Vanitie, with
some formal gravitie.'

1 That Pettie was a philanderer of sorts is plain enough in several passages
like the following: 'But here [Admetus] aptly ended his talke upon her
mouth, and they entred into sutch privy conference, their lips beeing
joyned most closely together, *that* I can not report the meaning of it unto
you, but if it please one of you to leane hitherward a little I will shew you
the manner of it.'
2 With no copyright laws, of course, Elizabethan authors had no protection.
Thus Gascoigne's *Hundreth sundrie Flowres* (1573) were delivered during
the author's absence in Holland through a certain 'G.T.' and 'H.W.' to
the printer. Similarly Shakespeare's sonnets emerged, in 1609, into print.

A PETITE PALLACE OF
PETTIE HIS PLEASURE

A petite Pallace

of Pettie *his pleasure*:

Contaynyng many pretie Hystories
by him set foorth in comely colours,
and most delightfully dis-
coursed.

*Omne tulit punctum,
qui miscuit vtile dulce.*

To the gentle Gentlewomen Readers.

GENTLE READERS, whom by my will I woulde have onely Gentlewomen, and therefore to you I direct my woords. May it please you to understand, that the great desire I have to procure your delight, hath caused me somwhat to transgresse the boundes of faithfull freindship: for havinge with great earnestnesse obtained of my very freinde Master *George Pettie* the copie of certaine Histories by himself upon his owne and certaine of his   10 freinds private occasions drawn into discourses, I saw sutch wittie & pithie pleasantnes contayned in them, that I thought I could not any way do greater pleasure or better service to your noble sexe, then to publish them in print, to your common profit & pleasure. And though I am sure hereby to incur his displeasure, for that he willed me in any wise to keepe them secret: yet if it please you thankfully to accept my goodwill, I force the lesse of his ill wil. For to speake my fancy without feigninge, I care not to displease twentie men, to please one   20 woman: for the freindship amongst men, is to be counted but colde kindnesse, in respect of the fervent affection beetweene men and women: and our nature, is rather to doate of women, then to love men. And yet it lyeth in your powers so to thinke of his doings, and to yeeld him sutch courteous consideration for the same, that hee shal have more cause to thank me, then think ill of my faithles dealing towards him. Which if your courtesies

shall perfourme, you shall increase my dutie towardes
you, and his good will towards mee: you shall make me
shew my will and him his skill another time to pleasure
you: you shall binde both of us to remaine ready at
your commaundements. For mine owne part, I can chal-
eng no part of praise or thankes for this woorke, for that
I have taken no paines therein, neither by addinge Argument, Note, or any thinge, but even have set them
forth as they were sent mee: only I have christened them
10 with the name of a *Pallace of Pleasure*. I dare not compare this woorke with the former Pallaces of Pleasure,
because comparisons are odious, and because they containe Histories, translated out of grave authors & learned
writers: and this containeth discourses, devised by a
greene youthfull capacitie, and reported in a manner *ex
tempore*, as I my selfe for divers of them am able to tes-
tifie. I dare not commende them because I am partiall, I
dare dedicate them to you Gentlewomen, because you
are curteous. And that you may the better understande
20 the drift of these devises, I have caused the letter also
which my freinde sent mee with this worke, to be set
downe to your sight. Thus commending mine owne faithles enterprise, and my freinds fruitfull labour and learning, to your courteous protection, I wish you all, beuty
with bounty, and cumlinesse with curtesie, from my
lodging in Fleetstreete.

Yours readily to command.   R.B.

om. BCDEF

The Letter of G.P. to R.B.
Concerning this Woorke.

FORCED by your ernest importunity, and furthered by
mine owne idle oportunity, I have set downe in writinge, and accordynge to your request, sent unto you
certaine of those Tragicall trifles, whiche you have heard
mee in sundrie companies at sundrye times report, and
so neare as I could I have written them word for word as
I then told them: but if any of them seeme better unto
you now then they did then, you must attribute it to my   10
lisping lips, which perchaunce did somewhat disgrace
the grace of them: and yf any seeme worse now then
than [sic], you must impute it to this, that perchaunce
there was then some *Pallas* in place which furthered my
invention. For I am in that point of *Ovid* his opinion,
that, *Si cupiat sponte disertus erit.* But whether they
seeme unto you good or ill, I trust you will take them as
a token of good will, and that is the onely commoditie I
looke to reape by them. I pray you only to use them to
your owne private pleasure, and not to impart them to   20
other[s], perchaunce to my prejudice, for that divers
discourses touch neerely divers of my nere freindes: but
the best is, they are so darkely figured forth, that only
they whom they touch, can understand whom they
touch: yet to avoide all captious constructions, I pray
you in any wise let them bee an object only for your owne
eyes. If this mislike you in my discourses, that I make
Camma, use the example of the countesse of *Salisbury*,

the Dutches of *Savoy*, and sutch who were of far later
yeeres, then the auncient *Camma* is, with the like in divers other of the stories: you must consider that my
Camma is of fresher memory then any of them, and I
thinke in your judgment, of fresher hew then the fayrest
of them. Likewise, if you like not of some wordes and
phrases, used contrary to their common custome, you
must thinke, that seeing wee allowe of new fashions in
cutting of beardes, in long wasted doublets, in litle
short hose, in great cappes, in low hattes, and almost in
al things, it is as mutch reason wee should allow of new
fashions in phrases and wordes. But these faultes, or
whatsoever els, I care not to excuse unto you, who are
the only cause I committed them, by your ernest desire
to have mee set downe these trifles in writing. And as my
wordes hytherto have tended to this end, that you should
take these trifles well, so now I am to exhort you that
you will use them well: that with the spider you sucke
not out poyson out of them: that by some light example
you bee not the sooner incited to lightnesse. For beleeve
me (I speake it freindly, therefore take it freindly) I
thinke it more needfull to send you a bridell then a spur
that way. And if my example may bee a bridle to restraine you from vanity, doe but imitate mee hereafter,
or if my counsayle may contain you in continency, doe
but follow this advise: if you bee free, that you come not
into bondes: if you bee bound, *ut te redimas captum quam
queas minimo*: for trust me, the broad blasphemy of
Pigmalion, and the sodain *Apostacie*, or rather right con-
version of *Alexius*, have setled me in this fayth, that I
thinke him *Terq[ue] quaterq[ue] beatum, qui a consortio
mulierum se conhibere potest.* You mervayle, I am sure to
heare these wordes of mee, and that I should so soone
turne my tippet and recant, who but yesterday, as it

were, entred into heresy. But beleeve mee (my B.) *nun-quam nimis cito est ad bonos mores via. Qui non est hodie, cras minus aptus erit.*

Principiis obsta, sero medicina paratur,
   Cum mala per longas convaluere moras.
Errare humanum est, in errore perseverare, belluinum.
Sinnes oft assaied, are thought to be no sinne:
So sinne doth soyle the Soule it sinketh in.

Thus have I sent you in that booke some fruites of my former folly, and in this letter the profession of my present fayth, desiring you to use the one to your honest pleasure, and to follow the other to your godly profite. I meane, god willing, the next spring to goe on pilgrimage with *Alexius*, and if you were so devoutly disposed, I should thinke my selfe most happy to have sutch a companyon. From my lodging in Houlburn this. 12. of July. 10

   Tuus semper, aut suus nunquam: G.P.
      Omnia in mundo, immunda.

om. CDEF
12–16 I meane, god willing . . . to have sutch a companyon *om.* B
17 G.P. *om.* B

The Printer to all Readers of this Booke.

HAVING sumtime in my custodie this Booke in written hande, which by meanes of a special freind of mine was committed unto mee, I was by him eftsoones ernestly sollicited to publish the same in printe. Who beeing sutch an one, whose request I would not willinglie denie, I fell to perusinge the woorke, and perceyved at the first by the Auctours letter, that hee was not wylling to have it common, as thinkinge certaine poynts in it to bee to wanton to bee wrought by that wit which by this woorke appeareth to bee in hym: which, as I conjecture, mooved him to write to his freinde to keepe it private to his owne use, as may appeare by his freindes Epistle, and his Letter goyng beefore. Nevertheless, to accomplish the desire of the one, and not to incurre the displeasure of the other, as also to pleasure you, the freindly Readers hereof,

om. B
1 all/all the CD, the EF   Readers/Reader EF
8–15 perusinge the woorke . . . goyng beefore/CDEF read and therein found such sharpnes of wit, poudred with such pleasantnesse of invention, as I thought I could of dutie doo no lesse then yeelde unto him, in so friendly and reasonable a request. Nevertheless, having a special regard, not to attempt any thing that might justly provoke the aucthours displeasure, or offende any godly man or woman of what vocation soever. I have with great industry imployed my diligence to beare my selfe uprightly herein, well perceiving that these histories were by himselfe uppon his owne, and certain of his friendes private occasions, drawne into sundry discourses, and by him penned, rather for his owne private exercise, then to have them come abrode to the view of al men (the view/view EF).
15 Nevertheless/Thus willing therefore CDEF

I have put the same in printe, using my discretion in
omitting sutch matter as in the Aucthours judgement
might seeme offencive, and yet I trust not leaving im-
perfection in the discourse, wherof if I have not gelded
to mutch, I thinke I have deserved the lesse blame. And
consideryng that in matters of pleasure, the Prynter
may sooner offende in printyng to mutch, then in pub-
lishyng to litle: I have applyed myselfe to the contrary,
hopynge that how mutch the lesse I have printed, reserv-
ynge the discourse perfect, so mutch the lesse I shalbe   10
blamed for the deede. As for the Gentleman that wrote
this woorke, and his freinde that procured it to bee published: as they are unknowen to mee both, so had I conference with neither, wherby the lesse I could use their
advice in abridging any thinge, which may bee some
cause of the disgracinge of that, which doubtlesse the
Auctour had penned with great excellency, and eloquence. If herein, as I feare, I have offended, I am willing, beeynge advertysed therof, to bee refourmed, cravinge pardon of him especyally, and of all other freindly   20

1 put the same in printe/imprinted the woorke *CDEF*   using/partly
using *CDEF*

2 the Aucthours judgement/my judgment to the Auctour *CDEF*

5 to mutch . . . blame/too much, or have gelded as much as was needful, I am sure I have deserved the lesse reproofe *CDEF*

5 And/For *CDEF*

8 contrary/more commendable part *CDEF*

9 lesse/lesse of some matters *CDEF*   10 discourse/discourses *CDEF*

10 shalbe/am to be *CDEF*

12 and his freinde that procured it to bee published *om. CDEF*

13 they are/he was *CDEF*   both *om. CDEF*

13 had I/had I no *CDEF*   14 neither/him *CDEF*   wherby the lesse
I could/neyther coulde I *CDEF*   their/his *CDEF*

16–17 the Auctour/he *CDEF*

18–p.10, 6 I have offended . . . caryed away/*CDEF read* I gaine his displeasure for leaving in somethyng whiche he would not have been seene, or incur
your yll wylles, for any errour committed, I earnestly crave pardon both
of hym and you: assuring you, that it lieth in your power so to thinke of

Readers, for the oversightes whatsoever herein committed: for whose pleasure and profite I have left undoone,
and doone, whatsoever I have doone in this behalfe. I
have also of my selfe added an argument to every history, that the effect of the discourse may bee the more
easily caryed away.

Fare yee hartely well.

his dooinges, and to yeelde hym such courteous considerations for the
same, that he shall have more cause to thanke me, then to thynke yll of
my dealynges in this respect. VVhich if your courtesies shall perfourme,
ye shall encrease my duetie towardes you, and his good wyll towardes
me: ye shall make me shewe my wyll, and hym his skill another tyme to
pleasure you: and bynde both of us to remayne ready at your commaundement. As for myne owne part I am able to assure you, it is for your
pleasure and profite that I have left undoone, and doone whatsoever I
have doone, in this behalfe.

[Sig.] R.W. *EF*

Sinorix and Camma.

[SINORIX, cheif governour of *Sienna* in *Italy*, glauncynge his eyes upon the glitteryng bewtie of *Camma*, wife to *Sinnatus*, a Gentilman of the same citie: falleth into extreame love with her, and assaieth sundry waies to win her goodwill. But perceivinge his practices to take no wished effect, and supposinge the husbandes life to hinder his love, causeth him to bee murthered by a ruffian. *Camma*, to the intent she might bee revenged upon the cheif conspiratour, in grauntinge him marriage, dispatcheth her selfe in drinkinge to him, and him in pledging her in a draught of poyson, which she had prepared for that purpose.]   10

As amongest all the bondes of benevolence and good
wil, there is none more honorable, auncient, or honest
then Mariage, so in my fansie there is none that doth
more firmely fasten, and inseparably unite us together
then the same estate doth, or wherein the fruites of true
freendship do more plenteously appeare: In the Father
is a certayne severe love and carefull good will towardes
the childe, the childe beareth a fearefull affection and aw-
full obedience towards the Father: the Master hath an
imperious regarde of the servant, the servant a servile   20
care of the master. The frendship amongest men is
grounded uppon no law, and dissolved upon every light
occasion: the good will of kinsfolke is commonly colde,
as mutch of custome as of devotion: but in this stately
state of Matrimonie, there is nothing fearefull, nothing
fayned, all things are done faithfully without doubting,
truely without doublyng, willingly without constraint,
joyfully without complaint: yea there is sutch a generall

consent and mutuall agreement between the man and
wife, that they both wish and will, covet and crave one
thing. And as a sience grafted in a strange stalke, their
natures being united by grothe, they beecome one, and
together beare one fruite: so the love of the wife planted
in the breast of her husband, their harts by continuance
of love become one, one sence and one soule serveth them
both. And as the sience severed from the stocke with-
ereth away, if it bee not grafted in some other: so a loving
wife seperated from the societie of her husband, with-
ereth away in woe, and leadeth a life no lesse pleasant
then death, as the sequele of this history shall shew,
wherin you shall see a mervaylous Mirrour of blessed
Matrimony, and a terrible tipe of beastly tyrannie.

In the Citie *Sienna* was a married couple, the husbande named *Sinnatus*, the wife called *Camma*, who as
they were by estate worshipfull, by vertue honorable,
and by goodnesse gracious, so were they in ritches fortunate, in children fruitfull, in friends flowrishinge, and
in love so loyall eche to other, that they long time led a
lovinge and quiet life together: but either fortune envying their prosperity, or the divell displeased with
their vertuous life, or God disposed to try their truth,
and make them patterns to their posterity, converted
this happy life to heavy estate, and raysed up one *Synorix* to raze and beat down the firme foundacion of their
faithfull buildinge and bydinge together. For this *Sinorix* glauncing his gazing eyes on the blazinge beuty of
Camma, received so deep an impression, of her perfection in his hart, that immediately he fixed his fancie
upon her comely corps. And beinge the chiefe ruler of the

---

1 mutuall/natural *CDEF*   3 & 8 sience/sienes *BCD*, siens *EF*
3 stalke/stocke *BCDEF*   7 soule/desire *BCDEF*
15 Sienna/Scienna *CDE*, Syenna *F*

citie, hee perswaded him self that there was none in the
city so stout but would stoup to his lure, nor none so
faire but would faine imploy them selves to pleasure
him: but on the other side the renowmed vertue of
Camma came to his minde, which perswaded an impossibility to his purpose: and floting thus betweene hope
and dispaire he entred into these termes.

O miserable wretch that I am, to whom shall I addresse
my complaintes, is it the heavenly powers and goddes of love that have deprived mee of my sences, and
shewed their devine working in mee, or is it the hellish
Hags and spirites of spight that have bereeved mee of
reason, & executed their cruelty on mee? is it love that
leadeth me to this lust, or is it hate that haleth mee to
this hurt and mischiefe, no no the gods guide us to goodnesse, the furies of hell it is that force us to filthynesse:
neyther doth it any way deserve the name of love,
which bringeth such torment to my troubled minde,
that all the divels in the world could not do the like. But
see my rashnes why am I so blindly bolde beastly to
blaspheme against that which proceedes altogether of
nature, which nature hath imparted to all men, and
which I ought to follow without repininge or resistinge:
for so long as I follow nature as my guide I cannot doe
amisse, & seing nature hath taught us to love, why
should I not rather proove her precepts, then reprove
that which by natures lore is allowed: and touchinge
torment of minde, or either inconvenience that it bringeth, is it all able to impaire the least joy which I shall injoy in imbracinge my *Camma*, is it not meete that hee
which would reape should sowe, he that would gather
fruite should plant trees, hee that would reach the
sweete rose should now & then be scratched with the

2 to/at *CDEF*   23 I *om.B*   28 either/other *BCDEF*

sharpe briers? I meane is it meet if I purpose to possesse
so proper a peece, as *Camma* is, that I should fly no labour or refuse any peril in the pursute therof [?] And
hereupon he determined to follow the fury of his fancy
what pangues or perils soever hee incurred therby: and
having revolved many wayes in his minde how hee might
aspire to his purpose, at length he resolved upon this to
institute a sumptuous Banquet, wherto hee invited the
cheeif of the citie, among whom *Synnatus* and his wife
10   *Camma* were not forgotten, to wit the only autors of the
feaste. Now for the more royall receivinge of his guestes
he met them at the entry into his Palaice, and gave them
this greeting.

     Faire Ladies as I am right joyfull of your presence, so
am I no les sorowfull for the paines which you have taken
in undertaking so great a journey this dark and misty
evening, for the which I must account my selfe so mutch
the more beholdinge to you, by how much greater your
labour was in coming, and by how mutch lesse your
20   chere shalbe able to countervayle it now you are come:
& taking *Camma* by the hande, hee sayd softly unto her,
I pity the peines of these gentlewomen the les for that
you were in their company, whose piersing eyes as ce-
lestiall starres or heavenly lampes might serve for lightes
in the darke, whose sweete face might parfume the aier
from all noysome smels which might annoy them: and
by beholding your lovely lookes and perfect shape they
might take sutch delight, that the wearynesse of the
way could nothing molest or greeve them.

30   *Camma* hearing her selfe so greatly praysed of so great
a personages [*sic*] as hee was, could not keepe the Roseal
redde out of her Alablaster cheekes, and thinking no

2 fly/flee *BCDEF*   15 am I/I am *EF*   27 by *om. CDEF*

sutch serpentine malice to lie hid under these merry and sugred woordes, shee gave him this courteous answere.

If Sir the company had made no better provision for lights and other thinges necessary then sutch as you speake of, they might soone have slipt into the mier, but as I perceive by your woords you are disposed to jest and bee meery, so I am content for this once to bee made the instrument thereof, thereby to ease some part of the paines which you are like to take in receiving sutch troublesome guestes as wee are: and for our chere you neede take no thought, for it shalbe so mutch to good for us, by how mutch lesse wee have deserved any at all at your handes.

After this amarous incounter, he caused the company to sit downe to the banquet, and so disposed the matter, that *Camma* sat right over at the table against him, wherby hee freely fed his eyes on that meat which converted rather to nourishment of sicknesse, then to wholesome humours of health. For as the finest meates that bee, eaten by one in extremity of sicknesse, resolve not to pure bloud to strengthen the body, but to watrish humors to feede the fever and disease: so though her face and lookes were fine and sweete, and brought delight to all the beholders els, yet to him they wrought onely torment and trouble of minde: and notwithstanding hee perceived her beauty to breed his bane, & her lookes to procure the losse of his liberty, and that as the *Cocatrice* by sight only sleath, so shee by courteous countenance onely killed and wounded his hart, yet could he not refrain his eyes from beholding her, but according to the

---

1 sutch *om. CDEF*   16 right over at the table/at the table right over *CDEF*
18 nourishment/the nourishment *CDEF*
20 eaten *om. CDEF*   by/be *EF*
21 not to/not to be *DEF*   24 els, *mispr.*/eyes *CDEF*

nature of the sickly pacient, which cheifly desireth that which cheiflye is forbidden him, hee so incessantly threw his amarous glaunces towards her, that his eies were altogether bleared with her beauty, and shee also at the length began to perceive his loving loookes towards her, which made her looke pale in token of the litle pleasure shee tooke in his toyes, and of the great feare shee had least, some other should marke them, wherby her good name might come in question. The banquet beeing ended, every one prepared themselves to heare a stage playe, which was then ready to bee presented. But *Synorix* being able to play but one part, which was of a pore passionat lover, determyned to go forward with the tragedy already begun betweene *Camma* and him, and seeing her set out of the husbandes sight, placed him self by her, and entred into reasoning with her, to this purpose. If (faier lady) this simple banquet had bene so sweete and pleasant to your seemely selfe and the rest, as your sight is delightful to mee, I am perswaded you would not have changed your chere for *Nector* and *Ambrosia*, which the Poetes faygned to bee the foode of the goddes: but seeing there was no cause of delighte in the one, and the other contayneth that in it which may content the gods them selves, I shall desier you in good part to accept the one, and courteously to accounte me worthy to injoy the other. And though I have not here tofore by dutifull service manifested unto you the loyalty of my love, yet if my poore hart could signifie unto you the assaults it hath suffred for your sake, I doubt not but you would confesse, that by force of love I had woon you, & were worthy to weare you. For albeit by humane lawes your husband only have interest in you, yet by

10 one/one of them *BCDEF*   15 set/sit *EF*
15 the/her *BCDEF*   29 but/but that *CDEF*

natures lawes, which beinge more auncient ought to be of
more auctority, he ought to injoy you which joyeth most
in you, which loveth you best, & indureth most paine for
your sake: & for proufe of natures lawes, it may please
you to consider the quality of the shee woulfe who always choseth that woulfe for her make who is made most
leane and foule by following her: besides that, my tytle
marcheth under the ensigne of justice, which is a vertue
givinge to every one accordinge to his deserte, and that
the desert of love is onely love againe, I know you are   10
not to know: for all the goods in the worlde are not able
to requite good will, the one belonginge to the minde,
the others incident to the body, but from the equitie of
my cause I appeale to your good grace and favour, and
at the bar of your beauty I humbly holde up my handes,
meaning to be tried by your courtesy and mine owne
loyalty, and minding to abide your sentence either of
consent unto life, or of deniall unto death. *Camma* hearing this discourse, assone loked red for shame, as soone
pale for anger, neither would disdain let her make him   20
answere, neither would her greife give her leave to holde
hir peace, but standing a while in a maze betweene
silence and saying, at length shee brake of the one and
burst out into the other in this sort.

If (Sir) your banquet had bene no better, then this
your talke is pleasant to mee, I am perswaded the dishes
woulde have been taken whole from the Table without
touchinge, but as the one was far better then the company deserved, so the other for a far worse woman might
more fitly have served, and if your sweete meate have   30
sutche sower sauce, the next time you send for me, I will
make you sutch answere as was made to *Cratorus* the
Emperour by *Diogenes*, when he sent for him to make his

19 soone *om. EF* 32 Cratorus/Craterus *BCDEF* 33 Diogenes/Diogines *DEF*

abode with him in his courte, who answered he had rather be fed at *Athens* with salt, the*n* live with him in all delicacy: so for my part I promise you, I had rather be fed at home with bread and water then pay so derely for dainty dishes. Touching the paines you have indured for my sake, I take your wordes to bee as false towardes mee, as you would make my faith towards my husband, but admit they were true, seeing I have not willingly been the cause of them, I count not myself bound in conscience to countervayle them, only I am sory they were not bestowed on some more worthy your estate and lesse worthy an honest name then my selfe, which beinge the cheife ritches I have, I meane most diligently to keepe. The interest which cavilingly you cleime in me as it consisteth of false premises, so though the premises were true, yet the conclusion which you infer thereof followeth not necessarily, for were it so that your love were greater towardes me then my husbandes (which you can not induce me to beleeve) yet seeyng my husbande by order of law hath first taken possession of mee, your title succeeding his, your successe and sute must needes bee cold & naught: for as your selfe say of lawes, so of titles the first are ever of most force, and the most ancient of most auctoritie. Your Wolves example, though it shew your Foxely brayne, yet doth it inforce no sutch proofe to your purpose, but that by my former reason it may bee refelled, for y^t the Woulfe is free from the proper possession of any: but therin truly you observe *decoram* very duly, in usyng the example of a Beast in so beastly a cause: for like purpose, like proofe: like man, like matter. Your manly marchyng under the ensigne of Justice, if reason bee your captayne generall to lead you, I doubt not, but soone to tourne to a retire: for if it bee goodwill

23 most force/more force *EF*   24 Wolves/Wolvyshe *CDEF*

which you beare mee, I must needes graunt you duly
deserve the like agayne: but when you are able to proove
it goodwill to deflower my chastitie, to beereeve mee of
my good name, to despoyle mee of mine honour, to
cause mee to transgresse the boundes of honestie, to
infringe my faith towards my husband, to violate the
sacred Rytes of Matrimonie, to pollute the Temple of
the Lorde, with other innumerable enormities, when I
say you are able to proove these to proceed of good will,
then will I willingly yeelde consent to your request. But
see the unreasonablenesse of your suite, would you have
mee in shewyng curtesie towards you, commit cruelty towards my self? should I in extendyng mercie to you, bring
my selfe to miserie? should I place you in pleasure, and
displace my selfe of all joy? for what joy can a woman injoy havinge lost her chastitie, which ought to bee the joy
Jewell and Gemme of al Gentilwomen of my callyng and
countenance? your appeale from your owne cause to my
courtesie bewrayeth the naughtinesse therof, for if it bee
not ill, why sticke you not to it? if it bee good, why appeale you from it? but seeynge you have constituted mee
Judge in this case, you know it is not the part of a Judge
to deale partially, or to respect the man more then y^e
matter, or to tender more mine owne case then your
cause: therefore indifferently this sentence definitive I
give, I condemne you hencefoorth to perpetuall scilence
in this sute, and that you never hereafter open your
mouth herein, beeing a matter moste unseemely for
your honour, and most prejudiciall to my honestie: and
in abidyng this sentence (if you can bee content with
honest amitie) for the curtesie which I have alwayes
founde at your handes, and for the good will which you
pretend to beare mee, I promise you, you shall injoy the

10

20

30

23 partially/parcially *BCD*

seconde place in my harte, and you shall finde mee
freendly in all thinges, which either you with reason can
aske, or I with honestie graunt.

Synorix having heard this angell thus amiably pro-
nouncing these woords, was so rapt in admiration of hir
wisedom, and ravished in contemplation of her beutie,
that though shee had not injoyned him to silence, yet
had hee not had a woorde to say: and least his lookes
might beewray his love, and his countenance discover his
case, hee secretly and suddainly withdrew him selfe into
his chamber, to study what face to set on the matter: &
casting him self upon his bed, after hee had dreamed a
while upon his dotinge devises, at length he awaked out
of his wavering thoughtes, and recovered the possession
of his sences againe: by which time the play was ended,
and his guestes ready to depart, wherupon hee was
driven to come foorth of his chamber to take his leave of
them: and bidding his Misteris good night, hee gave her
sutch a looke, that his very eyes seemed to plead for
pity, so that what his tongue durst not, his eyes did.
His guestes beeinge gone, he disposed him selfe to rest,
but love, which was then his good Maister, willed him
otherwise to imploy that night, whiche was in examyning perticulerly every point of her answere. And though
the first part seemed sumwhat sharpe and rigorous, and
the second contained the confutation of his cause: yet
the third and last part seemed to be mixt with mettell
of more milde matter, which he repeated to himselfe a
thousand times, and there uppon, as uppon a firme
foundacion, determined to raise up his building again
with the two former partes of her answere had utterly
ransakt to the grounde. But mistaking the nature of the
ground wheron the foundation was layd, his building, as

4 Synorix/Sinorix *BCDEF*   31 with/which *BCDEF*

if it had been set in sandes, soone came to ruine: for by
that promise of freendship, which she freendly made him,
hee sinisterly conceived hope of obtayning that which
she neither with honour could promise, neither with honesty perfourme, and feeding him selfe with that vaine
hope in great braverie, as in a manner assured of the
victorie, hee wrote unto her to this effecte.

Albeit good Misteris, you have injoyned my tounge
to silence, yet my handes are at libertie, to bewray the
secrets of my harte: and though you have taken my   10
harte prisoner, yet my head hath free power to plead for
release and releife. Neither would I you should count
mee in the number of these cowardly Souldiours, which
at the first Canon that roareth, give over the siege of the
citie they assaulted, for I have been alwayes setled in
this opinion, that the more harde the fight is, the more
haughtie is the conquest, and the more doubtfull the
battayle, the more doubtie the victory. And as it is not
the part of a politike Captayne to put himself in perill,
without hope of pray, or prayse: so to win the Bulwarks 20
of your breast I count it a more ritche booty then *Caesar*
had in ransacking so manie Cities, and a more rare
prayse then ever *Alexander* had in subduing so many
nations. And though my presumption may seeme great
in practising one of so highe a calling as your sweet self,
yet seing in al degrees of freindship, equality is cheefly
considered, I trust you will clere me of crime that way:
neither would I, you should thinke my flight so free to
stoup at every stale, for as the haughty Hauke will not
pray on carrion, so neither will courtely silkes practise 30
country sluttes. But bicause I knowe that to bee in you,
which both concerneth my callynge, and consenteth
with my fancie, I have chosen you for the Goddesse of

13 these/those *BCDEF*   25 one/on one *BCDEF*

my devotions, humbly beseechinge you with pitie to
heare the prayers, whiche I with payne powre foorth
beefore you, that it may not bee sayd your name hath
been called on in vayne, whereby you may lose that honour, whiche others of dutie, and I of devotion doo [owe
B–F] unto you. The benefite which you bestow on mee
in graunting mee the second place in your hart, as I
must acknowledge though somwhat unthankfully, so
must I crave a greater though somwhat impudently: for
10   seeinge my whole heart and body are yours, mee thinkes
a peece of your heart is a poore peece of amendes. Way
the matter uprightly, consider my case courtiously, and
take compassion on mee speedely. Yours altogether,
Don Sinorix de Sienna. Camma having received and red
this letter was assayled diversely, sometime with sorowe
in thinking on the time shee first saw him or hee her,
sometime with repentance of her former promise made
him, sometime with pity on his part, sometime with
piety on her owne: but at length piety vanquished pity,
20   and caused her to send this rough reply to his letter.

The litle account you make of mee and my goodwill,
I perceive by the litle care you have to satisfie that
which I gave you in charge, you would yl have done as
the knight *Virla* did, who at the commaundement of his
lady *Zilia*, forbare the use of his toung & remained dum
the terme of .iij yeeres: but as you subtilly thinke to
discharge your self of my charge by writing and not
speakyng, so by writyng I simplie do you to understand,
y^t from henceforth you looke for no more at my handes
30   then at a straungers, I wil not say an enemies, for seyng
my promise was but upon condition, the condition beeing
broken, my promise is voyde: And seeing you have plaied

14 Sienna/Scientia *D*   16 the/the the *B, mispr.*
19 piety/pity *B*   24 Virla/Virle *BCDEF*

yᵉ pelting Merchant ventrer, to hazard that goodwill
and credite you had with mee to get more, the tempest
of my just displeased minde hath driven your sute
against the rough rockes of repulse, and you have made
shipwracke of all: your couragious persisting in your
purpose proveth you rather a desperate sot then a discrete
souldiour: for to hop against the hill, and strive against
the streame, hath ever bene counted extreeme folly: your
valiaunt ventring for a pray of value proceedes rather of
covetousnesse then of courage, for the valiant souldiour   10
seeketh glory, not gaine, but therin you may bee more
fitly resembled to the Caterpiller which cleaveth only to
good fruite, or to the Moath which most of all eateth
the best cloath, or to the Canker which commonly breedeth in the fayrest Rose, or to the Woulfe whiche by his
will wil kill yᵉ fattest sheepe. The equality which you
pretend to be between us is altogether unequal, for both
you exceede me in degree, and I excell you in honesty,
so yᵗ neither in calling nor quality is there any equal-
itie beetween us. Wheras you have chosen me for your   20
goddesse, I beseeche you suffer me to remaine an earthly
creature, and serve you that god which can bridle your
wanton desires, and give you grace to give your neighbours leave to live honestly by you. Least you take his
name in vain, who will verely punish your vanity at
the length, though for a time he suffer you to wallow in
your wickednes, for it is the prudent pollicy of god to
suffer yᵉ sinfull long time to swim in their sinne, to make
their sinking more sorowfull, by their sodaine shrink-
ing from prosperity to adversity. For adversity is ever   30
most bitter to him who hath longe time lived in prosperity: neither must you thinke that that which is
deferred is taken away, for as your selfe or any other

19 is there/there is *CDEF*   31 most/more *EF*   to/unto *CDEF*

that oweth mony, though you defer your creditour for
a time, yet you defraude him not altogether of his due,
so though God take dayes with you for a time, yet
assure your selfe hee will pay you truly at the length,
yea and perchance with large usury besides the due
det. For as a hauke the higher pitch shee flieth from the
ground with the more force shee stoupeth downe upon
her praye and can the more easely commaund it, or as a
stroke or blowe the higher it is lifted the hevier it lightes,
so gods vengance the longer it is deferred, the more it is
to be feared. And this good counsayle take of mee as the
last benefite which you shall ever receive at my handes.
Yours nothing at all *Constantio Camma. Sinorix* having
seen this rigorous resolution of his Misteris, went another
way to work, hee suborned an old woman of the citie,
wel seene in soliciting sutch sutes, to go unto her and to
present her from him with many ritch jewels, and which
hee willed her to tell, hee would willingly bestowe for
one simple consent of her good will. The olde woman
having done his shamefull message without shame, sayd
of her selfe in this sort.

Surely, Misteris *Camma*, if the experience which olde
yeeres have given mee, might crave credite for the counsayle which I shall give you, I would not wish you to
refuse the frendship of sutch a one as *Sinorix* is, who is
able to fill your purse with perles, and fulfil you with
pleasure every way: neither is it wisdome for you to
spend your golden yeeres but in golden pleasure, and
not to bee tied to one diet which bringeth satiety and
lothsomnesse, but to have choice of chaung which breedeth appetite and lustinesse. The chast eares of *Camma*

4 truly *om. CDEF*   the *om. EF*   6 shee/he *E*   flieth/fleeth *BC*, flyeth *D*
7 stoupeth/stopeth *B*   13 Constantio/Constantino *BCD*, Constantina *EF*
17 and/all *CDEF*   29 satiety/sacietie *BCDEF*

not able to indure this course discourse, shee cut of her
gostely counsayle with these cutting woords, gentlewoman, if you were indued with as many good conditions as you have lived yeeres, you would never have
undertaken so shameles a message and were it not more
for reverence of your yeeres, then respect of your errant,
I would make your filthy trade of life so famous, that
you should ever hereafter bee ashamed to shew your face
in any honest company. What do you thinke, though
mony can make you a baude, that it can make mee a har-   10
lot, and though you for gaine flie no filthinesse, that I for
glory follow no faithfulnesse, either towardes my spouse
and husband, either towardes my Lorde and god? Do
you judge me so covetous of coine, or so prodigall of
mine honour, that to get the one I wil loose the other?
Or doth hee that sent you thinke so abjectly of mee,
that gaine may more prevaile with mee then goodwill,
mony more then a man, coyne more then courtesie, Jewels more then gentlenesse, Perls more then perils and
paynes which hee hath indured for my sake: no let him   20
understand, if any thinge could have caused mee to
swarve from my duty, love of luker should not have allured mee therto. But as I am fully resolved, faythfully
to keepe my vow and promise made to my husband, so
I beeseeche him not to bestow any more labour in at-
tempting that, which hee shall never attaine unto: for
before this my resolution shalbee reversed, hee shall see
the dissolution of my body into dust. But if hee will not
thus give over his sute, hee will cause mee to make those
privy to his dealing, who will make him ashamed of it: 30
and for your part, you may packe you hence with this
your trashe and trumpery to those, which measure their

5 shameles/shamefull *DEF*   11 flie/flee *BCDEF*
22 love of luker should not have/love, not luker should have *BCDEF*

honour by the price of profite, and their glory by the
gwerdon of gayne. This honest woman beeing gone away
with a flea in her eare, *Camma* began to thinke of the matter with advysed deliberation, and entred into reasoning
with her selfe in this sort.

What fearfull folly is this in mee to contemne the
frendship of so great a lorde as *Synorix* is, whom the
greatest Lady in this lande would willingly receive for
husband, and yet I rigorously refuse for servaunt? What
is that honoure wheron I stand so stifly, shall it not rather
increase mine honour to have so honourable a servaunt?
And what is that chastity which I seke so charily to
keep, do not some men say that women alwaies live
chastly inough, so that they live charily inough, that is
so that they convay their matters so covertly that their
dooinges bee not commonly knowen, for otherwise to
incontinency were added impudency: likewise, for a
woman to enter into conversation with a rascall of no
reputation, can not but bee a great blemishe to the
brightnesse of her name, (for a foule adultrer is ever
woorse then the adultry itself) and it is a great signe she
greatly lotheth her husband when she liketh one better,
which is everi way worse: but to have a freende of res-
ervation whose very countenance may credit her & her
husband, me thinkes can be no great dishonour to either
the one or the other. What dishonour was it I pray you
to *Helen* when she left her husband *Menelaus* & went
with *Paris* to *Troy*? Did not ye whole glory of *Greece* to
her great glory go in armes to fetch her again? And if she
had not been counted a peece of price, or if by ye facte
she had defaced her honour, is it to be thought ye *Grecians*
would have continued ten yeeres in war continually to

3 of/on *CDEF*   10 wheron/wherupon *CDEF*   21 it is/is it not *BCDEF*
24 her & *om. CDEF*   25 can be no/can be *B*, cannot be *CDEF*

win her againe? But to leave honour and chastity, and come to commodity and safety, what do I knowe what perils will folow of this repulse: is it likely *Sinorix* wil put up this reproche paciently? may I not justly loke to have his love turned to hate, and that he will either by tyrannous meanes seeke the subversion of my husbande & his whole household, either by trecherous meanes woork the overthrow of me and my good name? For the first, *Edward* a kinge of England may serve for an example, who when the countesse of *Salesbury* would not consent to content his incontinent desire, he so raged against her parents and friends, yᵗ the father was forced to perswade his own daughter to folly: & the mother as a baud to prostitute her to the kinges lust, & bring her to his privy chamber. For the second, the Erle of *Pancalier* may serve for testimony who when yᵉ duchesse of *Savoy* would not yeeld to his lasscivious lust, wrought sutch wyles, yᵗ she was condemned for adultry, and judged to suffer most shamefull death by burning. Now to prevent either of these perils it lieth in my power, & seing of evils yᵉ least is to be chosen, I think it better then to hazard life, living, or good name, to lose that which shalbee no great losse to my husband or my self, for as the sun though it shine on us here in *Italy*, yet it giveth light likewise to those that are in England and other places: or as the sea hath fish for every man, or as one good dishe of meate may well suffice two persons though very hungry, so is there that in mee wherwith *Synnatus* may bee satisfied, and *Synorix* sufficed. And this incourageth mee hereto the rather, for that I see by experience in most of my neighbours, yᵗ those are ever most made of by their husbandes, who that way deale

10

20

30

10 Salesbury/Salisbury *BCDEF*   15–16 Pancalier/Pancaliar *CDEF*
30 hereto/thereto *CDEF*

most falsely with theyr husbandes. Besides that how
openly soever they deale in these affaires, theyr husbandes never heare of it, and though they do heare of it,
yet wil thei not harken unto it, and though they do in
a manner se it, yet will they not beleeve it, and though
they doo beeleeve it, yet will they love them the better
to have them leave it the sooner. Againe, what know I
whether my husband deale falsly with mee & row in some
other streame, which if it bee so, I shal but save my
soule in paying his debts, & exercise the vertue of justice
in requiting like for like. And touching corrupting of my
childrens bloud, I thinke it made more noble in partic-
ipating *with* a bloud more noble then my husbands is.
But canst thou harlot cal him husband, whom y^u meanest so wickedly to betray? Am I in my wits to use these
witles words? Is it my mouth y^t hath uttred this blasphemy, or was it the divel within me that delivered it
forth? No, if I were gyltie but in thought hereto, I
would restore ye fault with criminal penance, yea if I
felt any part in me apt to any such evil, I would cut it of
for feare of infecting the rest of ye body. Good god,
whether now is honour fled, which was ever wont to bee
the fairest flower in my garland? Whether now is chastity chased, which hath bene alwaies the cheifest stay
of my state? Shall the sunne of my shining life be now
eclipsed with an acte so filthy, that the very remembrance thereof is no lesse greevous then death? Why, was
Helen for all her heavenly hew, any other accounted then
a common harlot, and was it not only to bee revenged on
her and her champion *Paris*, that the *Grecians* continued
their siege so long? And touchinge the inconveniences I
may incur by this refusall, is any evill worse then [dis-
B-F] honesty? Is there any thinge to bee fled more then

offence? Is not the losse of goodes lesse, then of ones
good name? Is not an honourable death to bee preferred
before an infamous life [?] And touching yᵉ Countesse
before rehersed, had shee ever married with the kinge if
shee had not continued in her constancy to the ende?
And for the Duchesse of *Savoy* what hurt sustained shee
by that false accusation? Did it not make her glory and
vertue shew more splendently to the whole world? Yes
no doubt of it, for like as streames the more ye stop them
the higher they flow: and trees the more yee lop them the
greater they growe, or as Spices the more they are beaten
the sweeter sent they send forth: or as the herbe *Camamile* the more it is trodden downe the more it spreadeth
abroad, so vertue & honesty the more it is spited, the
more it sprouteth and springeth, for honour ever is the
reward of vertue, and doth accompany it as duly as the
shadow doth the body. And as the sun though it bee
under a cloud keepeth still his brightnes though wee see
it not, so vertue though it bee dimmed with divelishe
devises, yet it keepeth her strength and power still,
though to us it seeme utterly to bee extinguished, so
that so longe as I remaine vertuous & honest, I neede
not care what man, malice or the divell can devise
against mee. No no deare children you shall not by my
meanes bee suspected to bee bastardes, neither wil I
make thee sweet husband ashamed to shew thy face
amongest the best of them: and I wil let thee understand
the villany which that viper *Synorix* indevoureth to
death. And shall I deale so fondly in deede, is not the
repulse punishment inough, onlesse I beewray his dooinges to my husband and so procure him further displeasure? Yea I might thereby bee occasion to set them

10

20

30

together by the eares, whereby it might fall out (as the
event of battaile is alwayes doubtfull) that my husband
might bee hurt or slaine, and then the common report
would bee (as the people are ever prone to speake the
woorst) that I beeing an ill woman had conspired his
confusion and seh [set *B–F*] *Synorix* to slea him. And
though no sutch thing chauncet (as God forbid it
should) yet this at least I should bee sure to get by it,
that my husbande ever after would bee jelious over mee,
and right carefull would hee bee to keepe that which hee
saw others so busily to seeke. And sutch is the malice of
men, perchaunce hee would judge some light behaviour
in mee, to be the cause that incouraged *Synorix* to attempt my chastity. For men have this common opinion
amongest them, that as there is no smoake but where
there is some fire, so seldom is there any fervent love,
but where there hath bene some kindnesse shewed to
kindle ones desire. Moreover this toy may take him in
the head, that it is a practise between us two to prevent
suspicion & cloake our love, & with the firme perswasion
of my invincible chastity, to lull him a sleepe in security,
and then most to deceave him, when hee least suspect-
eth guile: and if at any time hee heare of it by other, I
may stop his mouth with this, that I my selfe tolde him
of it, which if I had ment to deale falsely with him, I
would not have done: yea what know I whether hee wil
like the better or the worse of mee, for breeding sutch a
bees nest in his braine: lastly I should derogate mutch
from mine owne vertue, and in a manner accuse my
selfe of pronenesse to fal that way, as though I were not
strong inough to withstand his assaultes without the assistance of my husband. Yes, god in whom I repose my
trust, shall fortifie mee against the fury of my foes, and

27 the worse/worse *CDEF*

give mee grace with wisdome to escape his wiles, with
charines to eschew his charmes, and with pietie to resist
his pravitie.

Now to returne to *Synorix*, so soone as that olde *Pandarina* had related unto him at large the answere of his
Misteris, hee fel from the place he sat, flat upon the
ground, and lay in a traunce a great while, and now
those sparks which beefore love had kindled in him, were
with continuall sighes so blowen, as it were with a payre
of bellowes, that they breake foorth into fierie flames, 10
and that which before was fancie, was now turned to
furie: for beyng come to himselfe, or rather beeinge
quight past himselfe, with staringe lookes, with pale
countenaunce, with fierie eyes, with gnashing teeth, with
trembling tongue, in rage he roared foorth these words.

And shall I thus be frustrate of my desire? shal I with
wordes and workes, with prayers and presentes, pursue
the goodwill of a daintie disdayninge dame, and receive
but labour for my love, and greeif for my goodwill? But
ah frantik foole, why doe I in my rage, rage against her 20
who is the most fayre and curteous creature under
heaven? No it is that churle *Synnatus* that soweth the
sede of my sorrow, it is his severitie towardes her, that
causeth her crueltie towardes mee: the feare shee hath of
him, is the cause she dareth not take compassion on my
passions: and shall hee swim in blisse, and I lie drencht
in deepe dispaire? Shal he be ingorged with pleasure, & I
pine away in paine? No I will make him feele that once,
which hee maketh me feele a thousand times a day. And
hereupon determined with himselfe by some meanes or 30
other to procure the death of *Synnatus*, thinking thereby
the sooner to obtaine his purpose of his wife. And callinge unto hym one of his swearing swash buckler ser-

13 with pale/pale *BCDEF*

vauntes, hee laide before him the platfourme of his purpose, and tolde hym plainely if hee woulde speedily
dispatch *Synnatus* out of the way, he would give him a
thousand crownes in his purse to keepe him in another
Country. His servaunt, though altogether past grace,
yet for fashion sake began to advise his maister more
wisely, saying.

For mine owne part it maketh no matter, for another
country is as good for mee as this, and I count any place
my country, where I may live wel and wealthily, but
for your part it beehooveth you to looke more warely
to your selfe, for that your love towardes *Camma* is
knowen to divers of this citie, by reason wherof, if I
should commit any sutch acte, it must needes bee
thought that you must needes bee accessarie therto,
which will turne, though not to your death, for that
none hath auctoritie above you to execute the rigour of
the lawes upon you, yet to your utter shame and reproche it can not but convert.

Tush (saith his master) the case is light, where counsayle can take place: what talkest thou to mee of shame,
that am by injurious and spitefull dealyng deprived the
use of reason, and dispossessed of my wittes and sences[?]
Neither am I the first that have played the like parte,
did not *David* the chosen servant of God, beeyng blasted
with the beutie of *Bersabe*, cause her husband *Urias* to
bee set in the forefront of the battayle to be slayne,
which doone hee married his wife? And why is it not
lawfull for mee to do the like? But I know the worst of
it, if thou wilt not take it upon thee, I will either do it
my selfe, or get some other that shall.

The man seeyng how his Maister was bent bothe to
satisfie his minde, and to gaine so good a summe of

13 this citie/the Citty *EF*   33 good/great *CDEF*

money promised to perfourme his charge which with
oportunity of time and place hee did. And seeyng
Synnatus on a time, (in ill time) passyng thorow a blind
lane of the Citie, hee shrowded himselfe in a corner, and
as hee came by, shot him thorow with a Pistol: which
doone hee foorthwith fled the countrey. *Camma* hearyng
of the cruell murther of her husbande, and by the cir-
cumstances, knowyng *Synorix* to bee the authour thereof,
tearynge her heyre, scratching her face, and beatyng her
body agaynst the ground, so soone as the fluddes of   10
teares had flowen so longe that the fountayne was drie,
so that her speeche might have passage, whiche before
the teares stopped, shee began to crie out in this carefull
manner.

O God, what unjustice is this in thee, to suffer the
earth remayne polluted with the bloud of innocentes?
Diddest thou cursse *Cain* for killing his brother *Abel*,
and wilt thou not crucifie *Synorix* for sleayng *Synnatus*?
Is thy hart now hardned that thou wilt not, or are thy
hands now weakened that thou canst not preserve thy ser- 20
vantes from the slaves of Sathan? If there bee no safetie
in innocencie, wherin shall wee repose our selves? If thou
bee not our protectour, who shall defend us? If the wicked
vanquish the vertuous, who shal set foorth thy honour
and glory, or who will so mutche as once call upon thy
name? But what meane I wretched wight to exclayme
agaynst God as the aucthour of my evill, wheras it is only
I my selfe that am guiltie of my husbandes death? It is I
that pampred up my beutie, to make it glister in the sight
of every gazynge eye, in the thriftlesse threade wherof   30
this Tirant was so intangled, that to unwinde himself
thereout hee hath wrought all this mischeif. It is I that

---

15 in thee *om. BCDEF*   16 remayne/to remayne *BCDEF*
28 I *om. BEF*   31 so *om. DEF*

would not detect his doynges to my husband, wherby hee might have prevented the perill which hung over his head. And seeyng I have been the cause of his death, shall I beyng a murtherer remayne alive? Did *Alcyone* seeynge the dead carkas of her husbande *Ceix* cast on shore, willingly cast her selfe into the Sea to accompany his death [?] And shall I see my sweet *Synnatus* slayne, and not drinke of the same cuppe? Did true *Thisbe* goare her gorgious body with the same sworde, wherwith princely *Piramus* had prickt him selfe to the hart: and are not my handes stronge inough to do the like? Did *Julietta* die upon the corps of her *Romeo*, and shall my body remayne on earth, *Synnatus* beyng buried? No gentle death come with thy direfull dart, and peirce my paynefull harte, and with one death rid mee out of a thousande deathes at once. For what thought do I thinke on my *Synnatus*, which doth not procure mee double death? What thing do I see belongyng to him, which is not a treble torment unto mee? But it is cowardlinesse to wish for death, and couragiousnesse valiantly to take it. Yes I can and will bestow my lyfe for my *Synnatus* sweete sake: but O God shall that Tyrant remayne alive to triumphe in his trechery, & vaunt in his villanie? Shall I not see his fattall day beefore my finall end [?] It is his bloud that wilbe a most sweete sacrifice to the ghost of *Synnatus*, not mine: and then can I ende my life contentedly when I have offred up this acceptable sacrifice: and untill sutch time as I have oportunity hereto, I will prolonge my dolefull dayes in direfull greefe, and onely the hope of revengment, shall heavily holde my lothsome life and sorowfull soule together? For other cause why I should desire life I have not, for that I am utterly

4 Alcyone/Alcione *BCDE*, Alicione *F*   19 unto/to *EF*
25 of/of my *CDEF*

deprived of all joyes of life. For as the bird that is bruised
with some blow lieth aloofe on the leaves, and heares
his felowes singe, and is not able to utter one warblinge
note out of his mournfull voice, but rather hates the
harmony which other birdes doo make, so I, my heart
beeing broosed and broken, sit solitarily alone and see
some hange about their husbandes neckes, some closely
clepe them in their armes, some trifle with them, some
talke with them, all which sight redoubleth my paine to
thinke myself deprived of those pleasures: yea to a   10
wretched wounded heart that dwels in dole, every pleasaunt sight turnes to bitter spight: and the onely objecte
which shall ever content my eyes, shall bee the distruction of that tyraunt, which hath brought mee to this
desolation.

Now *Synorix* thinking that time had taken away her
teares and sorrow, and supposinge that neither shee,
neither any other had suspected him for the murther of
her husband, began to enter into the listes of lust againe,
and with a new incountry of incontinency to set upon   20
her. But shee so mutch abhorred him, that if shee but
heard his name it caused her nature to fayle in her,
and all her sences to faint: so that when hee saw no pos-
ibility to impell her to impiety, hee ment to move her
in the way of mariage and caused her nere kinsfolke and
friends to solicite his sute unto her, who partly for feare
of his displeasure, partly for that they knew it would bee
greatly to her advauncement, laboured very ernestly in
the matter, and were so importunate upon her that no
answere would satisfie them. Now *Camma* seeing shee   30
could not be rid of her freends, and foreseeing that by
this meanes shee might bee rid of her enemies, agreed to
take him to husband. And the day of the solemnizing of

13 my/mine *EF*   32 enemies/enemie *BD*, enimie *C*, enemy *EF*

the mariage beeinge come, they went together to the temple of *Diana* wher al things according to custome beeing consummated, the bride wife (as the use was) dranke to her husband in drinke as hee thought, but indeede in poyson which shee had provided of purpose: and when shee saw hee had drunke up his death, shee sayd unto him goe now and in steed of thy mariage bed get thee a grave, for thy mariage is turnd to murther, a punishment most just for thy outragious lust and cruell tyranny, for vengeance asketh vengeance, & bloud bloud, and they yᵗ sowe slaughter, shalbee sure to reape ruine and destruction. Now *Synorix* hearing these woordes and feeling the force of the poyson to woorke within him, assaied all the remedies hee could to cure him selfe, but al in vain. *Camma* also feeling the poyson to prevaile within her, fell upon her knees beefore the aulter of *Diana* uttringe these woordes.

O goddesse, thou knowest how since the death of my sweete husband, this life hath beene most lothsome and sower unto mee, and that the only offeringe up of this sacrifice kept mee from him, which now in thy presence I have perfourmed I thinke my selfe to have satisfied my duty, and purchased therby a pasport to passe to the place and Paradise where my husband hath his habitation.

Immediatly upon this so well as shee could shee crauld home to her house, where shee was no sooner, but shee had certaine tydinges brought her that *Synorix* was deade. Wherwith with great joy shee cast her selfe downe upon her bed, and called her litle children about her, and blessing and bussing them sayd.

Alas pretty Impes who shal now defend you from your foes, who shall redresse your wronges? Your father

9 most *om. CDEF*   cruell/ruel *B, mispr.*   14 cure/heale *EF*

is gone, your mother is goinge, and you poore soules
must bide behinde to abide the brunt and bitter blastes
of this wretched world. Ah if the love which I bare my
husband had not beene exceeding great, nature woulde
have caused mee to have had some care of you, & for
your sakes to have suffred my self somtime longer to
live, but now as I have shewed my self a loving wife, so
have I scarce shewed my selfe a naturall mother. But
alas it was reason I shoulde prefer him beefore you, who
was the autor of you, & who blessed me with you. Wel I   10
see now my time is come, my toung begins to faile,
come dere children, & take your last conge of your lost
mother, god shield you from shame, God preserve you
from perill, God send you more prosperous fortune then
your poore parents had. And thus farewel my fruit,
farewel my flesh, farewel sweete babes, and O welcome
my *Synnatus*, whom I see in the skies ready to receive
mee, and so in sorrow and joy shee gave up the ghost.

Now I would wish you blazing starres which stande
upon your chastity, to take light at this lot, to take heed   20
by this harme, you see the husband slaine, the ruffian
fled, the lover poysoned, the wife dead, the freinds com-
fortles, the children parentlesse. [And can the preservation of one simple womans chastitie, countervaile all
these confusions? Had not the losse of her chastitie been
lesse then of her lyfe? yea and of so many soules, which
(no doubt) are in daunger of damnation by their desperate and sodayne death? and of her own especially, by
her wilfull and voluntary death? *B–F*] But it is naturally
incident to women to enter into extremities, they are   30
either to lovinge or to lothinge, to curteous or to coy, to
willinge or to wilfull, to mercifull or to mercilesse, to for-

1 you/your *E*   8 have *om. EF*   15 had/have had *BCDEF*

warde or to froward, to freindly or to feendly, the
meane they alwayes meanely account of. Otherwise shee
might with reason sooner then rigour have repressed his
rage. [she might with some continent curtesie have cooled
his incontinent desire: and better it had been to have
drawen hym on with delayes, then to have driven him
into sutch dispayre, and to have brought him into some
error, then to have put hym into sutch terror. *B–F*] But
howsoever my words run, I would not you should take
them to tend altogether to her dispraise, for as I must
condemne her crueltie, so can I not but commende her
constancie, & chastitie, and thinke her worthy to bee
compared to *Lucrece*, *Penelope*, or what woman soever
that ever had any preheminence of praise for her vertue.
And I woulde wishe my gallant youthes, which delight
to gaze in every garish glasse, and to have an Oare stirring in every beutifull boate, not to row past their
reache, not to fixe their fancie upon impossibilities, not
to suffer themselves to be blasted with the beames of
beautie, or scorched with the lightning of loving lookes:
sutch love towardes the married is ever without lawe,
sutch fire is without feare, sutch suits are without
shame, sutch Cankers, if they bee not at the beginning
cured, growe to the confusion of the whole body. Therefore Gentlewomen I leave it to your judgements to give
sentence, whether be more worthy reprehension, hee or
she. He had the law of love on his side, shee had the lawe
of men and of marriage on her part: love led him, which
the goddes themselves cannot resist, chastitie guided
her, whiche the goddes themselves have lost: he killed
him whom he counted his enemy, she killed him whom

16 in/on *DEF*
18 fancie/fancies *BCDEF*
22 without feare/with feare *EF*   30 goddes/goddesses *BCDEF*

she knew her fleshly freinde: shee with reason might
have prevented great mischiefe, his wings were to mutch
limed with lust to fly forth of his folly.

1 fleshly *om. BCDEF*
3 fly/flee *BCDEF*

Tereus and Progne.

[TEREUS Kinge of *Thrace*, enamored of *Progne*, daughter to *Pandion* Prince
of *Athens*, obtaineth her in marriage, and conveyeth her into his owne
countrey. *Progne*, desirous to see her sister *Philomela*, mooveth *Tereus* to
go to *Athens*, and to get licence to bringe her into *Thrace*, who on the way
fallinge into unlawfull likinge of her, forceth her to his pleasure, and cut-
teth out her tounge, that shee might tell no tales. *Progne*, havinge hereof
secret intelligence, in lew of that foule fact, murthereth his and her owne
Sunne, young *Itys*, and dresseth him in meates for his Fathers mouthe.
Whiche horrible deede when *Tereus* would have revenged uppon the
Mother and Aunt, they escape his handes, and are transfourmed into
Birdes.]

IF it were meete for mortall creatures to complaine of
their immortall creator, then truly may wee justly prepare complaint against our maker, for that of al his
creatures hee hath made man most miserable. Herbes,
Trees and plants hee hath framed without sence, wherby
they neither feele the force of winters blastes, neither yᵉ
fire of sommers blaze: foules, fishes and beastes hee hath
beereaved of a reasonable soule, wherby they beare the
brunt of their bodies onely, and are not molested with
the motions of the minde: but man hee hath made subjecte to infirmities of the body, to miseries of minde, to
all stormes of striefe and panges of paine: And as the
Cameleon chaungeth him selfe into yᵉ colour and hew of
every thing hee doth viewe, so man is made apt to bee
transfourmed into any misfortune, and to receive any
evill yᵗ raigneth upon the face of the earth: yea, if wee
consider the whole course of our life, wee begin with

9 Itys/Itis *C*   18 neither feele/never feele *DEF*   20 a *om. CDEF*
23 the *om. CDEF*   25 Cameleon/Camelion *CDEF*

cries, and end with cares: for we are no sooner out of our mothers wombe, but we forthwith cry to signifie the sorrow which will insue in our succeeding age: in our infancy our tender bodies are subjecte to many infirmities: in our childhood our weake mindes are troubled with many toyes: wee are plyed sore to silence, which is of hard digestion to us, wee feare the maisters lowringe lore, which is a continuall torment unto us: but oh, the sea of sorrow and waves of woe which then overwhelme us, when wee once arrive to mans estate, what vaine desires? What fantasticall follies? What careles and sparelesse spendinge? What prodigall pride? What fiery flames of love? What harebraind heates of hate? What pensife feare of parentes displeasure? What solitarinesse in single life? What minde to marry? What misery in mariage? What charge in children? What care of theyr instruction? What fear of their distruction, and touching our owne bodies, what often surfetinges? What perillous plewrises? What fearefull fevers? What daunger in warre? What perill in fight? Yea what sorrow which this age is not subjecte to? Lastly in olde age wee covetously carke for coine, wee toyle for trashe, wee thinke wee never have inough, wee thinke all to mutch that is spent, wee take litle pleasure in any thing, wee thinke the world is changed, and that it is far worse then it was when wee were younge, only bicause our bodies are changed, and our vitall heat so vanished away, that nothing seemeth pleasaunt unto us, though it bee the same it was woont to bee, so that wee thinke the alteration to bee in the thing, when it is in our selfe. And then not onely our memory fayleth, our wits waxe weake, and

10

20

30

---

6 silence/science *BCDEF*   8 lore/looke *BCDEF*   10 wee once/once we *EF*
17 fear of/fear for *E*   22 carke/care *DEF*   25 then/then when *EF*
30 is/was *EF*   31 and/we *BCDEF*

returne to infancy againe, but our bodies also are broken
with cares, taken with crampes, shaken with paulseies,
tormented with the stone, lamed with the goute, dried
with dropsies, our sight waxeth dim, our hearing deafe,
our smelling smal, our tasting untoothsome, our feelinge
feable, yea all our sences are almost without sence: & yet
we are loth to die & leave our worldly mucke, the feare
of approaching death doeth dayly daunt us, and at
length his deadly dartes doe utterly distroy us. And
surely the consideration of this our miserable estate doth
so resolve mee into sorrow, that if your presence did not
sprinkle mee with some deawe of delight, I should hardly
frame my wittes to procure you pleasure by any pleasant history, but rather continew a dolorous discourse
of our calamity. And yet the history I meane to tell
shall not bee altogether estraunged from the argument
of my former discourse, but though it manifest not our
manyfolde misery, yet shall it at least set foorth the
frailty of our felicity. The history is this.

The flowrishynge common wealth of *Athens* had to
their prince one *Pandion*, whose estate bothe fortune
beutified with great wealthe, and God blessed with
goodly children, to wit two daughters of excellent beutie,
the eldest named *Progne*, the youngest *Philomela*. Now
fame beeyng a tatlyng Goddesse, blazed the brute of
Progne abroade into divers countries, untill at length
the rumour of her renoume ronge about the eares of
Tereus kynge of *Thrace*, who beeynge a younge lustie
gallant, made no great account of the commendations
whiche were given her, knowyng, if hee were disposed to
marrie, hee might make his choyce amongst a great number as good as shee was, and more nere neighbours unto
him then *Athens* was. But destenies so drave that shortly
after this, on a night in his sleape hee seemed to see her

stand apparently before him (only a stronge imagination
assurynge him that it was shee) which sight sunke so
deeply into his heart and brought him sutch excessive
delight, that hee presently awaked, and missyng the
partie that procured him sutch pleasure, his joy was
tournd to anoy: neither coulde hee ever after that finde
any contentation in any thought or deed, but only in
this determination to goe have a true sight of her, whose
seemyng shadow had so dazeled his eyes: and with all
speed repayred his shippes, and prepared al thyngs nec-   10
essary for sutch a voyage, and by the help of good
wynde and will, shortly arrived there where his hart had
already cast anker: and sent ambassadours to the kyng
to certifie him of his commynge, who receyved him with
royaltie fit for his regall estate. And at the first incountry of the two princes *Tereus* sayde.

My commyng unto you O noble prynce is not as an
open enemie to invade you, for you see I am unarmed,
neither as a secret traytour to intrap you, for you know
I am your freend: but that you may not mervayle at   20
my sodayne cummyng, you shall understand it is to see
your daughter the Lady *Progne*, for you shall soone perceyve I pretende well unto her. *Pandian* answered.

As (most worthy prince) the cause of your comming
is friendly, so can I not but friendly accept it, and how
much I thinke my selfe honoured therby so mutch I
count my selfe bound unto you.

And after a litle parlee passed betweene them of the
estates of their realmes and manners of their countreies,
Pandion preferred him to the sight of his daughter,   30
whom after *Tereus* had saluted with a curteous conge,
hee entred into discoursing with in this sort.

If faire Lady, I should tell the truth of my comming

16 sayde/sayth *EF*   23 Pandian/Pandion *BCDEF*

into this country, I thinke you would take it but for a
trifling toy, yea if I should in woords plainly set downe
ye cause of this my interprised journey, and the case
which through your meanes I remaine in, I doubt you
would neither beleeve the cause, neither releeve my case:
for yt the straungnesse of the one would breed great in-
credulity & for the other the small acquaintance I have
with you & lesse deserts towards you can crave smal
curtesy: yet if it please you to know, neither the desire
to see this country, neither the renoume of your vertue
& beauty brought me hither, for though the report therof
be great, yet now I se I must needes say, yt fame hath
rather framed your praise maliciously then reported it
truly, for one good part reported to bee in you, I perceive by your countenance such confluence of good conditions, that I can not but counte the rumor which run
of you, rather sparing speeche then right reporte. But
the cause of my hasty comminge and heavy case is this,
it pleased the goddes to presente your seemely selfe to
my presence, in the same lovely likenesse wherin you
are at this present, what time I tooke sutch veiwe of
your sweete face, that approchinge this daye to your
fathers palaice, beefore I knew who you were, what you
were, or where you were, as you looked if you remember
it, out at your chamber window, I said to my servants,
loe yonder standes the peereles peragon princely *Progne*:
and since yt sight in my sleepe, I take the heavens to
witnesse I never injoyed one quiet sleepe, but continued in contemplation how I might be placed in possession of that personage which drave me into sutch admiration. Now seinge it pleased the gods thus miracu-
lously to move mee to traveile to see you, and seeing the

8 with/with with *B, mispr.*   14 for/for, for *BCDEF*
16 rumor/rumors *DEF*   25 at/of *EF*

sight of your sweete face hath fast fettred my fancy in
links of love, these may bee humbly to desire you, neither to resist the motion of the goddes, neither to rejecte the devotion of my good wil. And if I have preferred your love before all the Ladies of my owne land,
if I make you that profer which many princes have
pressed for, if neither wearines of way, neither perils of
sea could prohibite mee from pursuing your good will, if I
bee content to resigne my kingdome, liberty and all that
I have into your handes, I shall desire you not to con-   10
temne my curtesy, but to countervaile my paine and to
returne my goodwill with like love and affection. This
request also resteth to make unto you that you drive
mee not of with trifeling delayes, for neither will the extremity of my perplexity permit longe delay, neyther
will the estate my kingdome standeth in, suffer mee
longe to bee away.

Progne hearing the ernest sute of this prince, and seeinge nothing in him to be misliked, considering also what
haste his request required, stood not upon the nice   20
termes of her virginity, but with a reverence of majesty
made him this answere.

Most worthy prince whatsoever were the cause of
your comming into this countrey, the kinge my father
hath to holde himselfe mutch beeholding to your majestie, that it would please you too do him the honour to
visite him: but touching the cause you pretend, I doubt
not but your wisdome knoweth that dreames are doubtfull, and visions are altogether vaine and therfore I must
crave pardon if I hardly beleeve, yt upon so light a cause   30
you would undertake sutch heavy travayle: and I mutch
muse that in your sleepe the goddes had no seemlier
sight than my selfe to present unto you: but whether
before you came hether, the goddes moved your minde,

or whether beeing here your owne fancy forced your
affection towards mee, assure your selfe this, if your love
bee as loyall, as your wordes seeme wonderfull in shewing the originall therof, you shal not finde mee either so
discourteous as to contemne your goodwill, either so un-
gratefull as not to requite it, mary as I may, which is for
your harty goodwil to give you my hart, for any benefit
of my body it is not in mee to bestow on you: for if you
do mee that injury to exacte any thing at my handes lasciviously, honesty will not allow it, whose boundes I
meane not to transgresse, and if you doe mee that honour to pursue my good will in the way of mariage, perchance my parents will not permit it, who onely have
power to place mee at their pleasuer. So that as the one
halfe and moytie of mee is not mine, so the other part,
if your goodwill bee as greate as you pretend, shalbee
yours. Presently upon this he preferred his sute to her
parentes, who were no lesse glad of sutch a sonne in law,
then hee of sutch a wife. And so out of hand ye mariage
with great solemnity was celebrated. Which done hee
joyfully departed from his sorowfull father in law, and
in short time safely lande[d] with his wife in his owne
land, where they lived together the space of five yeeres
in sutch joy as they commonly injoy, who cary fortune
as it were upon their shoulders, and abound in al thinges
which they can wish or desire. But see the frailty of our
felicity, marke the misery which mortall men are subject to. A man would have thought this maried couple
in love so loyall, in estate so high, in all thinges so happy,
had bene placed in perpetuity of prosperity. But alas
what estate hath fortune ever made so invencible,
which vice can not vanquish? Who hath ever bene established in sutch felicity, but that wickednesse can woorke

9 mee *om. EF*

his overthrow? What love hath ever beene so fast bound, but by lust hath been loosed? Yea the most faithfull bond of frendship betweene *Tytus* and *Gysippus*, thorow luste was violated: the most naturall league of love betweene *Antiochus* and his owne sonne, through lust was broken: and this most loyall love betweene *Tereus* and *Progne* through lust was turnd to lothsome hate. For it fortuned that *Progne* after they had bene maried together a whyle entred into great desire to see her sister *Philomelia*, and lay very importunately upon her husband to go to *Athens* and request her father *Pandion* to let her come unto her. *Tereus* loved his wife so intirely that hee would deny her nothinge, but presently imbarkte him selfe and went to fetch *Philomela* unto her. And beeing arrived at *Athens*, hee made *Pandion*, privy to yᵉ cause of his comming. The olde man was assailed with great sorrowe to thinke hee must parte from his faire *Philomela* the only stay and comfort of his olde yeeres, but *Tereus* intreated so ernestly that hee could not denie him easely, and *Philomela* was so desirous to see her sister that had so lovingely sent for her, that shee hung about her fathers necke kist him and used al the flatteries shee could to force him to yeelde his consent to her departure, wherwith hee beeinge vanquished with weeping eyes in great griefe and dolour delyvered his daughter to *Tereus* saying.

It is not my daughter onely I deliver you but mine owne life, for assure your selfe my life can not last one minute longer, then I shall heare shee doth well, and if her returne bee not with speede, you shall heare of my speedy returne to the earth from whence I came.

Tereus desired him to bee of good chere promisinge

3 Tytus/Titus *DEF*   Gysippus/Gisippus *DEF*
10 Philomelia/Philomela *BCDEF*

to be as carefull of her well dooing as if shee were his owne sister or childe. Whereupon the olde man blessinge his daughter gave her unto him. But like a simple man hee committed the seely sheepe to the ravening Woulfe.

Nay, there was never blouddy tiger that did so terribly teare the litle Lambe, as this tiraunt did furiously fare with faire *Philomela*. For beeing in ship together, hee began filthily to fixe his fancy upon her, and castinge the feare of god from before his eies, rootinge the love of his wife out of his heart, contemninge the holy rites of matrimony, and the sacred state of virginity, hee fell to fleshly daliance with her, and attempted to win that point of her, which shee held more dere and precious then her life, and which ought to bee of curious regard to al women of honest behaviour. But having no other weapon but weepyng to defende her selfe, by pitiful exclemations and cries shee kept him from satisfiyng his insaciable desire. But as the ravenyng Woulfe having seazed in his tearyng clawes some seely Lambe, seekes some den to hide him in, that nothing hinder him from quietly injoyinge his pray, so hee was no sooner arrived on the coastes of his owne countrey, but that hee secretly convayed her to a graunge of his owne, far from any towne or citie, & there by force filthily deflowred her. The poore mayde thus piteously spoyled, so soone as her greif would give her leave to speake, spit foorth her venome agaynst his villanie in this sort.

Ah most tirrannous Traytor, hast thou thus betrayed my father and sister, haddest thou no other to worke thy wickednesse on but mee, who was the jewell of my father and the joy of my sister, and now by thy meanes shalbe the distruction of the one, and the desolation of the other? O that my handes had strength to teare these

33 these/those *BCDEF*

starynge eyes out of thy hatefull head, or that my mouth
were able to sounde the trumpet of this thy trumpery,
either to the court of my sister, or country of my father,
that thei might take revenge on thy villanie. O cursed
bee the wombe from whence thou camst, and the paps
whiche gave thee sucke: O cursed bee the cause of thy
conception, and the Father that begat thee, who if hee
never otherwise in his life offended, yet doth hee deserve
to bee plonged in the most paynfull pit of Hell, only for
begetting so wicked a sunne.   10

Tereus not able to indure this talke, and fearyng least
her words might bewray his wickednesse, made no more
ado but tooke his knife, and like a blouddy butcher, cut
her tounge foorth of her head. This done hee caused her
to bee locked fast in a chamber, takyng every thyng
from her wherby she might use violence towardes her
selfe, and so went home to the Queene *Progne* his wife,
with this forged tale.

I am sory sweete wife it is my chaunce to bee the
messenger of sutch sower newes unto you, but seeing of   20
force you must heare it, as good I now impart it, as
other here after report it unto you. And seeing it is an
accident which ordinarily happeneth to mortall wightes,
I trust of your selfe you will give sutch order to your sorowe, that you will suffer it to sinke no depelier into your
hearte then wisdome would it should: caryinge this in
your remembraunce that wee are borne to die, and that
even in our swathe cloutes death may aske his due. Alas
(saith she) and is *Pandion* departed? No (sayth hee)
Pandion liveth, but his life is sutch that death would   30
more delight him.

Then farewell my *Philomela* (sayth shee) thy death

6 whiche/y^t *E*, that *F*   25 into/unto *EF*
26 it/you *EF*   28 our/your *EF*

I know is cause of this desolation, and thy death shall soone abridge my daies. In deede (sayth hee) so it is the gods have had her up into heaven, as one to good to remaine on earth. Ah unjust goddes (sayth shee) shee is to good for them also, what pity, what pieti, what right, what reason is in them, to deprive her of life now in the prime of her life, beefore she have tasted the chiefe pleasures of life, or any way deserved the paine of death?

Ah sweete wife (sayth hee) I beeseech you by the love which you beare mee, to moderate your martirdome & asswage your sorrow, & only in mee to repose your felicitie: for I protest by these hands & teares which I shede to see your sorrow, that I wilbe to you in steede of a father & a sister: yea if you had a thousand fathers & a thousand sisters al their goodwils together, shuld not surmount mine alone.

These lovinge woordes caused her somewhat to cease from her sorrow, and shee began, to take the matter as paciently as her paine would permit her. But to returne to *Philomela* who beeinge kept close prisoner determined to pine herselfe to death, but the hope of revenge altered that determination, and shee began to cast in her head how she might open the injury to her sister, which that Tirant had offered them both: at length shee went this way to worke, shee wrought and imbrodred cunningly in cloath the whole discourse of her course and carefull case, which being finished, fortune so framed that a gentleman riding late in the night had lost his way, and seeing a light in her chamber a far of, drewe nere to the window, and called to *Philomela* inquiringe the way to the next towne, whereupon *Philomela* opened the window, & seeing him to bee a gentleman whom she thought would not sticke to put him selfe in some perill to redresse a Ladies wronge, shewed him the cloath which shee so cunningly had wrought, and in the first place thereof was plainly written, to whom it should bee delivered, and from whom. The gentleman tooke it at her handes, and plighted to her his fayth, safely and secretly to deliver it to the queene. See the just judgement of god, who will suffer no evill done secretly, but it shalbee manifested openly, as in times past hee made the infant *Daniell* an instrument to detecte the conspiracy of the two *Judas* judges, who falsely accused the good Lady *Susanna*, and other times other wayes: but this tiranny of *Tereus* was so terrible that the very stones in the walles would have beewrayed it, if there had been no other meanes used. Now *Progne* havinge this cloath convayed unto her, and fully understandinge how the case stoode, notwithstandinge her greife were great in the highest degree, yet (a mervailous thing a woman could do so) shee concealed ye matter secretly, hoping to be revenged more speedily. But yet her husbands villany towards her, caused her to inveigh against him in this vehement sort.

O divelish deepe dissembling of men, who would have thought that hee which pretended so great goodwill towards mee, would have intended so great ill against mee? Why if my person could not please him, could none but my sister satisfie him? and if hee thought her most meete for his mischeif, yet was it not villany inough to vanquish her virginity, but that hee must mangle and dismember her body also? but what pity is to bee looked for of sutch *Panthers* which passe not of piety? Hee sheweth his cursed carelesse kinde, hee plainely proves him selfe to proceed of the progenie of that traitor *Eneas*, who wrought the confusion of the good Queene *Dido*, who succoured him in his distres. It is evident hee is ingendred of *Jasons* race, who disloyally forsooke

15 were/was *EF*   29 carelesse/carls *B*, carles *C*   31 the/that *EF*

Medea y^t made him win ye golden fleece[.] Hee is discended of the stock of *Demopheon*, who through his
faithles dealing forced *Phyllis* to hange her selfe. Hee
seemes of the seede of *Theseus*, who left *Ariadne* in the
desertes, to bee devoured, through whose helpe hee subdued the Monster *Minotaur*, and escaped out of the intricate *Labirinth*. Hee commeth of *Nero* his cruel kinde,
who carnally abused his owne mother *Agrippina*, & then
caused her to bee slaine and ript open, that hee might
se the place wherin he lay beeing an infant in her belly.
So that what fruites but filthinesse is to bee gathered of
sutch graftes? What boughes but beastlines growe out
of sutch stems? no I will never make other account but
that faith which a man professeth is nothing els but forgery: truth which hee pretendeth nothing els but trifling:
love lust, woordes wyles, deeds deceit, vowes vanities,
faythfull promises faythlesse practises, ernest othes, errant artes to deceive, sorrows subtelties, sighes slightes,
groanes guiles, cries crafts, teares treason: yea all their
doinges nothing but baytes to intice us, hookes to intangle us, & ingins utterly to undoe us. O that my mouth
could cause my woords to mount above the skies, to
make ye gods bend downe their eyes to take vew of the
vilany of this viper, then no dout but either the city
would sinke wherin hee is, or the earth would open &
swalow him up, or the [*sic*] at least some plague should
bee thundred downe upon him, which might most paine-
fully punish him. Or why may not the gods use mee as
an instrument to execute their vengeance on him? The
wife of *Dionisias* the tirant wrought the will of the goddes on her husband, and miserably murthered him, and
why is it not lawfull for mee to doo the like? Yes I can

2 Demopheon/Demophon *BCDEF*   3 Phyllis/Phillis *BCDEF*
18 sighes/sights *EF*   26 the at least/at the least *BCDEF*

and will devise sutch exquisite punishment for this Tiraunt, that it shall feare all that come after from the like
filthinesse.

Now to further her furie shee had this oportunitie offred her, it was the same time of the yeere that the sacrifices of *Bacchus* were to bee celebrated, what time the
use was for the women to goe aboute the countrey disguised as if they had been mad, whereupon the Queene
tooke a troupe of women with her and gat to the graunge
where *Philo[mela]* was, brake open the doores, and
brought her home with her to her Palaice, and there they
two, the one with signes, and the other with woords,
entred into consultation how to bee revenged on the
trecherie of *Tereus*: and surely if a man bee disposed to
do his enemy a displeasure in deed, if he folow my counsayle, let him folow the counsayle of a woman, nay all
the Devils in Hell could not so have tormented *Tereus* as
they did, so that I thinke your selves wil say her fury ex-
ceeded his folly, and her severity in punishyng his crueltie in offendyng. For he had by her one only sweete
sunne named *Itys*. My tounge is not able to tell, and my
hart rendes in twayne to thinke, that a reasonable creature should so rage in rigour, that a woman should so
want compassion, that a mother should woorke sutch
mischiefe to her owne childe. For as I was about to tell
you, shee had by her husband one onely sonne, and shee
his owne mother miserably mente to murther him,
therby to bee revenged on her husband. O ruthlesse
rage, O merciles mother: I have read of a woman named
Althea who wrought the death of her owne sonne *Melea-*
ger, for that hee before had slaine two or three of her
bretheren, likewise *Agave* helped to teare in peeces her

5 her *om. EF*   14 Tereus/Terus *E, mispr.*
21 Itys/Itis *E*   30–31 Meleager/Meleagar *E*

own sonne *Penthey*, for that hee would not do honour to
the god *Bacchus*: but for a mother to murther, to mangle,
to make mans meate of her own childe beeing an innocent, an infant that never did or thought amisse, who
ever heard any thing more monstrous in nature, more
beastly in Tiranny, or more blouddy in cruelty? For
marke the manner of this murther, as her sister and shee
sate in her privy chaumber meditatinge of this mischeife,
in came *Itys* the prety elfe beeing two or three yeeres of
10   age, and seeing his mother sit sadly sayd unto her, Mam
how doost, why doest, weepe, and tooke her about the
necke and kist her, saying I will goe and call my dad to
come and play with thee: but shee like a tirannous Tiger
flong him from her saying: Away impe of impiety, how
like thy father thou art, not onely in favour, but in flattery also: I will make thee make thy Dad sport shortly:
the infant rose againe, and came run [running *B–F*] dug-
ling to her saying, why do you beate me mam, I have
learned my Criscrosse today so I have, and my father
20   sayth hee wil buie mee a golden coate, and then you
shannot kisse mee so you shannot, but this trifling
daliance could not turne her divelishnesse. But (O dread-
full deede, O lamentable case) shee tooke her prety babe
by the heare of the heade, and drew him into a privy corner provided for the purpose, and first cruelly cut of his
harmeles head, then butcherly quartered his comely
carkas, and betweene her sister and her dressed it in order
of meate, which done, (as the custome was in those feastes
of *Bacchus*) shee sent for the kinge her husband to suppe
30   with her, and set beefore him for the first service his owne
sun. Who after hee had fiercely fed on his owne fleshe, and
filled his belly with his owne bowels, hee asked for his
litle sonne *Itys*: the queene answered, why do you not

30 his/her *EF*

se him? I am sure you feele him, and as he stared about
the chamber to have seene him, out stept *Philomela*
from behinde a cloath of Arras, and flang the childes head
in the fathers face: wherby hee knew what banquet hee
had bene bid to, and so soone as his sences were come to
him, which that sower sight had taken away, hee drew
his rapier and thought to have offered up the bloud of
his wife and her sister for a sacrifice unto his sonne, but
they fled from him, and as *Ovid* reporteth were turned
into birds, meaninge they were not worthy humaine   10
shape or the use of reason, which were sutch cruell monsters altogether devoyd of ruth and reason. It were hard
here gentlewoman for you to give sentence, who more
offended of the husband or the wife, seeing the dooinges
of both the one and the other neere in the highest degree
of divelishnesse, such unbridled lust and beastly cruelty
in him, sutch monsterous mischiefe and murther in her,
in him sutch treason, in her sutch trechery, in him sutch
falsenesse, in her sutch furiousnesse, in him sutch devil-
ish desire, in her sutch revengful ire, in him sutch hellish   20
heat, in her sutch haggish hate, that I thinke them both
worthy to bee condemned to the most botomles pit in
Hell.

15 neere, *mispr.*/were
22 in/of *CDEF*

Germanicus and Agrippina.

[GERMANICUS, a younge Gentleman of small livyng, of the kin, and in the court of *Octavian* the Emperour, becummyng amorous of the Lady *Agrippina*, through great sute getteth her to wife: and through his valiencie winneth to bee proclaymed heyre apparant to the Empyre. Whose state *Tiberius* his cusin envying, dispatcheth him privily with poyson: and *Agrippina* for greif therof refusing all bodily sustenance, most miserably famisheth her self to death.]

THE Astronomers are of this opinion that the Planets
have preheminence over us, and that the Starres stir us
up to all our enterprises, but I am rather setled into this
sentence that not the Planets but our passions have the
cheife place in us, and that our owne desires not the destines dryve us to all our doynges: whiche opinion I may
justifie by the example of a Gentleman named *Germanicus*, whose fortune, neither the Fates fixed, neither the
Planets planted, neither the Starres stirred, neither the
destines drave, neither the Skies caused, but first his
owne fonde fancie framed, and then his owne ambitious
desire finished as by the sequele of this Hystorie you
shall see. For this Gentleman *Germanicus* frequentynge
the court of *Octavian* the Emperour, chaunced to fixe
his eyes on the face of a noble Gentlewoman named
Agrippina, the daughter of *M. Agrippa*, and as the
Mouse mumpeth so longe at the bayte, that at length
she is taken in trap, so hee bit so longe at the bayte of
her beutie, that at length hee was caught in *Cupids*
snare: and on a time as shee was at Cardes in the Presence chamber, this youth stoode staryng in her face in a

2 kin/kyn, kin B [*sic*], kindred *CDEF*   29 a *om. EF*

great studdy, which shee perceivynge to bryng him out
of his studdy, prayed him to reache her a boale of Wyne
which stoode uppon a Cupboord by: and as hee ap-
proched therewith to the place of her presence, his sences were so ravished with the sight of her sweete face,
that hee let the boale fall foorth of his handes: and re-
tiryng backe with seemly shamefastnesse, went for
more, and beeing come therwith shee thanked him for
his paines saying, I pray God that fall of the Wyne hinder not my winnyng and bryng mee ill lucke, for I know   10
many that connot [sic] away to have salt, or Drinke, or
any sutch like thynge fall towardes them.

Madame saith *Germanicus* I have often heard it dis-
puted in schooles that sutch as the cause of every thing
is, sutch wilbe the effect, and seeyng the cause of this
chaunce was good, I doubt not but the effect wil folow
accordyngly: and if any evill do insue therof I trust it
will light on my head through whose negligence it happened. *Agrip[pina]* answered. As I know not the cause,
so I feare not the effect greatly, and in deed as you say   20
hetherunto you have had the worst of it, for that
thereby you have been put to double paynes.

If that bee all (saith hee) rather then it shalbee sayd
any evill to have insued of this chaunce, I will perswade
my selfe that every payne whiche you shall put mee to,
shalbe double delight and treble pleasure unto mee. You
must use (sayth shee then) great eloquence to your selfe
to perswade you to sutch an impossibility. Oh if it please
you (sayth hee) there is an oratour which of late hath
taken up his dwelling within mee, who hath eloquence   30
to perswade mee to a far greater matter then this.

If (sayth shee) hee perswade you to thinges no more
behoufeful for your selfe then this, if you follow my

21 hetherunto/hitherto *BCDEF*

counsayle, you shall not give him house roome long.
Madame (sayth hee) it is an assured signe of a free and
freendly minde to give good counsayle, but it is harde
for one in bondage and out of his owne possession to
followe it. For what knoweth your honour whether hee
have already taken intire possession of the house wherin
hee is, which if it bee so, what wit is able to devise a writ
to remove him from thence? If sir (sayth shee) hee entred by order of law and payd you truely for it, it is reason hee injoy it, marie your folly was greate to retaine
sutch a tenant, but if hee intruded himselfe by force you
may lawfully extrude him by strength.

In deede (sayth hee) hee entred *vi et armis* forcibly,
but after upon certaine parlance passed betweene us, I
was content hee should remaine in peacible possession:
marie hee hath payd mee nothinge yet, but hee prom-
iseth so frankely that if the performance follow, a
house with beames of beaten golde, and pillers of precious stones will not countervaile the price of it: yea if I
were placed in quiet possession therof I would thinke
myself ritcher, I wil not say then the Emperour, but
which is most then god him selfe who possesseth heaven
and earth: and as the hope of obtayning the effecte of
that promise, heaveth mee up to heaven, so the doubt
to bee deceived therof driveth mee downe to hell.

And what joyly fellow (sayth shee) is this that prom-
iseth so frankely, will hee not promise golden hils and
perfourme durty dales? Would to god (sayth hee) your
semely selfe were so well acquainted with him as I am,
then would I make you judge of the worthynesse of the
thinge hee hath promised, for that you know the good-

12 extrude/exclude *EF*   18 of beaten/beaten of *E*   19 will/it will *EF*
22 most/more *EF*   god him selfe/the gods themselves *F*
22–23 possesseth heaven and earth/possesse their felicitie *F*

nes thereof none better? The lady smellinge the drift of his devises, and seeinge the ende of his talke seemed to tend to love and that touching her owne selfe, thought not good to draw on their discourse any longer, but concluded with this answere.

As I am altogether ignorant what your obscure talke meaneth, so care I not to bee acquainted with any sutch companion as your Landlord is, for so methinkes by you I may more fitly call him, then terme him your tenaunt: and so departed away into her lodginge: *Germanicus* likewise his Misteris beeing gone gat him to his chamber to entertaine his amarous conceites and beeing alone brake forth into these wordes.

O friendly fortune if continually hereafter thou furiously frowne upon mee, yet shall I all the dayes of my life count my selfe bound unto thee for the onely pleasure which this day thou hast done mee, in givinge mee occasion of talke with her, whose aungels voice made sutch heavenly harmony to my heavy heart, that where before it was plunged in perplexity, it is now placed in felicity, and where before it was oppressed with care, it is nowe refreshed with comfort. Yea every lovely lookes of her is able to cure mee if I were in most deepe distres of moste daungerous disease, every sweete woord proceding from her sugred lips, is of force to fetch mee from death to life. But alas how true do I trie that saying, that every commodity hath a discommodity annexed unto it, how dooth the remembraunce of this joy, put mee in minde of the annoy which the losse of this delight will procure mee? Yea it maketh all my sences shake to thinke, that some other shall injoy her more woorthy of her then my selfe: and yet who in this

3 to love/of love *EF*   18 of/to *EF*
31 shake/to shake *EF*

court, nay in all Christendome, nay in the whole worlde
is worthy of her? No if shee never have any untill shee
have one worthy of her every way, shee shall never have
any. And shall I then beeing but a poore gentleman
seeke to insinuate my selfe in place so high? Shall I by
my rude attempt purchase at least the displeasure of her
friendes and parentes, and perchaunce hers also, whom
to displease would be no lesse displeasant unto mee then
death? Alas and must love needes bee rewarded with
hate? Must curtesy needes bee countervayled with
crueltie? Must goodwil needes be returned with displeasure? Is it possible y^t bounti should not abide where
beuty doth abound, & that curtesy should not accompany her comlinesse? Yes I am sure at the least she wil
suffer me to love her, though her younge yeeres & high
estate will not suffer her to love mee: & though shee will
not accept me for husband, yet I am sure shee will not
rejecte mee for servaunt: and though shee will not receive my service, yet I doubt not but shee will courteously take the tendringe therof unto her. And touchinge her parentes displeasure, what care I to procure the
ill will of the whole world, so I may purchase her good
will. Yea if I should spend the most precious bloud in my
body in the pursuite of so pereles a peece, I would count
it as welbestowed as if it were shed in the quarrell of god
my prince or country. For shee is the goddesse whom I
wil honour with devotion, shee is the prince whom I
will obey with duty, shee is the country in whose cause
and quarrell I will spend life, living, and all that I have.
Neither is there mutch cause why her friendes should
storme much at the matter, for though my lands & revenewes are not great, yet am I of ye bloud royall, & nere
kinsman to themperour, who wil not suffer me to want

30 mutch/such *CDEF*

any thing pertayning to my estate & degree. Why *Ale-rane*, a youth like my self, practised the mightie emper-our *Otho* his daughter & darling *Adalesia*, stole her away & married her, and do I sticke to attempt the like w*ith* one of far meaner estate, though of far more worthi-nesse? And though frowning fortune tossed him for a while in yᵉ tempestious seas of adversiti, yet at yᵉ length he arrived at the haven of happy estate, and was recon-ciled to the good grace and favour of the Emperour againe. And though at the first my ship be shaken with   10 angry blastes, yet in time I doubt not but to bee safely landed on the shore, and have my share of that which the showres of shroad [shrewd *B–F*] fortune shall keepe mee from. Hee is not worthy to sucke the sweete who hath not first savored the sower. And as the beauty of a faire woman beeing placed by a foule, blaseth more brightly, so eche joy is made more pleasant by first tast-ing some sower sops of sorrow. Did not the perill which *Leander* ventred in the sea, and the paine which hee tooke in swimming, make his arrivall to the haven of his heav-   20 enly *Hero* more happy and pleasaunt? Yes no doubt of it, for besides the feelinge of the present pleasure, the re-memberance of the perill past delighteth. Beesides that by how mutch more a man hazardeth him selfe for his misteris sake, by so mutch the more hee manifesteth the constancy of his love, and meriteth meede at her handes the more woorthily. This saying also is no lesse tried then true that fortune ever favoureth the valiaunt, and things the more hard the more haughty, high, and heav-enly: neither is any thing hard to bee accomplished by   30 him which hardily enterpriseth it.

With these and sutch like sayinges incouraginge him

1–2 Alerane/Alearne *D, mispr.*   13 the/no *EF*   showres/shewers *F*
27 the *om. EF*   28 that/and *EF*

self, hee purposed to pursue his purpose, and failed not daily to attend upon his Misteris withal dutie and diligence and sought all occasions hee could to let her understande his loyall love and great good wyll towardes her, which she perceiving disdayned not acknowledge by her amiable and curtuous countinaunce towards him, wherewith he helde himselfe as well satisfied as if he had bene made Monarche of the whole world. And though he were often determined in woordes to present his sute

10 unto her, yet when it came to the poynt he shoulde have spoken, feare of offending her altogether disappointed his purpose, and made him mute in the matter he minded to utter, but at length perceiving that delay bred danger, for that she had many other suters, and feeling by experience, that as fire the more it is kept downe, the more it flameth up, so love the more he sought to suppresse him, the more fiery forces he expressed within him, he began to set feare aside and to force a supplye of courage in his faint harte, and seeing his Misteris sit in

20 the presence alone, he entred into reasoning with her in this manner.

Madame for that I see you without company I am the bolder to presume to preace in place, wherof though I be altogether unworthy, yet am I altogether willing to supplye it, and if my companie may content you as well as your sight satisfieth mee, I doubte not but you will accept it in good part: and so mutch the lesse I hope my company shalbe combersome unto you, for that you are busied about nothing wherto my presence may be prej-

30 udiciall. And verely when I consider the common cource of life which your sweete self, and other maides of your estate leade, methinkes it is altogether like the spendinge of your time at this present, which is with your

5 not/not to *BCDEF*

leave bee it spoken, idly, unfruitefully without pleasure
or profit, and if my credite were sutch with you to
crave credite for that which I shall speake, I would not
doubt but to perswade you to another trade of life more
commendable in the world, more honourable amongest
all men, and more acceptable in the sight of god. For beleeve mee I pity nothing more then virgins vaine piety,
who thinke they merit meede for livinge chastly, when in
deede they deserve blame for spending their time wastly.

Sir (sayth shee) as your company contenteth me wel   10
inough, so your talke liketh mee but a litle, for though I
must confesse I sit at this present without dooinge any
thinge, yet in my fancie it is better to bee idle, then ill
imployed, as your selfe are now in reprehendinge that
state of life, which excelleth all other as far as the sunne
doth a starre, or light darkenesse, and wherin I meane for
my part to passe the pilgrimage of this my short life, if either god dispose mee not, or my friendes force mee not
to the contrary.

God forbid (Madame saith he) you should continue   20
your time in any such trifling trade of lyfe, which indeede
is to be counted no lyfe at all, as the Grecian Ladies
most truly testyfie, who (as *Homer* reporteth) count
their age from the time of their marriage, not from the
day of their birth: and if they be demaunded how olde
they be, they begin to recken from their mariage and so
answer accordingly. For then onely (say they) we begin
to live, when we have a house to governe, and may commaunde over our children and servants.

Tush (saith the Lady) this is but the sentence and   30
proper opinion of one peculyer people, who perchaunce
by the nature of their country, or otherwise are more de-
sierus of husbands then other[s], neither is it any more

29 over *om*. CDEF   32 the *om*. EF

reason that we should be tied to their example, then
they be bound to follow our virgin *Vestals* or other,
who consume the whole course of their life without con-
taminating their corps with the company of men.
Nay rather (sayth he) without receivyng their perfection
from men, according to the opinion of *Aristotle*. But
Madame I did not produce that example as necessary
for all to follow, but as probable to prove and shew,
what course a count they made of virginitie, which you
so highly esteeme of. But to leave perticuler opinions,
and come to generall constitutions and customes, I
meane both naturall, humaine and devine lawes, and
you shall see them all to make agaynst you. And first if
you consider natures lawes, which in the dooynges of
creatures without reason are playnly set downe you
shall see no living wight in the universall world, but that
so soone as by age they are apt therto, apply themselves
to that life whereby their kinde may bee conserved and
number increased. Behold the high flyinge Faulcon
which soareth so high in the ayre that a man would
think she would stoope to neither Lure nor lust, yet shee
is no sooner an entermuer or at the fardest a white
Hauke, but that of her owne accorde shee commeth to
the call of the tassell gentle her make. Likewise the Doe
which flingeth so freely aboute the wooddes as though
she made no account of the male, yet shee is no sooner a
sores sister, but that shee seekes the society of the bucke.
Yea if it would please your seemely selfe to enter into
the consideration of your owne nature, or if your curtesy
would accounte mee worthy to have the examination of
your secrete thoughtes, I doubt not but you would confesse your selfe to flee a firy force of that naturall incli-

8 probable/profitable *DEF*   24 make/mate *DEF*
32 flee/feele *BCDEF*

nation which is in other creatures, which being so you must graunt to deale unnaturall in resisting that naturall motion which cannot bee ill or idle, bicause nature hath planted it in you: for God and nature doo nothinge vainely or vily. And in that some doe amisse in rebellinge against nature, their owne scrupulous nicenesse is the cause, when they will lay on them selves heavier burdens then they are able to beare, and refuse to beare those burthens whiche nature hath appointed them to beare: which are but light.

What talke you sir (sayth shee) so mutch of nature and of creatures without reason, as though wee ought to follow either the instinct of the one, either the example of the other. I have bene alwayes taught that reason is the rule to direct our dooinges by, and that wee ought to laye beefore us the actions of creatures indued with reason to follow and imitate. For if you sticke so strictly to the example of reasonles creatures, you should use the company of women but once or twice at the moste in the yeere, as most of them doo, with their females, whereto I am sure you would bee loth to bee tied.

Madame (sayth hee) a gentlewoman of this citie hath answerd this obj[e]ction alredy for me. Why then (saith she) wil you condemne their dooings in some poinctes, & place them for paternes to bee practised by in other some?

Yea why not (sayth hee) otherwise you might generally take exception against the example of men, for that some men in some matters do amisse. The good ever is to bee used, and the ill refused. But to come to the dooings of men which you seeme to desire, doth not every man so soone as his daughter is arrived to ripe yeres, travell to bestow her in mariage, wherby she may injoy

2 unnaturall/unnaturally *BDEF*

the fruits of love, & participate with the pleasures incident to that estate: wherby they plainly shew that the
cause why they begot them with pleasure, and bring them
up with pain, is to have them enter into that trade of life,
wherin not only them selves may live happily abounding
in all pleasure, but also by the fertill fruite of their body,
make their mortall parentes immortall: that when they
with age shalbee wasted and withered away the seede of
their seede may begin greenely to grow and flowrishingly
to spring, to the great comfort of both the father and
daughter. For what pleasure the graundfather takes in
the sportinge pastime of his proper daughters prety
children, I thinke you partly understand, and what delight the mother takes in the toyes of her litle sonne, you
soone shall perfectly perceive, if it please you friendly to
followe the friendly counsayle which I frankely preache
unto you. For do you thinke if virginity were of sutch
vertue, that parentes would not rather paine them selves
to keepe their deare daughters modest maides, then
straine them selves and their substance to joyne them in
Junos sacred bond? Yes perswade your sweete selfe if
your mother were so perswaded shee would rather locke
you up close in her closet, then suffer any to injoy the
soveraigne sight of your beuty, or once aspire to your
speeche whereby you might bee perswaded to some other
kinde of life. But shee experienced by yeeres knoweth
best what is best for your behoufe and would you should
followe her example and make no conscience to loose
that which shee her self hath lost, which except shee had
lost wee had lost so rare a Jewell as your seemely selfe
are, with what a losse it had bene to my self I dare not
say lest you count verity vanity, and truth trifling and

12 daughters *om. EF*   15 friendly/freely *BCDEF*   31 with/which *CDEF*
32 count/should count *CDEF*   verity/vertue *EF*

flattery. But to our purpose, you perceive as I sayd your
parentes pleased with the accesse of gentlemen unto you,
wherby you may conceive their minde is you should accept sutch service as they profer, and pertake with those
pleasures which they prefer unto you.

Why sir (sayth shee) you altogether mistake the
meaning of men in this matter, for when fathers tender
mariages to their daughters, it is not for any minde they
have to have them maried, but onely for feare least they
should fall to folly other wayes, for knowing the fickle   10
frailenesse of youth, and our proclivyty to pravity and
wickednesse, they provide us mariages to prevent mis-
chiefes: and seeinge of evils the least is to bee chosen,
they count mariage a lesse evill then lightnesse of our
life and beehaviour.

Alas good Madame (saith he) why do you so mutch
prophane the holy state of wedlocke, as to count it in ye
number of evils, wheras the goddes themselves have entred into that state, where as Princes pleasantly passe
their time therin, wheras by it only mankinde is pre-   20
served, and amitie and love amongst men conserved, of
the worthinesse wherof I am not worthy to open my
lippes.

Sir (sayth she) I speake it not of my self, but according to the opinion of the most wise and learned Philosophers that ever lived, amongest whom one *Aminius* so
mutche misliked of Marriage, that beeyng demaunded
why hee would not marie, answered, because there were
so manie inconveniences incident to that estate, that
the least of them is able to slea a thousande men.   30

Why Madame (saith hee) you must consider there is
nothyng in this mortall life so absolutely good and perfect but that there bee inconveniences as well, as commodities incurred therby: by that reason you may take

the Sunne out of the world for that it parcheth the sum-
mers greene, and blasteth away the beutie of those that
blaze their face therin. But to leave naturall & humaine
lawes and come to the devine precepts proceedyng from
Gods owne mouth: doth not God say it is not good for
man to live alone, and therefore made *Eve* for an helper
and comforter? Likewise in divers places of Scripture he
doth not only commend Marriage to us, saying, Marriage and the bed undefiled are honourable, but also
commaundeth us to it, saying: you shall forsake Father
and Mother and follow your wives.

Why sir (saith shee) and doth not God say it is good
for man not to touche a woman, and if thou bee unmar-
ried remayne so [?] But why alleadge you not this text,
it is better to marrie then to burn, wherby is playnly
shewed that Marriage is but a meane to medicine the
burnynge in concupiscence and lust, and as I sayd beefore of two evils the least, and therfore preferred. But
because wee bee entred into devine misteries, I could refer you to a place of scripture, where it is reported that in
Heaven Virgins cheeifly serve God and set foorth his
glorie. And *Mahamet* the great Turke (who was in
heaven) saith he saw there Virgins, who if they issued
foorth of Heaven would lighten the whole worlde with
their brightnesse, and if they chaunced to spit into the
sea, they would make the whole water as sweet as Honie,
but here is no mention of married folke.

Belike (saith hee) those Vyrgins bee like your self, and
then no mervayle though God be delighted with the
sight of them, whiche perchaunce is the cause hee hath
them in Heaven to attend upon him, as first *Heve* [*Hebe*
BCDF] and after *Ganymedes* did upon *Jupiter*. But
generally of women the scripture sayth that by bring-

19 bee *om. EF*   31 Heve, *mispr.*/Herbe *E*   Ganymedes/Ganymides *E*

inge forth of children they shalbee saved and injoy a
place in heaven, which must bee by mariage if honestly.
But bicause I am perswaded that it is onely for argument sake that you disalow mariage, and that you pretend otherwise in words then you intend to doo in
workes, I am content to give you the honour of the
fielde, and thus far to yeelde my consent to your opinion,
that virginity considered of it[s] owne nature simply
without circumstance is better then Matrimony, but bicause the one is full of perill, the other full of pleasure,   10
the one full of jepardy, the other full of security, the one
as rare as the blacke swan, the other as common as the
blacke crow, of good thinges I thinke the more common
the more commendable.

If (sayth shee) I have gotten any conquest hereby I
am to thanke mine own cause not your curtesy who yeeld
when you are able to stand no longer in defence.

Nay Madame say not so (sayth hee) for in that very
yelding to your opinion, I proved mariage better then
virginity for that is more common: neither would I have   20
you turne my scilence in this matter, into lacke of science and knowledge, or reprehend mee if I spare to inforce further proufe in a matter sufficiently prooved already, no more then you would rebuke a Spanniel which
ceaseth to hunt when hee seeth the Hauke seazed on the
Partridge. But you may mervaile madame what is the
cause that maketh mee perswade you thus earnestly to
mariage, which as mine owne unworthinesse willeth mee
to hide, so your incomparable curtesy incourageth me to
disclose, which maketh mee thinke that it is no smal   30
cause which can make you greately offended with him
who beareth you great goodwil, and that what sute soever I shal prefer unto you, you wil either graunt it or

15 hereby/thereby *CDEF*   20 is/it is *BCDEF*

forgive it, pardon it or pitie it. Therfore may it please
you to understand y^t since not long since I tooke large
view of your vertue and beauty, my hart hath beene so
inflamed with the bright beames therof, that nothing is
able to quenche it, but the water which floweth from the
fountayne that first infected mee, and if pity may so
mutch prevaile with you as to accept mee, I dare not say
for your husband, but for your slave and servaunt, assure your selfe there shall no doubt of daunger drive mee
from my duty towardes you, neither shall any Lady
whatsoever have more cause to rejoyce in the choice of
her servaunt then your selfe shall, for that I shall account my life no longer pleasaunt unto mee then it shall
be imployed in your service.

Agrippina dying her lily cheekes with *Vermilion* red,
and castinge her eies on the grounde gave him this
answere.

As I am to yeeld you thankes for your goodwill, so am
I not to yeeld consent to your request, for that I neither
minde to marry, neither thinke my self worthy to re-
tain any sutch servaunt: but if I were disposed to receive you any way, I thinke the best manner meane
inough for your worthynesse.

Immediately here upon there came company unto
them which made them brake of their talke, and *Agrippina* beeing got into her chamber began to thinke on the
sute made unto her by *Germanicus*, and by this time
Cupid had so cunningly carved and ingraved the Idoll
of his person and beehaviour in her heart, that shee
thought him worthy of a far more worthy wife then her
selfe: and perswadinge her selfe by his woordes and
lookes that his love was loyall without lust, true without
triflinge, and faythfull without faygninge, shee deter-

21 sutch/such a *EF*   27 Germanicus/Germannicus *E*

mined to accept it if her parentes would give their consent therto. Now *Germanicus* nothinge dismayed with
her former deniall for that it had a curteous close, so
soone as oportunity served, set on her againe in this sort.

Now Madame you have considered my case at leasure
I trust it will stand with your good pleasure to make mee
a more comfortable answere.

I beeseech you sir (sayth shee) to rest satisfied with
my former answere, for other as yet I am not able to
make you.   10

Alas Madame (sayth hee) the extremity of my passion
will not suffer long prolonginge of compassion, wherfore
I humbly beseech you presently to passe your sentence
either of bale or blisse, of salvation or damnation, of
life or death: for if the heavens have conspired my confusion, and that you meane rigorously to rejecte my
good will, I meane not long to remaine alive to trouble
you with any tedious sute, for I account it as good reason
to honour you with the sacrifice of my death, as I have
thought it convenient to bestow upon you the service of   20
my life.

Alas sir (sayth shee) this jesting is nothing joyfull
unto mee, and I pray you use no more of it for the re-
memberaunce of that which you speake of in sporte,
maketh mee feele the force therof in good ernest: for a
thousand deaths at once can not bee so dreadful unto
mee, as once to thinke I should live to procure the death
of any sutch as you are.

If sayth hee you count my wordes sporte, jest and
daliance, assure your selfe it is sport without pleasure,   30
jeste without joy, and daliance without delight, as tract
of time shall shortly try for true. But if you love not to
heare of my death, why like you not to give mee life,

9 am not able to/cannot *EF*   15 for/or *DEF*   27 should *om. DEF*

whiche you may do only by the consent of your good will [?]

Why sir (sayth shee) you know my consent consisteth not in my selfe but in my parents to whom I owe both awe and honour: therefore it beehooveth you first to seeke their consent.

Why Madame (sayth hee) shall I make more account of the meaner partes then of the heade, you are the heade and cheife in this choice, and therfore let mee receive one good worde of your good wil, and then let heaven and earth doo their woorst. It is not the coine, countenance, or credite of your parentes that I pursue for to winne, sutch wealth as your good will. I coulde bee content to leade a poore life all the dayes of my life, so that you bee maintayned according to your will and worthinesse.

Well (saith shee) seeing I am the only marke you shoot at, assay by all the meanes you may to get my freindes good will, and if you levell any thinge strait you shall not misse mee.

Germanicus upon this procured the Emperours letters to her father in his beehalfe, who havinge perused those letters sayd hee trusted the Emperour would give him leave to dispose of his owne accordinge to his owne pleasure, and that his daughter was to nere and deere unto him, to see her cast away upon one, who for lacke of yeeres wanted wisdome to governe her, and for lacke of landes, livyng to maintaine her: and calling his daughter beefore him, hee beegan to expostulate with her in this sorte.

Daughter, I ever here tofore thought you would have been a solace and comfort to my olde yeeres, and the prolonger of my life, but now I se you will increase my

32 and the/and be the *EF*

hoarie heares and bee the hastner of my death. Doeth
the tender care, the careful charge, and chargeable cost
which I have ever used in bringyng you up deserve this
at your handes that you should passe a graunt of your
goodwill in marriage without my consent? Is the pietie
towardes your parents, and the dutie of a daughter
towardes her father so utterly forgotten, that you will
prefer the love of an unthrift before my displeasure, & to
please him care not to displease your parentes, who
travayle to bestow you with one worthy your estate   10
and ours? No never thinke *Germanicus* shall injoy you
with my goodwill, nor never take mee for your father if
you graunt him your goodwill.

Agrippina hearing this cruell conclusion of her father,
with bashfull countenance and tremblynge tounge,
framed her answer in this fourme.

I beeseeche you good father not to thinke mee so
gracelesse a child as once to thinke, mutchlesse to do any
thing whiche may heape your heavinesse or hasten your
death, the least of which two, would bee more bitter unto   20
mee then death. For if it please you to understande, I
have not graunted my good will to any, unlesse your
consent bee gotten therto. Neither have I, as you say,
preferred the love of an unthrift beefore your displeasure, but as I cannot let that noble gentleman *Germanicus* to love mee, so can I not, to confesse the truth,
but love him: mary in hart only, for my body as you
gave it me so shall you dispose of it: and as I faithfully promise you by the love which of dutie I owe you,
that I will never have any to husbande without your   30
good will, so I humbly beeseeche you for the affection
which by nature you beare mee, that you will never
force mee to any without my good will. For if for the
transitorie life you have given me, you make mee pay so

derely as to be linked with one agaynst my likyng, I must
needes count it a hard pennyworthe, and well may I wish
that I had never beene borne. I beeseche you sir consider the inconveniences alwayes incident to those marriages, where there is more respect of money then of the
man, of honours then of honestie, of goods then of good
will of the parties eche to other. What strife, what jarres,
what debate at bed & at bourd, at home and abroade,
aboute this about that, never quietnesse with contentation, never merry countenance without counterfaityng,
never lovyng deedes without dissemblyng. And whence
but from this rotten roote springeth so many dishonest
women, so many ill livyng men? Is it not the lothyng of
never liked lips that maketh women stray from theyr
husbandes to straungers? And is it not either the difference of yeeres, either ye diversitie of manners, or dis-
agreement of natures, that maketh the husband forsake
his wife and follow other women? And where are any of
these differences or inequalities beetween the married,
but where the force of freendes not liberty of love linketh
them together? These thinges by your wisdome considered, I trust as you restraine mee from one whom I love,
so you will not constraine mee to any whom I love not.
In so dooing doubt you not but you shall finde in mee
modesty meete for a maide, vertue fit for a virgin, duty
meet for a daughter, obedience fit for a childe. Her father
having mildly heard her modest talke, tolde her hee
ment not to force her to any, but would provide her a
husband whom hee doubted not should like her better
every way then *Germanicus* did, and therfore willed her
to put out of her minde the likeinge shee had conceived
of him, and so gave hir leave to depart. And beeing in
her chamber shee began to devise all the meanes shee

22 restraine/straine *EF*   31 of her minde/of mind *EF*

could to roote out of her heart the love shee bare *Germanicus*: and assone revoked to her memory his lacke of living his litle countenance and credite, assone her fathers displeasure, and her owne preferment, with many other discommodities arising that way. But nothing prevayled, for as the bird caught in lime, or conny in hay, or deare in toyle, the more they strive the faster they sticke, so ye more diligently shee laboured to get out of the *Labyrinth* of love the more doubtfully was shee intricated therein. And as one climbing on high his feete   10 fayling and he in daunger to fall, more firmly fasteneth his hold then hee did before: so love seeinge him selfe ready to bee dislodged out of her breast, tooke sutch sure holde and fortified him selfe so strongly within her, that no force was of force to fetche him from thence. Which the good gentlewoman preceivinge thought best for her ease and quiet to yeeld to the sommonce of love to bee disposed at his pleasure. Wherin no doubte shee had reason, for as the swifte runninge streame if it bee not stopped runneth smoothly away without noyse, but   20 if there bee any dam or locke made to stay the course therof, it rageth and roareth and swelleth above the bankes, so love if wee obay his lore and yeeld unto his might dealeth gently with us and raigneth over us like a lovinge Lorde, but if wee withstande his force and seeke to stay the passage of his power, hee rageth over us like a cruell tiraunt. Which this gentlewoman as I sayd perceivinge, without any more resistance determined in her hart to love *Germanicus* only and ever.

Now *Germanicus* notwithstandinge the angry lookes   30 of the father, the frowninge face of the mother, and the straunge counterfayte countenance of the daughter, followed his sute so effectually, used sutch apt perswasions to the maide, and in short time insinuated him-

selfe so farre into hir familiaritie, that her parentes lowred
not so fast, but shee allured as fast, and thought shee
received no other contentation in the whole worlde but
in his company: which her parentes perceivinge, and
besides dreadinge the Emperours displeasure, thought
as good by their consent to let them goe together, as
by severitie to keepe them asunder whom the goddes
seemed to joyne together. And so mutch the rather they
were induced therto, for that they saw their daughter so
affected by *Germanicus*, that the hearinge of any other
husbande was hatefull and hurtfull unto her. And hereupon the mariage was concluded and consummated: and
to this bargaine only the fancy of *Germanicus* forced
him, nowe see whither his ambicious desire drave him:
for beeing in proper possession of his proper wife, he was
not able to maintain her according as his princely minde
desired, for y^t his owne lyving was litle, and her parentes
would not part *with* mutch, bicause shee had matched
her self not any thing to their minde: where upon in
hope of preferment and advauncing his estate, he applied him selfe diligently to the Emperours service, and
in shorte time with valiant exploytes atchived in warre,
and great wisdome and discretion shewed in time of
peace, hee wonne sutch credite with the Emperour, that
hee held him most deare unto him, and caused him to
bee proclaimed heire apparent to his crowne & Empire.
With which newes *Germanicus* congratulated his new
maried wife in this sort.

It is not unknowen unto mee (dere wife) that for my
sake you have somwhat sustained the ill will and displeasure of your freendes and parentes, it is not unknowen likewise to you that for your sake I have sustained some labour in seeking our preferment and get-

33 our/your *DEF*

ting the Emperours good will who only may prefer us: now as the one hath made your life lesse pleasant then I desire or you deserve, so the other shal advaunce our state so high, as your self can wish, or I be able to wield: so yt the commodities of the one, shall countervaile the inconveniences of the other. For you shall understand that the Emperour doth not only for the present time provide for me as if I were his owne child, but also for the time to come hath proclaimed mee sole heire to his Diademe and realme. Which estate as I never sought so   10
mutch as in thought for my selfe, knowing mee to bee altogether unworthy of it, so I thinke my selfe most happy to have aspired therto, only for your sake whom I know woorthy of all the honour in the world. For as it would have been a hel and horrour to my hart to have seene you live in meaner callinge then you are woorthy of, so will it bee a heavenly mirth to my minde to see you a prince in state as well as in stature beauty and vertue.

Master *Germanicus* (sayth shee) I promise you by the   20
love which I beare you, for greater bonde I have not to confirme my woords by, that it doth mee more good to see you thus pleasantly disposed then to here ye newes which you have imparted unto me, for th'one [*sic*] I am sure cannot hurt you, but what harme the other may procure you I feare to thinke and faint to say. Alas my *Germanicus* are you to know the perils which princely stat bringeth, the falshood in friendes, the treason in nobilyty, the rebellion in comminalty, the envy of the weake, the injury of the strong. Besides you see boy-   30
strous windes do most of all shake the highest towers, the higher the place is the sooner and sorer is the fall, the

2 life/selfe *EF*   3-4 our state/your estate *EF*   17 of *om. EF*
18 prince/Princesse *E*   25 you/me *DEF*

tree is ever weakest towardes the top, in greatest charge
are greatest cares, in largest seas are sorest tempestes,
envy alwayes shooteth at high markes, and a kingdom
is more easyly gotten then kept. For to get is the gift of
fortune, but to keepe is the power of prudency and wisdome, especially where there bee many that catch for it,
yea and when a man shall have no faithfull frendes in
savyng it. For *Ennius* saith flatly, there is no freendly or
faithfull dealinge to be looked for at any mans handes,
in matters pertayninge to a kingdome: and *Euripides*
makes it in a manner lawfull for a kingdomes sake to
transgresse the limittes of law, nature, and honesty.
Which opinions I may justifie by many examples, as of
Numitor and *Amulius* &c. who though they were naturall bretheren, yet *Amulius* beeinge the younger deposed
his elder brother from the kingdome of *Rome*, slue his
sonnes and made his daughters virgin *Vestales* that
they might not marry and have issue male to succeede
the crowne: likewise of *Romulus* and *Remus* who beeing
bretheren borne at one birth, yet bicause *Remus* should
injoy no part of the kingdome, *Romulus* found meanes to
make him away. The like is reported of *Eteocles* and
Polinices, of *Jugurth* towardes *Hyempsal* and *Adherball*:
all which were bretheren and by natures lawes most
neerely linked together. But of others that by bloud
have not beene so neere, which in cases of kingdomes
have dealt far worse, the examples are in straungnesse
wonderfull, in number infinite, and in successe so sorowfull, that it maketh mee colde at hart to consider of it.
I spake not this my *Germanicus* to forespeake you, you
may injoy the Empire quietly, and so I trust you shall,
but I know not what the matter is, methinkes my
minde gives mee some mischiefe will insue thereof. Alas

14 &c. *om. BCDEF*   23 Adherball/Adherbal *BCD*, Asdruball *EF*

(good husband) was it for my sake you sought the Empire? Doo you thinke I can not be content with th'estate which fortune shal assigne to you? Yes if it were to beg my bread from doore to doore as *Adalesia* did with her *Alerane*, I could bee contented therwith, so you were not tormented therewith. It is you (sweete husbande) that are the ritches which I seeke to possesse, you are the only honours which I looke for, you are the only kingdome which I care for, for so longe as I may injoy you, come poverty, come meane estate, come sicknesse,   10 yea come death it self so I may die betweene your armes. Therefore (good Master *Germanicus*) if you followe my counsayle, resigne your title to the Emperour againe to bestrow on some that hath more neede of it then (thanks bee given to god) wee have: for for my part I thinke my self indued with the greatest riches in the world, to wit your person and mine owne contented minde. And beesides the evils beefore rehersed incident to a kingdome this inconvenience is commonly incurred therby, that it altereth the nature of the person which taketh that   20 name upon him, for honours chaung manners, and no doubt the diversity of delightes which a prince possesseth bee but prickes to pleasure, inticementes to folly, and allurementes to lust. Was not *Saull* (I pray you) in the beginning of his raigne a good prince, but after declined to impiety? *Salomon* beegan his raigne godly, but afterwards gave him selfe in pray to women. *Caligula*, *Nero* and *Hannibal* beegan to raigne like good princes, but after the whole world was troubled with their tir-anny. I could aledge infinite other examples to like pur-   30 pose, but these shal suffice, neither do I alledge these, for that I feare ye chaunge of your good nature, but to feare you from the chaunge of your estate: and yet the

4 her *om. EF*

better I knowe your nature to bee, the more cause
have I to feare the alteration therof. For freshest colours
soonest fade, & ripest fruit are rifest rotten. But to leave
the louringe lottes which light on high estate, which are
more then I am able to reherse, let this request take
place with you, that seeinge for my sake onely you
coveted the empire, at my sute only you will forgoe it
againe.

Ah (sweet wife saith hee) imbracing her in his armes,
what is it under the Sunne whiche you may not commaunde mee to do without desiryng? But I beeseche you
suffer not the tender care you have of mee, to deprive
you of the honour due to you[.] For to cast the worste
of it, though open enemies or trecherous traytours, or
rude rebels shall set mee beesides my regall seate, and
deprive mee of life, yet shall you remayne a princesse,
and be matched agayne with some other more worthy
your estate, and so longe I care not what beetide of my
selfe.

Alas (sir saith shee) I beeseeche you use no more of
those wordes, onlesse you count my great greif your
great good. Can I live when you are dead, shall I bee
married again and you made away? In deed (saith hee) I
neede not use sutch extreeme doubtes in a matter nothyng daungerous for the numbers are infinite of those
who have wielded far more waightie empires then this
without hazarding them selves any way, as the Emperour *Octavian* hath consumed the whole course of his
life without perill, and *Alexander* beeyng but five and
thirtie yeeres of age tooke upon him the Monarchy of
the whole world. Besides if I should now refuse the Empire offred me, it were a signe of a base and ignoble
minde, and the Emperour woulde thinke I made no ac-

13 to/unto *DEF*   21 those/these *DEF*

count of his good will. Well saith shee do as God shall
put in your head, & of mee make this account, that
though you bee the meanest man in the citie yet will I
honour you as if you were the Emperour: and though
you make mee a Princesse, yet will I bee as obedient to
you as if I were your hyred hand mayde. Ah good wife
(saith hee) leave those termes of humilitie to those y^t
like them, or looke for them, for for my part I have you
in sutch reverent estimation, y^t I thinke the best state
which ever I shalbe able to bryng you to wilbe to base   10
for your worthinesse, and if it shall please you to rest
satisfied with the service I can do you, to remaine content with the callyng I can give you, to returne lovingly
the good will which I will beare you, it is all that ever I
will looke for at your hands, and the only felicitie I force
of in this life.

God forbid (maister *Germanicus* saith shee) that I
should either looke for service of you, or mislyke the lot
whiche you shall alow mee, or not restore with interest
the good will which you shall beare mee. Yes perswade   20
your selfe this, though you surmount mee in all other
thynges, yet wil I not fayle, if it bee possible, to exceede
you in good wil. Shortly upon this the whirlyng
wheele of Fortune turned theyr talke to teares, their
woordes to waylyng, their gladnesse to sadnesse, their
happinesse to heavinesse, yea their life to death. For a
certayne thirst of the kingdom, began to assaulte one
Tiberius a Gentleman in the Emperours court, who beeyng of the bloud royall, perswaded her selfe if *Germani-*
cus were made away, the Emperour beeyng dead, hee   30
should succeed in the Empire. Whiche greedie desire of
the kyngdom so blinded his understandyng, that hee
passed not to pervert both humaine and devine lawes

8 for for/for *EF*   24–5 theyr talke . . . to sadnesse *om.E*

for the accomplishyng therof, no rules of reason, no
bonde of freendship, no care of kynred, no feare of lawes,
no prickes of conscience, no respect of honestie, no regard of gods or men could prohibite him from his pestif-
erous purpose. For if freendship had been of force with
him, why they were familier friendes. If kinred, why ther
were nere kinsmen. If lawes, hee knew his deede contrarie to all lawes. If conscience, hee knew it terrible. If
honestie, hee knew it most wicked. If goddes or men,
hee knew it abhominable in the sight of bothe the one
and the other. But too true it is, desire of a kyngdome
careth neither for kith nor kin, friend nor foe, God nor
the divel, as by this trayterous Tyrant may bee playnly
prooved, who by poyson procured the death of this
worthy Gentleman *Germanicus*, to the intent to injoy
the kyngdome of *Rome*. Now *Agrippina* seeyng her
sweet husband so sodainly dead, was surprised with sutch
sodain sorrow, y^t for a long time she could neither
speake woord, neither let fal teare, but at length she
cast her self upon the corps of her *Germanicus*, kissyng
his colde cheekes, and imbracing his breathlesse bodie,
sighyng & sobbyng foorth these woords.

Alas wretched wight that I am, whose misery is like
to mine, whose griefe so great, whose life so lothsome? no
flowing teares, no griping groanes, no carefull cries, no
throbbing sighes can sufficiently set forth my sorrowes.
My life my love, my hope my husband, my joy my *Germanicus* is miserably murthered and made away. Ah
vaine desire of worldly dignity, ah divelish deede of
blouddy cruelty. But in vaine it is to complaine, when
my care is without cure, and none can redresse my
wronge. For goddes I know there are none, otherwise I
knowe the good should not bee so made away by the ill:

33 knowe/deeme *CDEF*

and men there are none that can medicine my malady,
and rayse my *Germanicus* to life againe: so that nothing
resteth for mee but by death to bee rid of the most bitter
panges of death. I could prolong my life and seeke by
some meanes to hasten the death of that tirant *Tiberius*,
but alas his death can not bring *Germanicus* to life, no let
him live stil on earth where I doubt not but hee shall ten
thousande times in his time, feele the force of death. For
hee wilbee so tormented with his owne example, that (as
the poets report of *Suspicion*) to bee plonged in all the   10
pits of hell will not bee so painfull unto him. Well the
gods (if there bee any) give him as he hath deserved, and
give me leave to goe to the ghost of my *Germanicus*.
Here upon shee resolved with her selfe, that as her husbande indeed [ended *B-F*] his life by receiving into his
body that which hee should not, so shee would end her
daies by not receivinge that which shee should, and so
defrauding her selfe of foode, distillinge her selfe as it
were into teares, pitifully pined away. And when the Emperour *Octavian* caused meate to bee thrust in her   20
throate, shee cast it up againe saying, sorowe was the
onely sustinance, and moane the meate which shee
either could or would take, and so in short time died.

I shall not neede here (gentlewoman) to exhort you to
take the death of your husbandes when you shalbe married, and when it shall happen more paciently, for that I
knowe your wisdomes to bee sutch that you will not so
wilfully worke your own confusions, neither doo I think
you are to know that wee must live by the livinge not by
the dead, and that there hath bene never any one hus-   30
band so good, but there may bee others found as good:
yea and though they bee not perfectly so good, yet in
respecte of chaung which most women delight in, they

11 unto him *om. BCDEF*

are commonly counted better: as your selves if you were once married perchaunce would saye, or at least thinke. But I thinke this needefull to put you in minde, that by the example of *Agrippina* you counsayle your husbandes to content themselves with their callinge not to soare to highe, and ftie [flie] above their seate, and with foolishe *Phaeton* and youthfull *Icarus* come to confusion. It is your partes also to way your husbandes wealth, and not to decke your heades and neckes with golde when hee hath none in his purse, not to swimme in silkes when hee is drowned in debt, not to abound in bravery when hee is pinched with poverty. For you knowe it is your parte to take sutch part as hee doth, whither it bee poverty or ritches, woe or wealth, pleasure or paine. But surely in my fancy that man is to bee begged for a foole who will prefer his wives pleasure before his owne and her profite, her will before his owne wealth, her vanity before his owne ability. And as it is great incivilyty and churlishnesse in a man to deny his wife any thing which is reasonable, so is it great imbecillity and childishnesse to graunte her any thing which is unreasonable, and hereof commeth the utter undooing of a great number of young gentlemen. And as is it wise and lovinge carefulnesse to provide well for ones wife, so is it fond and doatinge curiousnesse to seeke and provide better for her then hee would do for himselfe, whereof came the confusion of this noble Gentleman *Germanicus*.

6 seate/state *BC*, staye *DEF*
13 whither/whether *BCDEF*

Amphiaraus and Eriphile.

[AMPHIARAUS a Gentleman Argive, sueth for marriage to *Eriphile* a widow, either likyng others possessions better than persons. *Infortunio*, burnyng in fonde affection toward the same trull, seeyng *Amphiaraus* land preferred beefore his loyaltie, is at poynct to destroy himself. *Amphiaraus* hidyng himself to escape from the warres, is betraide by *Eriphile* for covetice of rewarde: and settynge foote within the *Theban* soyle, the earth openeth and swalloweth him up. *Eriphile* eftsoones a widow, profereth her love to her olde suter *Infortunio*, by whom beeyng repulsed, in choler she consumeth away and dieth.]   10

THE auncie[n]t Philosophers are of this mynde, that there is nothyng that doth more argue and shew a base mynde, then covetous desire of coyne & ritches, and nothyng more signe of a noble heart, then not to desire wealth if one want it, and liberally to bestow it, if hee have it. But I am of this minde, that nothynge doth more argue a mad minde, then to desire goods which never did good, but which have been alwayes the cause of all our calamities. What a world of men hath desire of wealth wasted in war? What huge heapes hath it drowned   20 in the Sea? What infinite numbers hath it caused Phisitions to kill? How many hath it mooved Lawiers to undoe? How many hath it driven Devines to sende to the Divell? Of how many Murthers, thefts, slaughters, parricides, patricides, treasons, rebellions, perjuries, forgeries, adultries, fornications, hath it been the cause? As *Jupiter* himselfe abused golde and pelfe to abuse

2 Argive/Argyve *BCDEF*   4 trull/rule *EF*   12 that *om. BCDEF*
18 all *om. DEF*   23–24 How many hath it driven Devines to sende to the
    Divell *om. CDEF*   25 patricides *om. EF*

Danae that virgin. But you will say though the desire of goods bee detestable, yet the possession is profitable. Wherto I pray you? to maintayne us in bravery, in gluttony, in venery, in securitie, in impunitie, in pride, in prodigalitie, yea to brynge us to perdition and distruction as kynge *Midas* wished that every thynge which hee touched might bee gold, wherby hee was starved to death. *Fabritius* an aunciant *Romain* waighed wealth so litle, that though hee had been Prince and Consul of *Rome* three or foure times, yet at his death hee had not so mutch goods as might suffice to bring him honorably to his grave, but was faine to bee buried at the common charge of the citie. But though the immoderate desire of ritches bee to bee reprehended, yet must I needes say that moderately to account of them is not [to *B–F*] bee misliked, for they are given us by God to passe the pilgrimage of our life withall, and we may use them and yet not abuse them, wee may make of them and yet not make our Goddes of them. And as by duely desiryng and truly usyng them, they convert to our commoditie, so by greedy covetinge and naughtie consumyng them, they turne to our trouble, care, and confusion: as partly beefore hath been shewed, and plainly here after by the hystorie folowing is prooved, which is this.

In *Greece* amongst the people called *Argives* dwelt one *Amphiaraus*, who beeyng a man of great possessions and wealth, heard of a Widdow in the same country of like livyng unto him selfe, her name was *Eriphile*, and her nature was sutch, that shee thought gaine sweet how so ever shee got it. It fortuned this Gentleman to come to her house to see and assay her in the way of Marriage, and not withstandyng hee had more likyng to the livyng

---

4–5 in securitie . . . to brynge us *om. EF*   5 to/into *CD*, in *EF*
8 Fabritius/Valerius *BCDEF*   16 by/of *EF*   27 like *om. EF*   32 to/in *EF*

0

then wil to the woman, yet hee laboured his sute as ernestly, as if hee had loved vehemently: and at convenient time commenced his sute in this sort.

Gentlewoman I think it not needful to enter into termes in commendation of mariage therby to perswade you the sooner therto, for that you know the dignity thereof, and have already tasted the pleasures and commodities beelonginge to the same: but this chiefelye lieth mee upon earnestly to perswade, and humbly to requeste at your handes, that when it shalbee your good pleasure to enter into that life againe, you will count mee worthy (though altogether unworthy) to serve you in steede of a steward to order and dispose your thinges as your seemely selfe shall please to appointe, and to ease you of the trouble of travailinge in your owne affaires: which I am sure for that you have not beene accustomed thereto, must needes mutch molest you. For it is not meete your young yeres should bee tied to any trouble or travaile, but to passe your time in pleasure according to your bringinge up and callinge, and accordinge to the custome of your kinde, and sexe. And that you may not thinke my sute to proceed of any desire to your goods, your selfe I thinke partly know and by litle inquiry may perfectly understande, that my landes and livinges are sufficient to maintaine the port and countenance of a Gentleman of worship: all which I willingly yeeld into your handes to bee disposed at your pleasure, if it shall please you to yeeld your body into my armes to bee imbraced at my pleasure: so yt in acceptinge my offer you shall not only increase your substance, but also have a gentleman at your commaundement, who shall make more account of you then of all the goods in the world. His talke

14 please/seeme *EF*

ended *Eriphile* smylinge made him this smooth answere.

Sir, by how mutch more I know the inconveniences and infinite troubles mixed with mariage, by so mutch lesse do I like to enter into that estate againe. And as I was once linked with one according to my liking, so looke I not to bee placed againe with any, in whom I can take sutch pleasure: And as by holy oth I firmely bounde my fayth unto him, so in this minde I am in, only my death shal dissolve that bond: and ye sower remem-
10   brance of my sweete husbandes death, shall take away the renewinge of all pleasures of life, and altogether mor-tifie in mee the minde to marry any more. For his love was so exceeding great towardes mee, that I feare to finde the like at your handes or any mans els. For where you professe to be my steward and servant, I am sure if you were once sure of that you seeke for, you would thinke your selfe good inough to bee my Lord and maister, and you would dispose my goods neither at my pleasure, nei-ther to my profite, but that which is mine should bee
20   yours and yours your owne. And where you pretend to prefer mee before al worldly goods, I take it rather for wordes of course then talke of troth, for as in the fayrest rose is soonest found a kanker, so in fairest speech is falshood and faigning rifest. For I knowe the fashion of you men is by your subtelty to deceive our simplicity, and by a fewe filed woordes to bring us into a fooles par-adise. Yea you have set it down as a setled sentence amongst you, that he which knoweth not how to dis-semble, knoweth not how to live. Therfore I yeeld no
30   other faith to your wordes than their faygned falshoode deserves, nor no other consent to your requeste, then the smal acquaintance you have with mee, may justly crave. But if hereafter in deedes I shall see as playne proufe of

22 troth/truth *E*, trueth *F*   33 of/in *EF*

perfect goodwill, as your wordes import likelyhood of
ernest love, perchaunce I shal bee as zelous to cast liking
towardes you, as now I am jelous to cast doubtes of you.
By this time dinner was served in, whereupon their talke
ceased, and presently after dinner the Gentleman had
occasion to depart. Now *Eriphile* beeinge alone in her
own house, beegan to discourse upon this matter by her
selfe, and notwithstandinge shee had no great minde to
the man, yet shee felt in her selfe a great lust to his
landes, and thought her selfe more then happy if shee   10
might have them safely assured and made over unto her:
and in this thought, uttred wordes to this sence.

Why what though I can not finde in my heart to love
and like him above all other. Is it requisite that every
mariage bee grounded on love, as though we see not
daily some to marry in respect of ritches, some in respecte
of honours, some by constraint of freindes, & some upon
sundri other considerations: and for my parte I count it
sufficient to have married once of meere love, and havinge lost him whom I did love intirely, I thinke it not   20
lawfull, or at least not possible, ever to love any againe
hartely. For true love ever decayeth, when the party
truly beeloved dieth. And as my heart is hardened to
take his death paciently, so will it not bee mollified to
suffer the love of any other to sinke therein deepely. Like
as the potters clay beeing once hardened in the Oven,
will not bee made soft againe to receive the impression
of any other forme. But to speake my fancy freely, I see
not how wee women are bound to love our husbandes so
mutch, wee are onely commaunded to honour and obay   30
them, which I count sufficiente, and more then for my
part I meane to perfourme. Besides that love consisteth
in the heart, now it is our bodies only that are bound to

19 once/one *F*   of/for *DEF*

our husbandes as by joyning of handes beefore the con-
gregation is plainely shewed. But if I determine not to
love him, how can I looke for any love at his handes?
Tush that is the least matter amongest a hundred, so
long as I may abound in bravery, ruffle in ritches, and
participate with his goods, I care not to communicate in
love with him: I am to olde now to live by love. And yet
wherefore is womens wit counted full of wyles, if I bee
not able so to dissemble the matter that hee maye thinke
I love him deeply, though I hate him deadly. But if it
should come to the woorst, that hee should perceive my
dissembling towardes him, and reward my colde kindenesse, with heate of hate, why I know the worst of it.
[My beautie is not so blasted, but enow will make account of me to my contentation. *B–F*]

So that all things considered I see not how I can doe
better then to accept this gentlemans offer, whose large
landes and revenewes are able to supplie al other wants
whatsoever. For what disease is so desperate which
mony may not medicine? what wound so deadly which
coine can not cure? What life so lothsome which goods
can not make gladsome? Shortly after this there made
repayre unto her house, a youth more wilfull then wise,
named *Infortunio*, who havinge seene her once or twice
beefore, was so bleared with her beauty that it dazeled
his sight, and tooke away his foresight in all things: and
comming to her presence hee proferred sutch lamentable
sute, and ghostly resemblances unto her, that a rigorous
repulse seemed sufficient to procure him a present death.
The Gentlewoman seeing the furious assaultes of this
freshe water souldiour, knew how to traine him to the
fielde of her falshood, and to make him march under the
ensigne of a marciles Misteris and cruell captaine: and
sometimes fed him with wordes of comfort, to put him

in hope, and by and by feared him with doubtes of deniall, to drive him into dispaire. And as the North East
winde first gathereth up the cloudes, and then by puffes
putteth them abroade agayne, so shee first by lovely
lookes allured to bringe him in, and then with frowninge
face lowred to drive him away: the only end beeing to
sport her selfe in his paine, yea and if shee could of his
good will to make some gaine. The poore gentleman perceivinge these haggard trickes, and that assoone shee
would be wel comming to the lure, and by and by checke   10
at it and soare away, was so amazed therat that hee
knew not what to resolve upon. And as a tree hewen
round with axes ready to fall with a blowe or twaine,
tottereth every way, beeing uncertaine which way to
fall, so his minde distracted with doubtfull devises, wavered unconstantly, nowe bending this way, now bowing
that way, willing to retire his desire, but not able to set
his fancy free. And not with standinge her perverse dealinge pitifully perplexed and terribly tormented him, yet
hee perswaded himselfe that as from most sharpe thornes,   20
to wit the Rose tree, spring most sweete flowers, so from
bitter annoy would come pleasaunt joy, and of his heavy
sute happy successe. Tush (saith hee) ye Merchant often
sliceth the seas, though not sure to returne with gaine.
The souldiour often ventreth his body in the field, though
not sure of booty: the husband man still tilleth the
ground though not certaine to save his seed: but yet
hope of good hap carieth all these to their enterprises,
and why should not the same hope worke the same effect
with mee? Yes nothing venter nothing have, I wil pur-   30
sue my purpose whatsoever come of it.

Now the gentlewoman (as I sayd) ceased not to bayte

---

2 North East/Northeast *BD*, Northest *CEF*   10 would/should *EF*
12 a/the *EF*   13 round/downe *DEF*   25 in the field/in field *BCDEF*

him continually with courtly banquets, as dissembled
favour, uncertaine hope, curteous congies, amiable
lookes and sutch like: but hee on the contrary as one that
ment truly, ceased not to feed her with faire words, with
faithfull promises, with ernest othes, with many a ritch
jewel and costly gifte, which she willingly received without condition, and wilyly kept without restitution. In
this mean while came the other wooer againe to renew
his sute afreshe, and seeinge this younge Gentleman, as
10   hee thought in great favour, began greatly to feare his
owne part, and thought the grasse had bene cut from under his feete: and as a conning *Pilot* seeing the seas rough
and the winde contrary to his course, casteth ancker
least his ship bee driven against the rockes, or into some
coast contrary to his minde: so this Gentleman fearinge
least wilfull waves in ye gentlewoman, should set her
fast in the sands of slipper subtelty, and dash his sute
against the rockes of repulse, hauld in the maine shete of
her minde, and by the anckers of advise so stayed her
20   course, that no wynde which my wilfull youthe could
blow, could cause her any thinge to bow or waver: and
by assuringe her to a large joynter hee was chosen to rule
her sterne, wher the other was kept stil under the
hatches. Who all this while that they were concluding
the contracte, was in his chaumber busily devisinge
verses in the praise of his Misteris: but hearing of the
sory successe of his sute, by a handmaide of the Gentlewoman, hee was so confounded in him selfe, that his in-
vencion was cleane marred, and his devise utterly dasht:
30   yea hee was so far from writinge that hee had not a
woord to saye or a thought to thinke. And surely in my
judgment hee reaped the right reward of his doatinge de-

10 great/greater *EF*   13 ancker/an anker *BCDEF*
14 his ship/the ship *DEF*   26 in the/in *EF*

sire, for there only grafts of greife must needes grow, where sutch raw conceite doth set, and sutch rashe consent dooth sowe. For neyther was his love grounded upon vertue, wherwith shee was not indued, neither upon beauty wherwith she was not adorned. For neither can cruelty be cloaked under vertue, neither the treason of untruth covered under beuty (for the disposition of the minde followeth the constitucion of the body) so that it was his own selfe will and fond fancy that drewe him into sutch depth of affection, and therefore with greife was faigne to gather the fruites of his folly. And beeing come to him selfe hee began to rage in this sort.

And is my true love thus triflyngly accounted of? Shall hee with his trash more prevayle then I with my truth? And will shee more respect gayne then good will? O iniquitie of times, O corruption of manners, O waveryng of women. Bee these the fruites of thy fayre lookes? Is this the hap of the hope thou puttest mee in? Is this the delight of the daliance thou usedst with mee? Herein truly thou mayst bee fitly resembled to the Cat, whiche playeth with the Mouse, whom straight shee meaneth to slay: or to the *Panther* who with his gay colours & sweet smell allureth other beastes unto him, and beeyng within his reache hee ravenously devoureth them. But if I should set thee foorth in thy colours I thinke the savage beastes would bee lothe to bee likened unto thee: for crueltie thou mayest compare with *Anaxarete*, who suffred *Iphis* to hange himself for her sake: for inconstancie with *Cressed*, who forsooke her trustie *Troylus*: for pride with *Angelica* who contemned all men: for treason with *Helen*, who ran away with *Paris* from her husbande *Menelaue* [*Menelaus B–F*]. But what rashnesse is this in mee to rage and rayle agaynst her, whereas it is

22 to *om. BCDEF*   25 thy *om. EF*

love, and the destines that have decreed my distruction.
For Marriages are guided by destiny, and God hath indued women with this propertie, to bee wedded to their
wils: Neither doth love learne of force the knots to knit,
shee serves but those which feele sweet fancies fit:
for as streames can not bee made to run against their
course, so unwilling love with teares nor truth cannot
bee won. So that this only choice is left for mee either to
die desperately, or to live lothsomely: and as the birde
inclosed in cage, the cage doare beeing set open, and the
Hauke her ennemy sitting without, watching for her
betweene death and prison piteously oppressed standeth
in doubt whether it bee better stil to remaine in prison,
or to goe forth to bee a pray for the hauke, so stande I in
doubt whether it bee better by loosing life to get liberty,
or by lyvinge to become thrall and bond, and live in continuall torment and vexation of minde. For love hath
taken so deepe roote in mee, that neither reason can rule,
neither wisdome wield my witched will. But as the byt-
inge of a mad dogge rageth and rankleth until it have
brought the body bitten to bane, so the poyson of love
is so spread into every part of mee that it will undoubtedly bringe mee to death and distruction. O cruell captaine *Cupid* is this the pay thou givest thy souldiours?
O vaine *Venus* is this the victory thou vouchsafest thy
champions? Wouldest thou have bene content thy darlinge *Adon* should rigorously have rejected thee, when
thou wert furiously inflamed with his love? But the parish priest forgetteth that ever hee was clarke, and those
that bee in happines themselves way not the heavinesse
of other[s]. Yea perchaunce thou favour the falshood of
this woman the rather, for that thou thy self playedst

1 love, and/love, God, and *BCDEF*   24 the/thy *E*   pay/prey *F*
28 his *om. EF*

the false harlot with thy husband *Vulcan* the smith, and madest him a forked toole more then before hee had in his shop: but remember yet how hee tooke thee and the adultrour *Mars* tardie in your trechery and lechery together starke naked in an iron nette, and then called all the goddes to take view of your vicious conversation, to thy utter shame and confusion. And so it may fall out that this your pupill may so longe delight in deceit, that shee may bee taken in the net which shee layeth to intangle other[s]. But what meane I to blaspheme against the gods who doe but punnish mee justly, for loving so lightly and onely mine owne careles faut, is the cause of this curelesse fate. Wherefore O death to thee I make ernest request, that thou wilt speedily send *Atropos* unto mee, to cut in sunder the twyst of my troublesome life: and seing my love doth loth mee, good death doe thou desire mee. I know thou sentst out processe for mee even in my swath cloutes, and now I beeseeche thee serve it on me, when I am most willinge and ready to appeare beefore thy presence. While this forelorne gentleman continued in these carefull contemplations, the mariage was consummated betweene the widdow and *Amphiaraus*, who lived quietly together about a yeere or two, shee shewinge a presentiall obedience towardes him, and hee bearinge an ordinary affection towardes her: but in short time it pleased god to give occasion to try the trechery of the one, & to worke the distruction of the other. For it fell so out that *Adrastus* king of yᵉ *Argives* was upon urgent causes mooved to infer war upon the *Thebanes*, and in mustringe his men hee thought *Amphiaraus* a meete man to make one of his captaines, and willed him to prepare him selfe for that

10

20

30

6 view/a view *EF*
13 curelesse/carelesse *EF*   fate/facte *CDE*

voyage, who beeing well seene in astronomy and other
secret sciences, knew if hee went to the warres hee
should not returne alive: for which cause hee covertly
hid himselfe in his owne house, makeing only his wife
privy therto. Now the kinge takinge muster of his men
missed *Amphiaraus*, and knowing the cause of his absence, was in great rage, sayinge hee thought hee had had
no sutch cowardes in his kingdome, and promised great re-
wardes to them that could bring tidings of him: *Eriphile*
havinge intelligence of this riche reward promised, was
merveylously set on fier in the desire therof: & notwithstandinge she was plentifully indued *with* ritches, yet
was she in desire as greedy as if she had been in estate
most needy: and as dropsy pacients drink and still be
drye, neither is any lycour able to alay their thurst, yea
the more they drinke the more they desire it, so she continually heaped in welth and yet was never satisfied: yea
the more she had the more she desired to have. And being possessed with this lothsome lust of lucre she entred
into reasoning with her selfe in this sort. Who unlesse
they be out of their wits wil refuse offered gold? no the
favour of gaine is sweet of what thing so ever it be gotten.
Why *Tarpeia* a *Romane* mayde did betray the Tower of
Rome for a few Bracelets to the *Sabines* that layed siege
to yᵉ citie, and shall not I for great Duches of Gold bewray
mu husbande to the Kinge, who meaneth by his meanes
to preserve our citie? for if it come to the worst, that he
never come home againe, why I know the worst of it,
two or three dayes weepinge will wash away al wo & sorrow, and then shal I be Lady of his landes and lyvings,
and be maried againe to some that perchaunce shall better content me every way then hee doth: and who is so
foolishe that will not be content to chaunge for the bet-

16 it *om. EF*   17 in/up *EF*   33 to/with *CDEF*

ter? and in this good minde gat to the King, and told him, that preferring the safety of his person, and the profit of the common wealth before her owne private pleasure, she was constrained to detect her loyall mate unto his royall majesty (which her deede she humbly desired him to conceale) and not withstanding the absence of her loving husband would greatly annoy her, yet the commoditie of her country, which she hoped through her husbandes help should be procured, would as greatlye joy her. And that she might savely see her sweet husband againe, with a few feined teares forcibly wroung forth, she humbly requested the King that he might be placed in sutch part of the battaile, that he might not be subjecte to the shot, and lie open to the army of the adversarye. The King plainly certified by her of the den wherein the foxe was hidden, geving her the promised reward went foorth with to unkennell him: who hearing of the Kinges comming, and by what meanes he was discovered, fell to raging against his wife and other like women for her sake in this sort.

Ah fonde foole that I was to repose any trust or confidence in women, whose sexe is subtil, whose kinde is cruell, who are constant only in unconstancy, who are wytty onely in wiles, who as *Aristotle* saith are monsters in nature, altogether imperfect, weake vessels, ignoraunt in al things, yea (which we may most lament) they are naturally indued with baites to allure men, with poyson to infect men, and with charmes to chaunge men from men to beastes, as *Cyrces* did the servauntes of *Ulisses*: yea what man hath ever been so wise but by women hath bene seduced to folly? as *Pharo* his daughter caused *Solomon* to fall to idolatry: what man hath

19 other like/other *B*, al *CDEF*   20 women/woman *E*
26 may most/must *EF*   29 Cyrces/Circes *EF*

ever been so godly but by women hath been depraved?
as *Bersabe* drove king David to divelishnesse: what man
hath ever bene so strong, who by women hath not bene
made to stoope? as *Dalila* tooke away yᵉ force of *Sampson* by cutting away his heire: who hath ever bene so
perfect, but by women hath bene drawn to imperfec-
tion? as *Adam* by the meanes of *Eve* loste the perfection
of Paradice: who hath ever bene so faithfull, but that
women have inforced them to infidelytie? as a hand-
mayde made *Peter* denie his mayster *Christ*: who so
valiaunt, but by women hath been v[a]nquished? as
Omphale made *Hercules* serve her and spinne amongst
her maides: and after by *Dynira* was done to death: who
so learned, but by women hath beene taught new
poyntes of schole? as *Tully* by *Terentia, Marcus Aurelius*
by *Faustina,* and *Ovid* by *Cornina* were often abused:
with infinet other[s]. But if the wise, the godly, the
strong, the perfect, the faithfull, the valiant, yᵉ learned,
have been bewitched beguiled & abused by women, is it
reason I should chalenge any proper or peculier fortune
to my self, and not remain content *with* the lot which is
common to al? yes I am content my rage in rule to binde,
but not withstandinge the comfort by other mens calamitie be miserable, yet it doth me good to thinke that
other[s] have been as sluttishly served by women as my
selfe, as *Tullia* conspired the death of her owne husband
Tarquinius, then of her Sister, and lastly maried the
brother of her owne husband who before was housband
to her owne Sister: as the fyftie daughters of *Danae* all
but one slue their husbandes the firste night of their
marriage: as *Candaules* by the counsell of his wife was

---

13 Dynira/Dyanira *BCD*, Deianira *EF*   14 hath/have *BCDE*
16 Faustina/Faustine *DEF*   Cornina/Corinna *EF*
23 but/but though *BCDEF*   29 Danae/Danaus *BCDEF*

slaine by *Gyges*, who after married her: as *Dyonisius*
notwithstanding his wary watch and watchful warenesse
for the preservation of his lyfe, was by his owne wife
Aristomacha miserably made away.

By this time the king was come into his house where
upon hee was driven with shame to shewe and presente
him selfe to his majesty, humbly cravinge pardon for
his offence, and seeing no remedy, made preparations
for the warres, disposing his livinge so well as the short-
nesse of time would give him leave, and dispossessinge   10
his wife of so mutch as hee could possibly. Which done
amongest the rest hee mournfully marched forward, but
hee no sooner set foote in the *Thebane* soyle, but that the
earth opened, & swallowed him up. Of which newes so
soone as his wife was partaker, for fashion sake shee put
finger in the eye, and attired herselfe in mourning apparell: but shee quickly cast it of againe and began to
cast in her head how shee might be sped of any other
husband: and callinge to minde ye deep affection wherin
Don infortunio was drowned towardes her, shee thought   20
none more fit to make a foole of then him, and therfore
by letters did him to understand, that considering his former goodwill towardes her, shee thought her selfe bound
in conscience to countervayle his curtesie, by any convenient meane shee might: and in that beefore time shee
set so light by his love, the cause was for that before his
comming shee had betrothed her selfe to *Amphiaraus*,
so that as th[e]n shee was not able to yeeld him the
meede of his merit: but now if his affection were not altered, & if hee were disposed to deale with her by order   30
of honesty & limits of law, he might bee paied his due
debt with double interest. Now the young gentleman

---

1 Gyges/Giges *EF*   11 so mutch/as much *EF*   15 sake *om. EF*
18 any/an *BCDEF*   30 order/the order *DEF*

by ye ayde of absence, by the assistance of time, by ye change of diet, by reme*m*brance of his repulse, by dregs of disdain by the vertue of necessity, and by the help of reason being fully cured of his folly: having heard also of the trechery which shee used towardes her other husband, rejected her offer, returning her answer, y^t beeing at liberty hee ment not to come in bondes, and beeing now set free from her fraud & falshood, he would no more bee trayned to her treison. Neither (sayth hee) doth that hold or castle merit mercy, which yeeldes rather for want of freshe supplie, then at the sute of the beseiger. Neither is ye prisoner to bee pitied, who beeinge judge, joyed only in staerity [*sic*] and cruelty: neither is that clientes cause to bee considered, who beeing a counsaylor, dealt in the cases of other[s] without conscience. The gentlewoman seeinge her selfe thus reprochfully repulsed, in very colorike conceites consumed away and died.

I am heere gentlewomen to admonish you not to suffer your selves to be caryed away with covetousnesse, you see to what miserable ende it brought this maried disloyall couple: and as wel for your sakes as mine owne I would wish you who are indued with wealth sufficient to make a man (as they say) & who are at your owne disposition and choice, not to yeeld your selves as a pray to any who hath no neede of your wealth, neither will gratefully accept your goodes, but rather frankly to bequeath your selves to some poore younger brother, who may thinke himself made by marrying you, who may thanke his wife onely for his wealth, who may impute his happiness onely to having you: whom you may binde to you by benefits, who will no doubt indevour to counterpeise your lyving with his love, and your

13 staerity, *mispr.*/severity

goodes with his good will: who will rather serve you,
then seeke superiorytie over you: who will rather be
your man then your master: your Liege, then your
Lorde: your subject then your soveraigne: wherby you
shal live as you list, your profits shall pleasure you,
your gooddes shall do you good. And what so ever bee
your common saying, that you must as well love to
live, as live to love, yet surely in my fancie I thinke
it farre better for a married couple to live together
without livinge, then without love: for what litle liv-   10
ing will suffice nature, who knoweth not, but what
lothed lives be where love doth lack, looke but into the
lives of the parties, but now reported unto you. And if
you credite not my report of them, no more but marke
your poore neighbours how quietly and merily they
passe theyr time in povertie, assisted only by the calme
of contentment and love: and then convert your eyes to
the view of many other estates, and looke how unpleas-
antly and uncontentedly they spende their daies, molested by the stormes of strife, debate, and hate. Which   20
contemplation I hope wil so confirme your judgements
that you will alwaies prefer love before living: or at
least not so to respect thone, as to neglect the other: or
at least, if it be posible, to joine the one *with* the other.
Another thing also the death of *Eriphile* may drive into
your mindes, that you rage not lyke tyraunts over those,
whom your beautye hath made your bon[d]slaves: for
you must know that it is more glory to use the victory
moderately, then to get it mightely: and farre more
holdes have been woonne by clemencie, then by crueltie.   30
For when the inhabitants know the captaines curtesie,
they wil rather yeeld to his assured mercy, then stand to
the doubtfull event of battayle: so gentlewomen if you

24 least/best *BCF*, the best *E*   26 rage/raigne *CDEF*

minde to make breach into the harts of many, and to
win the fort of their faithes unto you, if you crave to
conquer the goodwilles, and to be courted with the service of suters, you must with modestie make much of
them, with curtesie countervaile their kindnesse, with
gratefulnesse accept their good wil, with liberalitie requight their love, and with honest plainenesse answer to
their demaundes: you must not feede them with falshood, draw them on with delay, and torment them with
trifling as *Eriphile* dyd her *Infortunio*, to her owne in-
fortunate hap as it luckely afterwards did light: for it is
Gods word and will that such measure as is me[e]t shall
be measured againe, and they that delight to drowne
other[s] in dolour, shall not swimme long in pleasure
them selves: I knowe not what effecte my wordes will
take, for that I know not how you courtlye dames accounte of my cunninge: but before mine owne face I am
able to assure you this, that the girles of our parish
think that welch *Sir Richard* him selfe can not make a
better preache then I can: but it may be you wil thinke
me over saucy with my lisping lips to prefer persuasions
to them, who are as voyde of folly every way as my selfe
of wit any way. Yet considering how quietlye you tooke
the rude railing of *Amphiaraus* against you, I neede not
doubt but that you will take in good part wordes whiche
are well ment towardes you, and if not follow them, yet
not mislike them, and rather waigh the will of the
speaker, then the worth of the wordes.

25 wordes/the wordes *EF*

Icilius and Virginia.

[ICILIUS a younge Gentleman of Rome, fallynge in love with *Virginia*, is
refused by her friendes for want of sufficient wealth, but privily contract-
eth himselfe unto her, and departeth into the warres. *Appius Claudius*
burning with unchaste lust of the same mayden, the better to obtayne
her, causeth *Clodius* his client to clayme her for his bondslave, and giveth
wrongfull judgement on his side. But *Virginius* her father, at her ernest
request, slayeth her with his owne handes to preserve her virginitie from
the villainie of *Appius*, who for that fact is cast into prison, where
desperatly hee doth himself to death.]   10

IT is a doubt often debated but not yet decided, whether
love discendeth from the heavens, deriveth of our owne
nature, proceedeth of the similitude of manners, commeth of acquaintance and familiarity, taketh originall
of our education and bringinge up together, whether it
ariseth of beauty or of vertue, whether it entreth in at
the eyes, or first bee rooted in the hart, whether the
cause come from the party that loveth or the party
loved, or whether it bee in our power to love or to leave,
I leave to other[s] to resolve upon, for for my part (I   20
yeeld god thankes for it) I have as yet been so litle
troubled with love, that I know not what it is, nor from
whence it commeth, and when I muse theron I am as bad
troubled as *Symonides* was to thinke and say what god
was: but if an opinion grounded upon reason without
any proper experience on mine owne part may take place,
I thinke love cheifly to bee grounded upon the similitude
of manners shewed and signified by familiarity and abode
together. For it is daily seene that those parties who

2 in/into *DEF*   6 Clodius/Claudus *EF*   12 our/her *EF*
19 or whether/whether *CDEF*   20 leave to/leave for *EF*

at the first incountry and vew have rather disliked then loved ech other, by continuance of conversation and by conferring eche others conditions and nature together, have fallen into the fire of most fervent affection. For true love and faythful freindship is to will and to nill one thinge, to have one object of appetite, and to have like effect of affection. I know there are infinite instances to bee given to this assertion, for that some have beene surprised with love only upon a loving looke, some upon a curteous word, some upon a single sight, some upon a vaine vision, some upon a doubtful dreame, some upon an uncertaine report, and some some other way. But as one swallow makes not sommer, so one particularity concludeth no generality. And as an *Æthiopian* is sayd generally to bee blacke though his teeth bee white, for that for the most partes of him hee is black, so I thinke love may bee sayd generally to proceede of the similitude of manners, for that for the most part it doth so. And besides infinite other examples which I can alleage for proofe hereof, the historie which you shal presently heare shall also confirme it.

In the renowmed citie of *Rome* made his abode one *Icilius*, who though hee were a gentleman of a worshipful house, yet by reason that his parentes were yet lyvinge, his patrimony was not great, neither his livinge more than might suffice to maintaine the porte of the place and countenance hee caried in the citie, by reason wherof hee remained unmaried, as beeing not able to maintayne a wife according to the estate of his callinge. It was his chaunce amongest other youthfull company to passe the time for the space of a sennight in feasting and makinge merry at the house of one *L. Virginius*, a

10 a single/single *EF*
20 hereof/thereof *EF*
18 it doth so *om. EF*
23 a gentleman/Gentleman *E*

worshipful gentleman of the same citie, who had to
daughter a damsell named *Virginia*, who as shee was of
ripe yeres, so was shee of ripe judgement and discretion
in every point beelonginge to a vertuous virgin & modest
maide. Her shape though it were not precise, yet was it
perfecte: her face though it were not blasinge, yet was it
beautifull: her corps though it were not curious, yet was
it comely: and as nature plentifully planted perfection
in her, so God superaboundantly bestowed his benefits
upon her, sutch gravity in gesture, sutch modesty in   10
manners, sutch curtesy in conversation, sutch troth in
talke, sutch wit in reasoning, that *Minerva* her selfe
could not have mended her: that it was doutfull whether
men were more rapte into admiration of her wisdome, or
ravished in contemplation of her beauty, the one con-
tayninge contentment for the body, the other solace and
delight for the minde. Now *Icilius* being in the company
and society of this saint used litle other behaviour towardes her above his common regard to all the Gentlewomen of the troupe, but spent his time in dauncinge,   20
dysinge, cardinge, and other sutch pastimes. And notwithstanding this while he often felt a certaine restraint
of liberty in his affections, an alteration of minde and as
it were a civell assault and discord within him selfe, yet
by reason of his younge yeres and small practise in the
pangues of love, hee could not conjecture the cause of
his sodaine passions: but this made him most to muse,
that when hee was in his most dumps, if shee chaunced
to present her selfe to his presence, his heart was presently lightned of that which lay so heavy in his stomake,   30
and as when the sun shineth the cloudes vanish away, so
when her beauty blazed in place, the cloudes of care were
cleare consumed. Likewise beeinge often desirous to

25 his *om. CDEF*   33 cleare/clean *DEF*

talke with her, & injoy the present pleasure of her pleasant speeche, his sences were so ravished with the sight of her, yᵗ he could not utter one word unto her. Sitting also at the table with her & casting a gazinge glaunce round about him, his sight was never satisfied untill hee had lent her a looke, and seemed only to resolve his fancy upon her face. But notwithstange all this hee did not thorowly perceive the cause of his sodain trouble of minde, and thought it as it was a toy lightly taken so would it bee lightly left againe, and therfore departed from her fathers house without preferring any sute unto her, or adding execution to the advantage of the time and place. But beeinge gone home, and gotten solitarily to his chamber, good god what mountaines of smooke did scaldinge sighes send foorth of his mouth, what drops of bloud did galdinge greife make his heart to bleed, what flouddes of teares did flow from his eyes, what carefull complaints did hee send unto the skies? saying O heavens why heape you my heavinesse? O planets why plant you my paine? O destines why decree yee my distruction? O Gods why deprive you mee of liberty, nowe my younge yeeres chalenge to live most freely[?] O fortune why doest thou mixe my sweete meate with sutch sower sauce yᵗ is more bitter then gall, and nolesse pleasaunt then death unto mee? Must the litle delight which I tooke in the company of *Virginia* (wherof I fully understood not her to bee the cause neither) bee countervayled with sutch direfull dispight? and for the pleasure which her presence procured mee, must her absence purchase me sutch displeasure? then to true doe I finde that every dram of delight hath a pound of spight, and every inch of joy, an ell of annoy annexed unto it: then well may I curse the chaunce, yᵉ cause and the company

9 it/that *BCD, om. EF*   26 tooke/take *EF*

which caused mee to come to that place, which hath
caught mee in sutch bondage. And may I terme it bondage to live in the service and contemplation of my *Virginia*? Is it slavery to bee thrall to vertue? It is her
bountie not her beutie that bindeth mee, it is her curtesy,
not her comlinesse that I care for, it is her perfection
not her person that I passe of, it is her conditions not her
colour that I account of: for beuty bideth not, comeli-
nesse continueth not, personage perisheth, coulour fadeth, but bounty, curtesie, perfection, and conditions re-   10
maine for ever. So that if I live in bondage, it is to vertue,
if I bee a slave I am vertues slave. But doth vertue use to
torment men thus, beelike that is the cause there are so
few honest and vertuous? No I ought not to count my
trouble a torment, but the fine gold must bee purified
in the flaming fire, & white silver is wrought in blacke
pitch: glory must bee gotten thorow depth of daunger,
and pleasure must bee purchased with the price of paine.
And though absence now be some torment to try mee,
and though dolour now drowne mee in the seas of sor-   20
row, yet doubt I not but shortly to swim in the fluds of
feliciti, and take land there where my heart hath already
pitcht his abode. But O presumptuous foole, whether
doth folly force mee? doo I hope to win her whom my
unworthynesse willeth me not so mutch as to wish for?
Yea which way soever I goe to worke, I am sure to have
a colde sute of it: for if I profer her my service dis-
honestly, why her vertue abhorreth it: if I make love in
way of mariage, her estate and ritches refuseth it. O god
and shall goods bee more accounted of then goodwill?   30
lucre more then love? Is the counsayle of *Themistocles*
altogether rejected, who willeth men rather to marry
their daughters to a man that wanteth mony, then to

1 which/that *EF*   27 her *om. DEF*

mony y^t wanteth a man to use it? Is the world so blinded in covetousnesse to prefer livinge before learning, wealth before wit? Then farewell true freindship if it bee not grounded upon love: then farewell true love if mariage bee not the end of it: then farewell true mariage if mony make it: then resteth for mee onely to beewayle my evill hap, to lament my luckelesse love, and never to attempt that I am like never to attaine unto.

By this time the earth was covered with a darke mantell, and by reason that the Sun was departed out of our *Horizon*, the light of the starres which the Sun lendeth them, beegan to appeare in the firmamente, where upon this poore passionate lover weried with woe, disposed him selfe to rest: but hee whose bane love hath brued, neither by night nor by day, neither in company nor solitary, neither sleeping nor waking, can take any rest or quiet. For hee was no sooner in a slumber but the goddesse of his devotions presently presented her selfe beefore him, sayinge: Myne owne, why doest thou thus torment thy selfe for my sake, who suffer no litle greife to see thy great sorrow, wherfore be bolde to aske any thing at my hands honestly, and bee sure I will graunt it willingly: for I perswade my selfe the heavens have reserved mee for thee. *Icilius* hearinge (as hee hoped) this heavenly voice, and seeing (as hee thought) that saint by his bed side, with open armes reached to imbrace her, but beeinge awaked with open eyes hee saw hee was deceived: which sodaine fall from heaven to hell tooke away his breath from him for a while, but beeing come to him selfe hee began to cry out in this carefull manner.

O God, is it not sufficient to vexe mee with vanities in the day time, unlesse thou torment mee with visions also in the night? have I not woe inough awake, but that bee-

5 the *om. EF*   15 nor by day/nor day *DEF*

sides I must have sorrow in sleepe? What greevous offence have I committed, that deserveth sutch greevous
punishment? if this bee the rewarde of them that love,
woe, woe bee to them that hate: thou hast commaunded
us all to love one another, and if thou thus punishe the
fulfillers of thy law, what shall beecome of the trans-
gressors therof? but if thou bee disposed to punish mee,
and displeased with my deedes, never suffer mee hereafter to do any thynge but cast mee into sutch a sleepe
wherin I was erwhile, and therein let mee continue con-   10
tinually. O happy was *Endymion*, who longe time injoyed the like sleepe. O ten times happie are the dead, if
death bee any thynge like this sleepe. But O hundred
times unhappie am I, to whom wakyng is waylefull,
wheras to all thynges els it is joyfull. But was this but a
vision which deluded mee? was it but a dreame whiche I
doated on? And if it were but a dreame, doth it portend
nothyng? and may there be effect in dreames? Yea god
wot commonly the contrary: or (as *Cato* saith) wee see
sleeping that which wee wish for wakyng. So that neither   20
in dreaming nor doing, neither in sleepyng nor seeyng,
neither in thinkyng nor sayinge, finde I any cause of
comfort or see any signe of solace. This youthe passed
his time so longe in these and sutch like passions, that
ye carefull cariage of his eyes bewrayed his carefull
minde, and his pale countenance his painfull case.
Which a special freend of his perceivyng, tooke sutch
compassion and pitie on his painfull state, that hee
sought all meanes possible to sift out the cause of his
sorrow, to the intent to seeke some medicine for his   30
maladie. And havyng oportunitie of time and place,
hee brake with him in this sorte.

Good freende, if I should shew you what great sorrow

11 Endymion/Endimion *BCDEF*   29 all meanes/al the meanes *CDEF*

I sustayne by your heavinesse, you would perchaunce
judge my words to proceede rather of flattery and trifling then of truth: but no more but trie how willyng I
wilbe to ease your payne, and by that judge how greatly
it greeveth mee. But how great so ever my greeif bee, my
wonder is more then great to see you transfourmed from
the estate of a pleasant Gentleman into sutch solitarie
regardes, that you seeme rather a *Tymon* of *Athens*, then
a courtier of *Italy*: and so mutche the more cause I have
of mervayle, by how mutch lesse I see any apparent
cause which should worke any sutch alteration in you.
For if want of worldly wealth coulde worke your woe,
why you want nothyng: if you would eate golde (as they
say) you might have it. If losse of freendes molest you,
why you have an infinite number whiche love you intirely. If you bee disposed to travayle to see straunge
countries, your parents wilbee well pleased with your
departure. If you bee wearie of your single life, your
freendes will foorthwith provide for your Marriage. If
any repulse receyved of any dayntie dame doo daunt
you, why the Goddes them selves have suffred the like:
as *Daphne* a seely damsel refused the God *Phoebus*:
Syrinx a simple mayde rejected the God *Pan*, with
infinite other[s]. If you have fixed your fancie in place
you thinke impossible to possesse, why you have reason
to rule your affection, you have wit to compasse your
desire, you have freends to further it, you want
nothynge to finish it. With this his colour beegan to
chaunge, and hee fetcht a deepe sighe or two, whereby
his freend perceived hee had touched the cause of his
calamitie, and sore of his sorrow, praying him very ernestly to unfolde the secrets of his thoughtes unto him,
sayinge two wittes are better then one, and that which you

23 Syrinx/Sirinx *BCDEF*

blinded perchaunce by love can not see, I stirred up by
desire to doo you good, may perceive. And for secrecy
in your affaires, assure your selfe, that never *Pithias* to
his *Damon*, *Pylades* to his *Orestes*, nor *Gysippus* to his
Titus was more true, then I will bee to you. And though
your learninge and wit to knowe what is best for your
owne behalfe bee far better then mine, yet the simple-
nesse of my wit shalbee supplied with the sincerenesse
of my will, which shalbe alwayes so ready prest to pleasure you, that if my service may satisfie you, you shall
commaund mee, if my company may content you, I will
never be out of your sight: if I may any way stand you
in any steede, account mee your owne only.

Icilius hearing this friendly discourse could not but
say in his heart, O friend unfained, O love most loyall, O
curtesy incomparable and imbracinge fast his freend in
his armes sayd, if al the miseries in the world did muster in multitudes about mee, yet this thing only is of
force to fence mee from their furies, to thinke I injoy so
firme a friend as your selfe are, and if I may live but to
requite some part of your good wil, it is the second felicity I loke for in this life. But touching the cause of my
perplexity I must crave pardon if I make courtsy to disclose it, for that many evils cary this nature, rather to
bee concealed with griefe, then revealed in hope of releife. And as a greene wound by taking the aire spredeth
farther abroad and is the hardlier healed, so I thinke my
tormente and greife beeinge once discovered, would not
bee so easely cured. If (sayth his frend) the originall of
your evil proceede of love as in my fancy it doth, then
undoubtedly the more it is uncovered the sooner is it
cured, for as coales of fire covered cloase with ashes
keepe their heate longe time, but lying open soone waxe

10

20

30

4 Gysippus/Gisippus *CDEF*   26 a/the *EF*

colde and blacke, so the firy flames of love raked up in
silence, burne furiously within a man, but beeinge by discourse disclosed they soone convert from flame to fume
and smoake. Wherefore (good freinde) sticke not to im-
parte unto mee this matter which doth import you so
nere, promising you by the inviolable bond of freindship
to travaile so ernestly in your affaires, that what wanteth in power, you shall finde in the paines which I will
take in your cause. Alas sweet freind (saith *Icilius*)
rather then you should thinke I have any diffidence or
distrust in you, or thinke you unwoorthy of credite in
any cause whatsoever, I will make you privy to the
cause of my paine what pange or perill so ever I incur
therby. Wherefore you shal understand that since the
time I was at the house of *L. Virginius,* as you partly
know, the conditions of his daughter did so well content
mee, her nature agreed so well with mine, her affections
were so framed to my fancy, that I am constrained to
resigne my liberty captive unto her, and to make her
person the prison of my hart. And the lesse hope I have
of obtayning her, the more doo I love: and the more
deeply I doo desire her, the more deadly doo I dispaire
of her: which is the cause of all my care and summe of
all my sorow: yea this is it which hath made mee an
enemie to my selfe, a straunger to my freindes, to abandon all good company, to sit in solitarinesse, and this is
it which, if it bee not in time provided for, will prevente
by death all other mischeifs. God forbid good freind
(sayth his freind) that so light a cause should so deepely
distres you: what, doo you thinke either so supersti-
tiously of her, either so abjectly of your selfe, that you
deeme this matter so impossible to bee brought to passe?

6 inviolable/invincible *EF*   11 of credite/in credite *E*
15 you/you may *E*   20–21 have of/have *E*   22 deepely *om. EF*

Why her person is not of sutch perfection, but that yours may match it: her freindes are not of sutch state, but that yours may stand by them: her position is not so greate, but your parentes are able to make yours equall unto it. No, doubt not but your love shall sort to lucky ende, and have sutch successe you seeke for: and I am hartely glad, that seeinge it was your chaunce to loose your liberty, it is lodged in sutch a place, which is rather to bee counted a Paradise of pleasure, then a prison of paine, of whose worthynes I would somwhat say, but that   10 perchaunce you will thinke mee partiall to the party, and besides that I should rather kindle newe coales in you, then quench olde flames. But bicause I perswade my selfe I may doe somewhat with the partie which putteth you to this paine, doubt not to commit this charge to mee, and I warrant you I will discharge it to your contentation. Ah deare freind (sayth *Icilius*) if I thought you as well able to give order to my sorrow and redresse my woe, as I see you willing to comfort my carefulnesse and keepe mee from dispaire,   20 I should thinke my self the happiest wight in the world, and I would account of you as the preserver of my life, but I can not tell what the matter is, mee-thinkes the more fervent is my fire, the more faint is my feare. Phy (sayth his freind) you shew your selfe to [*sic*] very a coward, fortune you knowe favoureth not the faint hearted, neither are they woorthy to win the pray you presse for, and therefore for shame take a good heart unto you, and doe your indevour, and let mee alone with the rest: there is no hauke soareth so highe but shee will   30 stoupe to some praye, neither any so rammishe and wilde but in time shee may bee reclaimed and made to the lure. And if you follow my advise, I think good you

25 Phy/Fye *B*, Fie *CDEF*   31 rammishe/ramage *BCD*, rammage *EF*

solicite her by letters untill sutch time you have convenient time to goe thither your selfe. Which counsayle hee forthwith put in execution, and indited a letter to his Mistris in this manner.

Good Mistris, to set foorth in woordes the fervency of my affection, & vehemency of my passion, I thinke would be both tedious to you, and I am sure greevous to my self for that the remembraunce of my passions would bee as it were a renewing of my paine, and though I altogether use silence therein, yet the lothsome life which I leade, may by report advertise you of my lucklesse love, and my drousy lookes to all which see them, are signes sufficient of my drouping heart. Therfore may it please you plainly to understand, that beeinge at Mayster *Virginius* your fathers house, I received sutch contentation in your company and sight, that since I have bene deprived therof, I thinke my selfe deprived of all the pleasures of life: And onlesse your curtesy surmounte my desertes, and that you vouchsafe to pity my painfull estate, I shal have just cause to say, that at your fathers I received in steede of meate misery, for drinke dolour, yea I may count my fare fire, and my cheere very deere which must cost mee no lesse then the losse of my liberty at least. But if yet at the last course it shall please you to send and serve in to the table of my troubled minde some confectes of comfort with the fruites of freindship, I shall thinke my selfe to have fared most daintily, wheras otherwise I shall count my selfe intreated disdainfully. Looke not good Mistris to my livyng but to my love, way not my wealth but my will, marke not my mony but my meaning in the way of honest and lawfull mariage, and speedily send the messenger of present consolation to him, which pineth away in paine and is yours only and ever: ICILIUS.

Virginia havinge vewed this letter, and likinge it never the worse for his sake that sent it, replied unto it in this short and sober sort.

Sir, bicause I knowe in my selfe no sutch due desert any way, to drive you to sutch deepe desire, I am the hardlyer induced to beleeve your wordes, and though I adhibited full credite unto them, yet perchaunce as yet my fancy is not fully framed to like so well of you as you eyther desire or deserve: and though I coulde finde in my heart to like you above all other[s], yet I know not   10 whether my freindes will yeeld their consent therto. So that it is in mee only to thanke you for your goodwil, but not to satisfie your request. Yours as shee may:

VIRGINIA.

This letter bringinge some comforte to his carefull minde, made him make hast to repaire in person to the place of her presence, where hee presented her his sute with sutch assured signes of perfect love and loyalty, that shee thought with good conscience shee could not contemne his good will. But her parentes for that   20 hee was not able, his father beeing alive to make her sutch joynter as they injoyned him to, deferred the consummation of the mariage from time to time, hopinge that time would mortifie the affection of either the one or the other lover. But as the smith his forge by casting on colde water [it *B–F*] burneth more fiercely, so their love by these delayes increased more vehemently, which caused them to betroth themselves eche to other. But *Icilius* indued with a couragious minde, perceivinge the lacke of livinge to hinder his happinesse, determined to   30 goe to the warres and by dint of sworde to win either coine or credite, or to loose life and love. And beeinge on point to take his journey hee gave his Misteris this farewell. If ever woful creature had cause to complayne his

carefull case, then undoubtedly may I duely preace for
the formost place. The horse now and then ceaseth from
his travaile, the Asse from bearing the Oxe from drawing, and so of all other creatures, but my poore heart is
never at rest, but as the wheele continually turneth, so
my minde continually tosseth, still devising how I may
aspire to the ende of my desires, and bee placed in full
possession of your perfecte person. And having revolved
many wayes in my minde, I am now resolved upon this
to goe to the warres and there to win with prowesse and
payn, that which god and fortune have denied mee:
where the remembraunce of your seemely selfe shall
arme mee with sutch courage, that I shall count nothing
daungerous to attempt or hard to attaine. And whatsoever woorthy feates you shall heare I shall enterprise, I
shall desire you to perswade your selfe that they are
done for your sake. And if in my absence it shal please
you to continue constant in goodwill towardes mee, it is
the onely shield that shall shadowe mee in field and fight.
Remember *Penelope* passed twenty yeeres in the absence
of her *Ulisses*, and assure your selfe *Ulisses* never hazarded him selfe in more perils, then I will put my selfe
to for your sake.

Virginia having heard this short and sower discourse,
castinge her selfe into his armes, after shee had bee-
dewed his face with the teares which fell from her eyes,
replied in this sort.

Ah (*Maister Icilius*) my tounge is not able to tell the
hurt which my hart sustayneth by the covetous cruelty
of my parentes, who in a greedy desire of goods, go about
to stay mee from that whereupon my life doth stay and
depende, and were it not that your great curtesie and
love towardes mee did somwhat moderate and mitigate

26 the *om. BCDEF*

my martirdome, I should never bee able to beare the un-
supportable burthen therof. But now I understande by
you I shall lose your companie, which was my only comforte and consolation, what resteth for mee, but notwithstandinge I was never married, yet to continue and
leade a wofull widowes lothsome life, and to spende my
golden yeeres in galdynge greeife. I could rehearse unto
you, and you your selfe can better tell, the infinite and
imminent perils which alwayes wayte on warre, but that
I doubt therby I should rather increase your greeif, then   10
alter your determination, but this request at least, yea
and perchaunce the last, let mee make unto you, that in
warre you be warie, in battaile rather to backward then
to bolde in field rather to flying then to forwarde, and if
you take no care of your selfe, yet make some spare of
mee. For perswade your selfe this, out of every wound
which your body shall receive, will issue as well my bloud
as yours. And for constancie in your absence assure
your selfe, *Virginia* will alway bee the vowed vassall of
Icilius. And as the Laurell or Bay tree ceaseth not to bee   20
green, notwithstandyng the parchyng Sommer, and
pinchyng Winter, so will I never cease to bee fresh in
freendship, and green in godwill towardes you, notwithstandyng the sharpe stormes of absence, the distance of place, and difference of time. But here teares
stayed the talk of the one, and time tooke away any
longer abode of the other, wherupon they were constrained after a few carefull kisses, to give eche other a
faintyng farewell. Neither is it easie to poynte foorth the
payne wherwith this partinge pinched bothe these poore   30
lovers, but surely in my fancie of al greifes it is most
gripyng when freindes are forced to parte eche from other,

14 flying/fleeing *BCDEF*   18 And/As *BCDEF*   25 here/her *EF*
29 poynte/paint *BCDEF*   30 these/those *EF*

when one hart is placed in two places, when one member is torne as it were from another, when ownes selfe is separated from him selfe, or at least his seconde selfe. But their partyng was not so paynfull, but that shortly after their meetyng was as mornefull. For not longe after the departure of *Icilius*: as *Virginia* walked abroad somwhat to recreate and solace her sorrowfull selfe, it was her fortune unfortunately to bee seene by one *Appius Claudius*, one of the *Decemvirs*, who were the cheife rulers of the citie, who by the furies of Hell was so set on fire in libidinous lust towardes that virgin, that he sought all the meanes possible to winne her to his wicked will: but seeyng her to firmely fortified in vertue, to bee by consent vanquished by villany, hee determined by force to force her to his filthinesse. And as nothinge is so impossible which frantike furie will not enterprise, nothyng so shamefull whiche unbrideled desire will not undertake, nothing so false which fleshly filthinesse will not forge, so to brynge his purpose to passe hee coyned this devise, hee caused one *Marcus Cloudius* a client of his, to lay clayme to the mayde as his bonde slave: Who partly for awe of the tyrant, partly beeyng apt of himselfe to undertake any evill, tooke the matter upon him, and the next time hee tooke her out of her fathers house, hee layde handes upon her, commaunding her to folow him home, to the end *Appius* might have had his pleasure of her. But by the pitiful exclamation of the mayde and her nurse, a greate multitude of people began to muster about them, who hearyng whose daughter shee was, and that shee was beetrothed to *Icilius*, thought it unseemly that in the absence of her father and freind (who were both in the warres) she should bee violently

2 ownes/ones *BEF*, ons *CD*   15 is *om. EF*
20 Cloudius/Claudius *BCDEF*

caried into bondage, the title beeyng not discussed by
the lawes, and thereupon with held *M. Cloudius* from
havynge hir away. Who seeynge his might overmatcht
by the multitude, tolde them hee ment not to deale by
force, but his minde was for the playne proufe of his
tytle and interest in her, to have her beefore the cheif
magistrate of the citie, and only judge in civil contro-
versies, who was *Appius Claudius* the only author of
this evill. Beeyng come beefore him, hee tolde a solemne
tale for the confirmation of his right in the mayde, say- 10
ing shee was the daughter of a bond woman of his, that
in her infancy shee was stolen from her mother, conveyed to *Virginius*, and from that time brought up at
his house and taken for his naturall childe, and for
proufe hereof hee brought in two or three knightes of the
post to depose. The freindes of the maide not able to re-
fell [*sic*] this forged tale, desired of the *Judas* judge that
the matter might bee adjourned untill the comming of
her father *Virginius*. *Apius* answered that hee thought
it good the matter should hange in suspence untill the 20
returne of her supposed father, but it was no reason but
that hee who pretended, yea and had prooved to have
sutch right to her, should have her in his custody, untill
the matter were more examined: and upon his honour
hee promised shee should bee foorth comminge to appeare at the time of her fathers approche. The people
hearinge this injurious judgment of *Appius*, rather mur-
mured at it, then durst make resistance against it, by
reason wherof *Marcus Cloudius* beegan to draw the maid
to bee defloured, as the tiger in *Hyrcane* wooddes haleth 30
the lambe to bee devoured. But god ye righter of al
wrongs and protector of all pure virgins, prevented the
perill which hong over her head, & sent home from ye

21 but it was no/yet was it not *EF*   no/not *CD*

warres to succour her, her uncle *Numitorius*, and her
spouse *Icilius*: who hearinge the haynousnesse of the
matter, presently presed to the place where *Appius*
sate in judgement, but hee commaunded his officers to
keepe *Icilius* backe, wherupon *Icilius* inveighed against
him in this sort.

Albeit (O *Appius*) by force you keepe mee from keepe-
ing mine owne out of your handes, yet shall you not stay
my toung from detecting the villany which you indevour
10   to doe. For the truth is, this virgin is betrothed to mee,
and my minde is to marrie her a chast maide, therfore
assure your selfe if it lie in mee to let, shee shal not remaine one minute of an houre out of her fathers house.
Is it not sufficiente for you to deprive the people of the
cheife pillors of their liberty, but that our wives and
children also must live in slavery to your tirrany? Exercise your cruelty on our bodies, at least let chastity
bee in safety. Ought princes to give light of life to their
people, and wil you make your selfe a mirrour of mis-
20   cheife to your posterity? But if you minde to take her
away from us by force and from her, her virginity, never
thinke to doe it while I have any breath left in my body,
for in this just cause and quarrell of my wife, life shall
sooner leave mee then loyalty. *Appius* thinking the
power of *Icilius* would prevaile above his, for that the
multitude mervaylously inclined to his side, sayd hee
would have another time to represse the rebellious rage
of *Icilius*, and touchinge the maide for her fathers sake
hee was content to defer the pronouncinge of sentence
30   against her, untill the nexte court day that her father
might bee present, in the meane while hee would intreate *Marcus Cloudius* to forbeare his right: but if her
father came not by the next court day, hee would defer

10 to/unto *DEF*   22 left *om. EF*

the execution of justice for no mans plesure. Presently
upon this hee dispatched letters to the captaine generall
of the army, that hee should not in any wise dismisse
Virginius or suffer him to come home: but *Icilius* had
sent for him with such speede that he had leave to depart beefore those letters came to the captayne, so it
pleased god to prevent the pollicy and wicked purpose
of *Appius*. Now *Virginius* beeinge come to *Rome*, went
with his daughter to the judgement place, and did there
lamentably implore the helpe of the people, sayinge: while
I with the rest of the souldiours have hazarded our lives
in the defence of you and your children, I am in daunger
to have mine owne daughter dispoyled: & wheras by
my helpe our city is preserved from enemies, I my
selfe am brought to sutch misery, as if it were taken by
our enemies and utterly razed to the ground. For what
greater villany can bee done to the vanquished, then to
see beefore their eyes their wives and children defloured
and defiled? But neighbours and freindes if you suffer
mee to sustaine this injury, assure your selves your
staffe standeth next to the dore, and looke no longer to
bee husbands over your wives, and parentes over your
children, then it shall please these tirantes to give you
leave. Any evill at the first entring in of it may easely
bee avoyded, but let one or two presidentes passe patiently without resisting, and it will run into a custome,
and from thence to a law, and you will never bee able
after to rid your handes of it. And if your owne safety
drive you not to succour mee, yet let my old yeeres, my
hoary heires, the honest port which I have ever main-
tained, and the chast life of my daughter move you to
put to your handes to helpe redresse my wronge. By

23 these/the *EF*   25–26 patiently/quietly *EF*
32 redresse/to redresse *CDEF*

this time *Appius* was come to the judgement place with
a great troupe of armed men, and seeing *Virginius* there
contrary to his expectation, and perceyving no colour of
law could cloud his dooings, hee set down his owne will
for a law, and sayd hee would defraud *Marcus Cloudius*
no longer of his right, and seeinge the maide was convicted by proufe and witnes to bee his bond maid, he
gave sentence that he should presently have her away,
not suffering her father to alleage any thing for her free-
dome. *Virginius* seeing this extreeme dealing of *Appius*
threatningly shooke his hands at him, saying, I have
beetrothed my daughter to *Icilius* not to thee (O *Ap-*
pius) & I have brought her up to bee an honest maried
woman, not thy harlot. What doest thou thinke under
the pretence of bondage, to make her bound to thy
beastlinesse? *Appius* not regarding his rayling caused
his officers to make the multitude give place to *Marcus*
Cloudius that hee might quietly cary away his bond
mayd, by reason wherof *Virginia* was left voide of helpe
and rescue, which her father perceivinge and seeing him
self not able to deliver her out of her enemies handes, to
defer the time hopinge still for helpe, hee used this pollicy: hee desired *Appius* hee might have his daughter
aside, and betweene her nurce and her examine the matter, that if it were found hee were but her fained father,
hee might the more willingly depart with her. Which
beeing by *Appius* graunted, they three went aside together, where *Virginia* fell downe upon her knees and
made this ruthles request unto her father.

I perceive (deare father) it is not without great cause
that the philosophers were of this opinion, that the
greatest felicity is never to bee borne, and the second
soone to die, now seeing by your meanes I am deprived

5 Cloudius/Claudius *BCDEF*   6 his/this *EF*

of the first I beseech you by your meanes let mee injoy
the second: and to countervayle the lucklesse and lothsome life which you have given mee, vouchsafe to bestow
on mee an honourable death. And as by your fatherly
care I have continued a continent virgin hetherto,
so by your furthering aide I pray you let mee dye an
honest mayde presently: least my life hereafter, contaminate ye commendation of my life heretofore: and
seeing I can bee no longer suffred to live honestly, good
father let mee die honourably[.] For an honourable death   10
is alwayes to bee preferred beefore an infamous life, of
evils the least is to bee chosen, and death of body is to
bee counted a lesse evill, then distruction of body and
soule. I thinke I may by more right crave your helpe
herein, for that partly by your meanes I am fallen into
this extremity, for yt you would not agree to ye consummation of the mariage betweene *Icilius* and mee, and
howe you can deliver mee, but by delivering mee to
death I see not, for that your power is to weake to
wreak the wrong which is offred mee, and your force is   20
to feeble to fence mee from the fury of my foes. Therfore seeing hee will needes have my body (sweet father)
let him have it dead, that I may not feele the filthinesse
which hee purposeth to force mee to. Her father melting
into teares at her pitifull sute, carefully kissing her, commended her couragious minde, rather confirming her in
her constant couragiousnesse, then disswadinge her from
her purpose. By this time the tirantes traine beegan to
flocke aboute them to have her away, which *Virginius*
seeing snatched a butchers knife from the shambels and   30
thrust therewith his daughter to the heart, saying: O
daughter, by this only meane wherby I may doe I make
thee free. *Icilius* seeinge his spouse thus spoyled, spent

13 distruction/the destruction *CDEF*

no time in triflinge teares, but by the helpe of his father in lawe *Virginius*, prosecuted the matter so ernestly against *Appius* that hee was throwen into prison, where for shame of his deede and dread of deserved punnishment, hee did him selfe desperately to death.

You see here Gentlewomen, a most lamentable death of a most vertuous virgin, wherein you may note a noble minde in her to desyre it, a stout courage in her father to doe it, and most outragious tyranny in *Appius* to drive them to it: wherby you may learne that vertue and chastity is to bee preferred beefore worlde or wealth, beefore freind or father, before love or living, before life or death. Therefore, if I were either in wit able or otherwise worthy to give you counsayle, I would advise you to avoyde the traines of sutch tyrauntes, to keepe you out of the sight of sutch seedsuckers, and to fly from sutch *Senes fornecatores*: sutch raveninge wolves in sheepes cloathinge are rediest to devoure sutch sweete sheepe, sutch olde dogs ever bite sorest, sutch gravity for the most parte contayneth most incontinency. For if their lust were not more then outragious, either their great discretion would represse it, either their many yeeres would mortify it, either their owne wives would satisfie it. But use of evill maketh us thinke it no abuse, sinnes oft assayed are thought to bee no sinne, and these grayheaded gamesters have the habite of this mischeife so deeply rooted in them, that concupiscence will frie their fleshe, till breath doe leave their bodyes.

And as I would you should avoide these olde youthes in the way of wickednesse, so if my wish might wield your willes, you should neither medle with them in the way of mariage. For perfect love can never bee without

9 most/a most *EF*   17 fornecatores/fornicatores *BCDEF*
21 not/no *DEF*   31 your/our *EF*

equality, there can bee no good agreement of affections, where there is sutch difference of yeeres. Can fire & water, can flowers & frost, can warmth and winter, can mirth & melancholy agree together? No surely Gentlewomen but if you wil have it so, I wil beleeve this matter mooveth you nothing: Yet what say you to another point, & that a most perilous point, when to impotencie shalbe added Jelousy? This is a pill of harde digestion, this is a pill which if it bee a litle chewed, it will bee so bitter that you will never bee able to abide it. For when sutch an one shall measure your deedes by his owne desire, and your life present by his owne life past, when hee shall thinke you to bee naught, bicause hee him selfe hath bene naught: good god how cloasely then will hee mew you up? how carefully will hee looke to you? How lothsomely will hee cloy you with his company? Then will you wishe you unmaried, then will you wishe you had maried with a younge man: [with young men you shalbee sure to have the dueties of mariage every way performed *B–F*]: they wil love and not doate, they will bee zelous and not Jelous. And if your parentes in some curious or covetous respecte goe about otherwise to dispose of you, humbly request them you may chuse where you like, and link where you love, that you may bee married to a man rather then mony, to quiet rather then coine. Dutifully tell them that sutch presinesse of parentes brought *Pyramus* and *Thisbe* to a wofull end, *Romeo* and *Julietta* to untimely death, and drave *Virginius* miserably to murther his owne daughter *Virginia*.

10

20

13 hee *om. EF*   18 had/had bin *EF*
27 Pyramus/Piramus *BCDEF*   Thisbe/Thesbe *EF*   a *om. BCDEF*

Admetus and Alcest.

[ADMETUS sonne to ATYS kynge of *Lybia*, fallynge in love with *Alcest*,
daughter to *Lycabas* kynge of *Assur*, who recompenced him with sem-
blable affection, are restrayned eche from other by their parentes, but
beeyng secretly married, wander in wildernesses like poore pilgrimes.
Atys shortly after dieth, wherof *Admetus* beyng advertised, returneth
with his wyfe, and is established in the kyngdom. The destines graunt
him a double date of life if hee can finde one to die for him, which *Alcest*
her self perfourmeth: for whose death *Admetus* most wofully lamentyng,
10   she was eftsoones by *Proserpina* restoared to her life, and lover agayne.]

It is a saying no lesse common then commonly proved
true, that Marriages are guided by destinie, & amongst
all the contractes which concerne the life of man, I think
they only bee not in our owne power or pleasure: which
may plainly appeare by this, that when the choice of
sutch marriages doth chaunce unto us as wee our selves
can wish, when they may by their parents & freindes
countenance us, by their dowry and portion profit us,
by theyr person and bewtie pleasure us, by their ver-
20   tue and perfection every way place us in paradise, yet it
is often seen that wee set litle by them, neither make
any account of sutch profitable profers, but by a contrarie course of the heavens and destinies, are caried, as
it were agaynst our willes, some other way, and caused
to settle in affection there where heaven and earth seeme
to withstand our desire, where freindes frowne on us,
where wealth wants, where there is neither fecilitie in
pursuyng, neither felicitie in possessing: which the history which you shal heare shall more playnly set forth
30   unto you.

2 Lybia/Libia *CDEF*   in/into *EF*   29 which *om. EF*

There raygned in the lande of *Lybia* one *Atys*, who
had to his neighbour more neere then was necessary one
Lycabas kynge of *Assur*, which princes rather covetynge
their neighbours dominions, then contentyng themselves
with their owne, incroched eche one upon others right,
and continued continuall warre one against the other.
But at length *Atys*, whether hee were weried and wasted
with warre, or whether hee had occasion to bend his
force some other way, or whether hee were disposed to
enter into league and amitie with his neighbours I know   10
not, but hee sent his one [owne *B–F*] sonne *Admetus* to
Lycabas to parlee of a peace. Now *Lycabas* either thinkyng hee had him at some advantage, either not minding
to put up injuries beefore received, would accept no conditions of peace, but by *Admetus* sent his father flat defiance. So that the warre continued between them in as
great rage as it had done the former time of their raygne.
But yet hate caused not sutch hoate skirmishes between
the parentes, but that love forced as fierce assaultes between the children. For it was so that *Lycabas* had a   20
daughter named *Alcest*, who what time *Admetus* was in
her fathers court to intreate of peace, chaunced out at
her chaumber window to have a sight of him, and hee at
the same time happened to incounter a vewe of her. And
as small drops of rayne ingender great flouddes, and as
of litle seedes grow greate trees, so of this litle looke and
sight grew sutch great love and delight that death it
selfe could not dissolve it. For as women bee of delicate
and fine mettall, and therefore soone subject to love, so
Alcest after this first sight was so overgone in goodwill   30
towardes *Admetus*, that shee fixed her only felicitie in

7 and/or *CDEF*   12 a *om. DEF*   16 that *om. EF*
17 their/the *EF*   22 of/a *CDEF*   at/of *CDEF*   23 a *om. EF*
25–26 as of/as *EF*

framyng in her fancie the fourme of his face, and printyng in her heart the perfection of his person. And as
nothyng breedeth bane to the body sooner then trouble
of minde, so shee persevered so longe in sutch pensive
passyons, and carefull cogitations, that her body was
brought so lo for lacke of the use of sleepe and meate,
that shee was fayne to keepe her bed: and by reason
that shee covertly concealed her greife, it burned so furiously within her, that it had almost cleane consumed
her away. Her father seeinge her in this heavy case, assembled all the learned phisitions hee could learne of in
the country, who havinge seene her were all altogether
ignorant of her disease, and were at their wits ende what
medicine to apply to her malady. Some thought it a con-
sumption, some a burning fever, some a melancholy
humor, some one thing, some another. And her father
examyning her how it held her, and what disease she
thought it to bee, shee answered that it was a sicknesse
which it pleased god to sende her, and that it was not in
ye helpe of Phisicke to heale her, but her health was
onely to bee had at gods handes. Nowe *Admetus* on the
other side havinge the profer of many princes made him
in the way of mariage, made very carelesse account
thereof, and seemed in his minde to bee very angry with
those offers: and as the sight of meat is very lothsome
to him whose stomacke is ill or hath already eaten his
fill, so that litle sight which hee had of *Alcest* had fed his
fancy so full, that to see, or so mutch as think, of any
other woman was most greevous unto him. And notwithstandinge the gripinge paine of love caused some graftes
of greife to begin to growe in his heart: yet by reason
that hee had the conducting of the army royall under
his father, hee was so busily occupied that he had no
great leasure to lodge any loving thoughts within his

breast. But see howe the destinies dealt to drive this bargaine thorow. There aroase a quarrell beetweene the two armies touchinge certaine pointes wherin the law of armes was thought to bee broken, to decide which controversy *Admetus* was sent post to *Lycabas*: who sitting by his daughters bed side, had woorde brought him that *Admetus* was come to the court to impart matters of importance unto him. Nowe at this instant there chaunced one of the Phisitions to hold *Alcest* by the arme and to feele her pulses, and where before they beate very feebly as if shee had beene ready to yeelde to the sommance of death, shee no sooner heard that message brought up to her father, but that her pulses began to beat with great force and livelinesse: which the phisition perceivinge perswaded him selfe hee had found the cause of her calamity: but for more assured proufe hee whistered [*sic*] the king in the eare desiring him that *Admetus* might bee sent for thither and there to make relation of his message unto him: which the kinge caused to bee done accordingly. *Admetus* was no sooner admitted into the chamber, but her pulses beegan to beate againe with wonderfull swiftnesse, and so continued all the while hee was in the chaumber. Who seeinge his love in sutch daunger of her life, though hee understood not the cause therof, yet hee cast sutch a carefull countenance towardes her, that shee easely perceived hee did participate in payne with her: which made her cast sutch glaunces of goodwill towardes him, that hee easely understood it was for his sake shee sustained sutch sorrow and sicknesse. But the feare of her father, who was his mortall foe, and the urgent necessity of his affaires, forced him to depart without manifesting unto her the

10

20

30

1 this/the *EF*   9 arme/armes *EF*   10 and to/to *BCDEF*
25 a *om. BCDEF*

manifolde good will hee bare her. And though his departure were litle better then death to the damsell, yet
for that shee knew her love to bee incountred with like
affection (wherof before shee stoode in doubt), shee beegan to drive away the darke cloudes of dispaire and to
suffer the bright light of hope to shine upon her. *Admetus*
beeing gone, the Phisition tooke the king asyde and
tolde him his daughters disease was not derived of any
distemperature of the body but only of the disquiet-
nesse of the minde: and to tell you the truth plainely
(saith hee) it is only the fervent affection shee beareth
to that younge prince *Admetus* your enemy that forceth
this feeblenesse and faintnes in her. And told the kinge
by what meanes hee tried the truth therof. The kinge at
these wordes was mervailously disquieted perswading
himself that it was so in deede, and that *Admetus* on the
other side bare affection to his daughter, for that all the
time of his talke with him, hee continually turned his
eyes towards her bed, and wold often times give him
answeres nothinge pertinent to the questions which hee
proposed unto him, as having his cogitations conversaunt in other matters. Upon this the king went to his
daughter, & as the phisition first ministreth to his patient bitter pilles and purgations to expell grose and ill
humours, and then applieth lenitives and restoratives to
breede and bringe againe good bloud, so hee first used
sharpe threatnings unto her to expell the force and fury
of her love, and then used gentle perswasions to restore
her to her former helth and quiet of minde. But neither
the sowernesse of the one, neither the sweetnesse of the
other could prevayle, for salves seldome helpe an overlong suffred sore, it is to late to shut the stable dore when

12 to that/to the *EF*   23 first *om. EF*
29 quiet of minde/quyet mynde *CDEF*

the steede is stolen, it booteth not to stop the breach
when the towne is overflowen: it is to late to dislodge
love out of ones breast, when it hath infected beefore
every parte of the body. For as sowninge mortifieth
every member, as pestilence infecteth every part, as poyson pierseth every vaine, so love if it bee not in time
looked too, will bringe both body and minde to utter confusion. For this virgin was so vanquished by love, that
shee neither forced her fathers faire wordes, neither
feared his fierce threatninges, but tolde him plainly shee   10
would not deny the love she bare *Admetus*, neither could
cast out of her minde the liking shee had conceived of
him: and therfore humbly craved pardon if (sayth shee)
it bee an offence to love him honestly, which deserveth
it worthily. But her father in a fury flunge from her sayinge, shee should never injoy him with joye, and that
shee should never finde any more fatherly furtherance
at his handes, then the greatest enemy hee had. The
younge princesse perceivinge her fathers goodwill thus
alienated from her, reposed her onely comforte and con-   20
fidence in *Admetus*, hoping that hee would stande her in
steede of both a freind, phere, and father. And with as
convenient speede as shee could, wrought a letter to him
to this ende.

    If (most peerelesse prince) necessity or love had law, I
might bee thought perchaunce to transgresse the law
and limyttes of modesty in first givinge the onset where
as I ought not easely to have yelded beeing assaulted.
But seeinge necessity and lacke of oportunity, by reason of the rigour of the warres perchaunce causeth you   30
to conceale that which you would discover, and vehe-
mente love and fervent desire forceth mee to discover

11 bare/bare to *DEF*   14 an *om. DEF*
21 would/should *CDEF*   23 wrought/wrote *BCDEF*

that which I should conceale, I thinke it lesse offence by
this meanes to supplye your wante and satisfie mine
owne desire, then, by standing upon the nice termes of
my maidens estate, to suffer both of us to pine away in
paine for lacke of beeing privy to eche others minde and
purpose. Therfore you shall understand the cause of my
writing is this. What time your good hap (I hope) was to
bee at my fathers court, I did perceive (if desire to have
it so did not deceive mee) that your affection was great
towardes mee, and that you seemed not a litle to bee
pinched with my payne, to ease you of which greife I
thought it my duty to certify you, that the certaine hope
which I therby conceived of your love and good will, did
presently restoare mee to perfect health, and further to
let you understand, that the only cause of my sicknesse
was the first sight which I had of you, and the dispaire
that I should never bee so fortunate as to obtaine you.
Now as the same hand which did hurt mee, did helpe mee,
so if I have any way wounded you, I shalbee ready to
make you what playster it please you to heale your hurt[.]
And judginge the sincerity of your minde by the cleere-
nesse of mine owne conscience, I commit my selfe wholy
into your handes, presuminge thus far of your perfect
love towardes mee, that you will not any way seeke the
disperagement of mine honour (which I hold far more
deere then love or life) but accept mee for your lawfull
and loving spouse. And that way you only and at any
time shall dispose of mee at your pleasure. My father by
ill fortune hath found out our love, and stormeth greatly
therat, so that I thinke his haggard hart is by no meanes
to bee reclaimed. But I thinke indirect dealinge by the
daughter may bee used, when the father by rage rather

then reason is ruled. Therfore if you thinke so good, I will secretly conveigh my selfe to what place you will have mee, but I commit this matter to your wisdome, and my selfe to you, remayninge yours onely and ever:

ALCEST.

Now *Admetus* ever after his returne from the court of *Lycabas* was driven into sutch dolefull dumpes, and governed his charge of men with sutch heavy cheere, that his father examining him very stractly of the cause therof, inforced him to confesse his carefull case. Which hee no sooner heard, but hee forthwith discharged him of his charge, saying hee was fitter to bee one of *Cupids* carpet captaines, then to march under the mainly [manly *B–F*] ensigne of *Mars* : and that he would have no sutch lascivious knights in his army. For (sayth hee) if any part of the body be putrified, it must bee cut of for feare of infectinge the whole body. And tolde him plainly if hee went forward with his folly, hee woulde never take him for his sonne, neither should hee ever succeed in the kingdome by this consent. The younge prince withdrew himselfe out of his fathers presence, and got him to his pavilion or tente, where hee was no sooner sadly set downe, but hee was presented by a trusty messenger with yᵉ letter of *Alcest*, which so soone as hee had red, hee seemed to bee rapt into the thirde heaven : but considering on the other side the difficulty of reapinge the fruites of his love, and wayinge the perill of his fathers displeasure, hee was throwen into the deepest dungeon of hell. And as a boate borne by the tide against the winde, feeleth double force, and is compeld to yeelde both to winde and wave, so this young prince, beeinge driven by the force of love againste the minde and pleasure of

7 Lycabas/Licabas *DEF*   9 stractly/streictlye *B*, strictly *CDEF*
27 his *om. CDEF*   32 againste/and *EF*

his father, felte double dolour, and was tormented with both. But at length love gat the victory, and all other doubtes cast aside, hee returned his Misteris this answere.

Who was ever exalted to the highest degree of happinesse, and driven to the deepest extremitie of evill at once but I? who ever flowrished in felicitie, and faded in miserie together but I? who was ever placed in paradise and plunged in perplexitie joyntly but I? for heaven it selfe cannot yeelde mee better blisse then the consent of your goodwill and love, (most peerlesse prince & princely peece) and hell it selfe cannot yeelde mee more bitter bale, then to bee destitute of meanes to injoy the fruites of your favour and benefite of your beutie. If *Craesus* came and offered mee all his wealth, if *Alexander* yeelded mee his empire, if *Juno* came from heaven with her kingdomes, *Pallas* with her wisdome, or *Venus* with her *Helen*, assure thy selfe (sweet Mistris) that neither any one of them, neither all of them together, should bee so gratefully or gladly received of mee, as the profer which your letters have made mee. And canst thou (deare wenche) prefer my love before thine owne life, my plesure before thy fathers displeasure, my contentment before thine owne commoditie, and shall any doubt of daunger drive mee from the dutie whiche I ought to doe unto thee? No let father fret, let freindes frowne, let lyving bee lost, let kingdome bee made from mee, let hap what hap wil, thou hast promised to bee mine, and I protest by the heavens to bee thine. What though the kinge your father bee greatly incensed agaynst mee, what care I for any mans freindship if I have your favour? What though the way unto you bee longe and daungerous? What passe I to passe a thousande perils

14 and/and the *CDEF*   22 & 24 thine/thy *CDEF*

to pleasure you? what though mine enemies lie in wayte for mee? What way I to be hewen in an hundred peeces in your presence? Yea if I had a thousand lives I thinke the loosinge of them all litle inough to requite the greate goodwill and curtesie you have shewed mee. But mee-thinkes I heare you say, the spendyng or losse of my life, is the greatest losse and evill that possibly can hap-pen unto you, and therefore I must take heede how I hazarde it. Well I will (sweet wenche) preserve my life only to serve thee, and the care I have of you shall cause   10 me to have care of my selfe. But touchyng the con-veigh of our affayres I am at my wits end which way to worke, for if your father chafe at this matter, mine rag-eth and stormeth, and watcheth mee so narrowly that not so mutche as my lookes but hee looketh to them. But I will ease him of this labour ere it bee longe, for this life I am not able to indure longe: yea I had rather live with you in most misery (if hee may possibly bee miserable that injoyeth sutch a jewell as you are) then here in most happinesse (whiche of mee is not to bee   20 had without you) therfore wayward fortune hath only left us this way, if it please you so mutch to dishonour your selfe, and to doo mee so mutche honour, as meet mee the tenth of this moneth at the chappell of *Diana*, standyng as you know sixe leagues from your fathers court, I wil there god willing meet you, and a priest with mee to marrie us, which done wee will shift our selves into Pilgrims apparell, and so disguised indure together sutch fortune as the fates shall assygne us. And thus till then I byd you farewell.   30
    Yours ever, or his owne never: ADMETUS.
    Now see the valiantnesse of a vyrgin, or rather con-sider the force of love which maketh the weake strong,

1 mine/my *EF*   2 an/a *EF*   6 or/and *EF*

the witlesse wise, the simple subtil, yea and the most cowards most couragious. For the day prescribed in the letter of *Admetus* beeyng come, the younge princesse beefore day attired her selfe in one of her Pages apparell, and trudged out of the citie as if shee had been sent to the Campe on some message: and so fast as her faynte legges (but strengthned by love) could cary her, she hasted thorow the desert and waylesse woods to this for-lorne chappel, where the God whom shee only honoured was ready to receive her: Who though at ye first hee knew her not, but thought shee had been *Cupid* or *Mercury* fallen from the heavens, yet at length by her loving lookes cast upon him, he knew who it was, and imbrasing her fast in his armes sayde, if *Jupiter* (sweet wenche) should see thee in this Pages apparell, no doubt but hee would forgoe his *Ganymedes*, and take thee up into heaven in his steede. O moste soveraygne Lady and mistris, what service shall I ever bee able to doo you, which may countervayle this kindenesse? What dutie can bee a due recompence to this goodwill? If I by any meanes can quite this curtesy, I never doubt to bee deemed un-gratefull while I live. But accept (good Lady) I beseech you that which is in mee to perfourme, which is the faithfullest hart that ever was vowed to Lady: which when it swarveth from you, let al the torments of *Tan-talus*, *Tytius*, *Sisiphus* and all the rufull rout of hell bee heaped upon me. *Alcest* hearinge him so earnest sayd:

Few wordes (most worthy prince) are inough to win credite to a matter already beleeved: for onely upon con-fidence of your constant and faithfull hart towardes mee, I have thus unadvisedly adventured mine honour as you see, desiringe you not sinisterly to thinke of this my attempt, beeing boldned therto by the greate love

9 God/Sainct *CDEF*   26 Sisiphus/Sysiphus *DEF*

which I bare towardes you, and by the loyalty which I looke for of you towards mee. Ah sayth *Admetus,* if I should make any ill interpretation of your vertuous love and sincere affection towardes mee, I were the veriest villain on earth, for I take god to witnesse I take your forward will for sutch freindly good wil, that I doubt my desertes will never bee able so to answere therto as I desire. But here hee aptly ended his talke upon her mouth, and they entred into sutch privy conference, their lips beeing joyned most closely together, y^t I can not report   10 the meaninge of it unto you, but if it please one of you to leane hitherward a litle I will shew you the manner of it. Now havinge continued some time therin, they at the length entred into the temple, wher the mariage accordinge to the sacred rites was solemnly celebrated: which done they entred into a poore cotage, in steede of a princely pallace, joyning to the temple, where longe they durst not tary for feare of apprehension by postes which pursued them. Therfore puttinge on their pilgrims apparell againe, they wente hand in hand and   20 harte in harte, waylfully and wilfully, wandring out of their owne native country, to avoide their parentes punnishment and displeasure. O lamentable lots of love which drave two princes from theyr pleasant pallaices, from their flourishinge freindes, from their traine of servauntes, from their sumptuous fare, from their gorgeous garmentes, from variety of delightes, from secure quietnesse, yea from heavenly happinesse, to wilde wildernesse, to deserte dennes, to carefull caves, to hard cheere, with hawes and hippes, to pilgrims peltes, to   30 perill of spoyling, to daunger of devouring, to misery of minde, to affliction of body, yea to hellish heavines. O

20 againe *om. BCDEF*   23 O lamentable/See gentlewomen the lamentable
   BCDEF   24 drave/drove *EF*

pitiles parentes to prefer their owne hate beefore theyr childrens love, their owne displeasures before their childrens pleasure, to forget y^t themselves were once younge and subject to love, to measure the firy flames of youth, by the dead coales of age, to governe their children by their owne lust which now is, not which was in times past, to seeke to alter their naturall affection from their children upon so light a cause, shewinge themselves rebels to nature, to indevour to undoe the destines and disappointe the appointment of the goddes, shewing themselves traitours to the goddes. But the one of them, the father of *Admetus* reaped the just reward of his rigour. For *Atys* after the departure of his sonne tooke the matter very heavily, abandoned all pleasures, avoyded all company, and spent most part of his time in discoursinge with himselfe in this sorrowfull sort.

If nature by the devine providence of god did not move us to the maintenance of mankinde, surely the charge of children is sutch a heavy burthen, that it would fear men from entring into the holy state of matrimony. For to omit the inconveniences of their infancy, which are infinite, when they drawe once to mans estate, what time they should bee a stay to our staggering state, good God what troubles doe they torment us with? What cares doe they consume as [*sic*] with? What annoyes doo they afflict our olde yeeres with all? They say wee are renewed and revived as it were in our offspringe, but wee may say wee die dayly in thinkinge of the desperate deedes of our children. And as the spider feeleth if her web bee prickt but with the point of a pin, so if our childred [*sic*] bee touched but with the least trouble that is, wee feele the force of it to perce us to the hart. But how well this tender care is by them considered, alas it

13 Atys/he *BCDEF*   17 devine *om. EF*

maketh my hart bleed to think if wee looke for obedience of them, and that they shoulde follow our counsayle in the convaighe of their affaires, why they thinke
wee doate, and that their owne wits are far better then
ours: if wee warne them to bee wary and thrifty, they
thinke it proceedeth rather of covetousnesse then of
kindenes: if wee provide them no mariages, it is bicause
wee will departe with no livinge to them: if wee perswade them to mariage, it is bicause wee would have
them forsake all good felowship, & live like clownes in 10
the countrey by the Plowe tayle: If wee perswade them
to learnynge it is that they might live by it without our
charge: if wee perswade them to one wife rather then
another, it is bicause the one is ritcher then the other: if
wee looke severely on them, wee love them not: if wee
use them familiarly, wee feede them with flattery bicause wee will give them litle: and so of all our loving
dooinges they make these leud devises: yea when wee
have brought them up with greate care and coste, when
wee have travailed all our time by sea and by land, 20
early and late, in paine and in peril, to heape up treasure
for them, when wee have by continuall toyle shortned
our owne lives to lengthen and inlarge their livinges and
possessions, yet if wee suffer them not to royst and to
riot, to spill and to spoyle, to swashe and to lashe, to lend
and to spende, yea and to followe the fury of their owne
frantike fancies in all things, this forsooth is our recompence, they with an end of our lives to have our livings.
Alas a lamentable case, why hath not nature caused love
to ascend as well as discend? Why hath shee indued the 30
Storke with this property to feede his damme, when shee
is olde, and men with sutch malice to wish their parents

2 our *om. EF*   9 would/will *DEF*
10 forsake/to forsake *EF*   24 and to/and *CDEF*

death when they are aged? But I speake perchaunce of
mine owne proper greife, god forbid it should bee a common case, for my sonne (Ah why doo I call him sonne)
hath not only wisht my death but wrought it. Hee knew
hee was my onely delight, hee knew I coulde not live hee
beeing out of my sight: hee knew his desperate disobe-
dience would drive mee to a desperate death. And could
hee so mutch doate of a light damsell, to force so litle of
his loving father? Alas a wife is to bee preferred before
father and freind. But had hee none to fixe his fancy on
but the daughter of my most furious foe? Alas love hath
no respecte of persons. Yet was not my goodwill and consent to bee craved therin? Alas hee saw no possibility to
obtaine it. But now alas I would graunt my goodwil,
but now alas it is to late: his feare of my fury is to great
ever to bee found, his fault is to great ever to looke mee
in the face more, and my sorrowe is to great ever to bee
saluted. And thereupon got him to bed and in five dayes
space his naturall moysture with secret sorrowe was so
soken away, that hee could no longer continue his careful life, but yeelded willingly to desired death. So it
pleased God to provide for the poore pilgrimes, who having past many a fearful forrest and daungerous desert,
were now come to the sea shoare mindinge to take ship
and travell into unknowen coastes, where they might
not by any meanes bee knowne, and beeing on ship borde
they heard the mayster of the ship make report that
Atys king of the *Lybians* was dead. Whereupon *Admetus*
desired to bee set on shoare againe, and dissemblinge
the cause thereof, pretended some other matter and got
to the next towne wherwith the mony and jewels hee had
about him, hee furnished him selfe and his lady with the

8 hee/he not *D*, he now *EF*   12 no/not *EF*   28 Lybians/Lybyans *BC*,
Libians *DEF*   32 about/bought *EF*   him selfe/him *EF*

best apparell could bee provided in the towne, and with
sutch a trayne of men as hee coulde there take up: whiche
done hee made the greatest expedition hee coulde unto
his owne country where hee was royally received as
prince, and shortly after joyfully crowned Kinge. And
beeing quietly, setled in the regall seate, hee presently
dispatched Ambassadours to *Lycabas* his fathers foe,
and his father in law, whose ambassade contained these
two pointes, the one to intreat a peace for his people, the
other to crave a pardon for his wife, who willingly   10
graunted both the one and the other. Wherby hee now
lived in great quiet and tranquillity. A mervaylous mu-
tabylity of fortune which in the space of a moneth could
bring him from happy joy to heavy annoy, and then
from annoy againe to greater joy then his former joy.
For as the sunne having bene long time overwhelmed
with darke cloudes, when it hath bannished them from
aboute it, seemes to shyne more brightly then at any
time beefore, so the state and condition of this prince
havinge bene covered with the cloudes of care, now it   20
was cleared of them, seemed more pleasaunt and happy
then at any time before. And verely as sharpe sauce
gives a good taste to sweete meate, so trouble and adversity, makes quiet and prosperity for [farre *B–F*] more
pleasaunt. For hee knoweth not the pleasure of plenty,
who hath not felt the paine of penury, hee takes no delight in meate, who is never hongry; hee careth not
for ease who was never troubled with any disease. But
notwithstandinge the happy life of this prince, albeit
hee abounded in as great ritches as hee required, albeit   30
hee had as many kingedomes as hee coveted, albeit hee
had sutch a wife as hee wished for, yea and injoyed all
things which either god could give him, fortune further

10 a *om. EF*   19 state/estate *EF*   24 quiet/quietnes *BCDEF*

him to, or nature bestow upon him: yet to shew that
there is no sunne shineth so bright but that cloudes may
over cast it, no ground so good but that it bringeth forth
weeds as well as flowers, no kinge so surely garded, but
that the gamesome goddes fortune will at least checke
him, if not mate him, no state so plentifull in pleasure,
but that it is mixed with paine, hee had some weedes of
wo which began to grow up amongst his flowers of felicity, & some chippes of sory chaunce did light in the
heape of his happynesse. Yea fortune presented her selfe
once agayne upon the stage and ment to have one flinge
more at him. For this prince possessinge sutch a pleasaunte life, tooke great delight in good house keepinge,
and gave sutch good entertainment to straungers that
his fame was far spred into forrain countries: yea the
rumor thereof reached to the skies, in so mutch that
Apollo (as the poets report) having occasion to discend
from heaven to the earth, went to see the entertaine-
ment of *Admetus*: who was so royally received by him,
that the god thought good with some great kindnesse to
requite his great curtesie. And as *Philemon* and *Laucis*
[*Bucis B–F*], for their harty house keepinge, were preserved by the goddes from drowning when al the cuntry
and people besides were overflowen, so the god *Apollo*
ment to preserve his life, when all his countrey and
people then lyving should lie full loe in their graves. And
of the destinies of death obtained thus much for him,
that if when the time and terme of his naturall life drewe
to an end, yf any coulde bee found who would willingly
die & loose their owne life for him, hee should begin the
course of his life againe, and continue on earth another
age. Now when the time of his naturall life drew to an
ende, there was diligent inquiry made who would bee

10

20

30

12 a *om. DEF*   25 his countrey/the Countrie *EF*

content to abridge their owne dayes, to prolong their
princes life. And first the question was put to his freindes
(who were neerest to them selves) then to his kinsfolke
(whose love was as mutch of custome as of kindenesse)
then to his subjectes (whose affection was as mutch for
feare as for favour) then to his servauntes (who thought
their life as sweete as their mayster did his) then to his
children (who thought it reason that as their father did
first enter into this life hee should first depart out of this
life) so that there could none bee founde so franke of   10
their life to set this prince free from the force of death.
Now *Alcest* seeing the death of her deare husband draw
neere, and knowinge her owne life without his life and
love would bee but lothsome unto her, of her owne accorde offred her selfe to bee sacrificed for her husbandes
sake, and to hasten her owne death to prolonge his life.
O loyall loving wife, O wight good inough for god him
selfe. And yet had shee a husband good inough for her
selfe, for hee loved her so intirely that though by loosing
her hee might have gained life long time, yet would hee   20
not by any meanes consent to her death, sayinge, without her life his life would bee more greevous unto him
then a thousand deathes. But shee preswaded with him
against herself all that shee could saying, I would not (O
peerles prince) you should take the matter so kindly at
my hands, as though for your sake only I offred up my
life, it is in deede the commodity of your country and
mine owne, beeinge under your domynion, which driveth
mee hereto, knowinge my selfe unable to governe them
you beeing gone. And considering the dayly warre, the   30
spoylefull wastes, the bloudy blastes, the troublesome
strife which your realme is subject too, I thought you

11 this/his *DE*   17–18 god him selfe/gods themselves *EF*
20 long/a long *EF*   27 life/selfe *EF*

had not loved mee so litle as to leave mee behinde you to
beare on my weake backe sutch a heavy burthen, as I
thinke *Atlas* him selfe could scarce sustaine. Againe, considering that death is but a fleeting from one life into
another, and that from a most miserable life to a most
happy life, yea from bale to blisse, from care to quiet,
from Purgatory to Paradise, I thought you had not envied mee so mutch, as to thinke mee unwoorthy of it.
Doo you not know that *Cleovis* [*Cleobis B–F*] and *Byton*
had death bestowed upon them as the best gifte which
God could devise to give them, and doe you thinke it can
doe mee harme, especially seeing I may therby doe you
good? Alas sweet wife (sayth *Admetus*) this your piety is
unprofitable which is subject to so many perils. But if
death bee so good (good wife) let mee injoy it, who am
injoyned to it, and to whom onely it will be good, for
death is onely good to mee [to *B–F*] whom it is given,
not to you who are not appointed to it. For it is not lawfull for any to leave this life without speciall permission
of the goddes. And as in our court it is lawful for none to
have accesse unto us unlesse by us hee bee sent for, so
neither is it lawfull for any to appeare before the heavenly throne, unlesse by the goddes hee be sommoned.
Neither wil death bee so easy to you as to mee, whose
nature is apt to yeelde unto it. For you see fruite whiche
is not ripe, will scarce with strength bee torne from the
tree, wheras that which is ripe falleth easely of it[s] owne
accord. Therefore (good wife) give mee leave to die to
whom it wilbee onely good and easy to die. Why sweet
husband (sayth shee) the god *Appollo* allowed any that
would to die for you, otherwise to what purpose was
that which hee obtayned of the destinies for you? And

4 into/to *EF*   9 Byton/Biton *DEF*   13 piety/pittie *EF*
27 falleth/falleth away *CDEF*

for the uneasines of death, nothing can bee uneasy or hard unto a willing heart. But bicause your pleasure is so, I am content to continue my carefull life, and with sorrowe to survive you. And so left her husbande and went privily to the Aulter and offred up her selfe to death to prolonge her husbands life. Which when the king knew, hee would presently have spoyled him selfe, but his handes had not the power to doe it, for that by the decree of the destinies hee must now of force live an-other age on earth. Which when hee saw, hee filled the court with sutch pitifull wayling, sutch bitter weeping, sutch hellishe houlinge, that it pearced the heavens and mooved the gods to take remorse on his misery. And *Proserpine* yͤ goddes of hell especiallye pitying yͤ part-ing of this loving couple (for yͭ she her selfe knew the paine of partinge from freinds, beeing by *Dys* stolen from her mother *Ceres*) put life into his wife againe, and with speed sent her unto him. Who beeing certified here of in his sleepe, early in yͤ morning waited for her com-ming seing her come a far of hee had much a do to kepe his soule in his body from flying to meet her. Beeing come hee received her as joyfully, as shee came willingly, & so they lived longe time together in most contented happinesse.

This seemeth straunge unto you (Gentlewoman) that a woman should die and then live againe, but the mean-inge of it is this, that you should die to your selves and live to your husbandes, that you should counte their life your life, their death your distruction: that you should not care to disease your selves to please them: that you should in all thinges frame your selves to their fancies:

2 unto/to *EF*   12 pearced/pleased *EF*   20 seing/and seing *BCDEF*
21 flying/fleing *BCDEF*   22 hee received her as joyfully/as joyfully he
    receyved her *CDEF*   26 then *om. CDEF*

that if you see them disposed to mirth, you should indevour to bee pleasaunt: if they bee solemne, you should
bee sad: if they hard, you havinge: if they delight in
haukes, that you should love Spanniels: if they hunting,
you houndes: if they good company, you good house-
keeping: if they bee hastie, that you should bee pacient:
if they bee jelous, that you should lay aside all light
lookes: if they frowne, that you feare: if they smile, that
you laugh: if they kisse, that you cleepe, or at least give
them two for one: and so that in all thinges you should
conforme your selves to their contentacion: so shall
there bee one will in two minds, one hart in two bodies,
and two bodies in one flesh. Meethinkes I heare my wish,
wishe mee sutch a wife as I have spoken of, verily (good
wish) you with your wealth great wealth, and God make
mee woorthy of you wish and your wishe and if I might
have my wish I am perswaded you should have your
wish. But if I bee so good a husband as *Admetus* was, if I
forgoe father, freindes, and livinge, if I bee content to
chaunge joy for annoy, court for care, pleasure for pilgrimage for my wives sake, if I had rather die my selfe
then shee should, if shee beeinge dead, with mournfull
cries I move the Gods to raise her to life againe, I shall
thinke my selfe worthy of so good a wife as *Alcest* was. I
shall hap [hope *B–F*] to have a wife who with *Cleopatra*
will sting her selfe to death with serpentes at the death
of her *Antonius*: who with *Hylonomo* will slay her selfe
at the death of her *Cyllar*: who with *Singer* will vanish
away into aire for the losse of her *Picus*: and who with
Alcest will bee content to lose her life to preserve her
Admetus.

2 solemne/solenne *D*, sullen *EF*   27 Hylonomo/Hylomono *CDEF*
28 Cyllar/Cillar *DEF*   Singer/Synger *CDEF*
29 aire/the ayre *CDEF*

Scilla and Minos.

[SCILLA, daughter to *Nisus* kynge of *Alcathoe*, disdaynefully rejecting the humble sute of *Iphis*, a yonge Gentleman of her fathers Courte, becommeth unadvisedly amorous of kynge *Minos*, her fathers and countries mortall foe, lyinge in siege aboute the Citie. To whom by the counsell of *Pandarina* shee beetrayeth her father, in stealyng away his golden hayre, and presentinge it unto *Minos* in token of her love, whiche hee reprochefully rejecteth. And beeyng imbarked to depart homewards, shee assayeth to swim after him, and is drowned in the Sea.]

MANY are of opinion that the vertues of love are very   10
many, & that it is of force to reduce us from savagenesse
to civilnesse, from folly to wit, from covetousnesse to liberalitie, from clownishnesse to courtlinesse, yea from al
vice to all vertue. But if the effects therof bee rightly
considered, I see not but that wee may more justly say,
that the inconveniences of love bee infinite, and that it
bringeth us from modesty to impudencie, from learnynge to lewdnesse, from stayed firmnes to staggering
fickelnesse, from liberalitie to prodigalitie, from warinesse to wilfulnesse, from good beehaviour to dissolute   20
livinge, from reason to rage, yea from all goodnesse to
all vanitie. As may be justified by the goddes themselves, by the godliest men that ever were, by the
wisest men that ever were, and by the valiantest men
that ever were. Who by love have been brought to most
outragious impietie, to moste extreeme foly, and most
vile villany. But Gentlewomen, bicause most of you
bee maydes (I meane at least taken so) I will manifest

23 men *om. CDEF*
26 most/to most *EF*

unto you the mischeif of love by the example of a mayde, in that estate (though I hope not every way) like unto your selves, that admonished thereby, you may avoyde the like inconvenience in your selves.

Therfore you shall understande that over the towne *Alcathoé* raigned one *Nysus* [*Nisus* B–F], who had to daughter a damsell named *Scilla*, a proper sweet wenche, in goodlinesse a goddesse, in shape *Venus* her selfe, in shew a saynt, in perfection of person peerelesse: but in deedes a dayntie dame, in manners a mercilesse mayde, and in workes a wilfull wenche, as by her life you shall perceyve. For there was attendant upon her father in his court a proper youth named *Iphis*, who, as the freshest colours soonest fade the hue, and as the finest mettals soonest breake, so the more noble bloud hee came of, and the finer wit hee was indued withall, the sooner was hee made thrall and subjecte to love: And the more couragious minde hee had, ye more haughtie conquest did hee indevour to atchive. For beeyng in the dayly sight of *Scilla*, hee beegan firmely to fixe his fonde fancie upon her fine face. And by reason of his younge yeeres beeyng ignorant that under moste greene grasse lie most great snakes, and under intisinge baytes intanglyng hookes, hee bit so greedely at the bayte of her beutie, that hee swallowed downe the hooke of hatefull hurte, and hurtful heavinesse to his heart. But like a man hee sought meanes to subdue his sorrow and to vanquish this virgin, and first like a bashfull younge man hee solicited his sute by pitiful lookes, thinkyng therby to let her understande his desire. But shee on the other side perceivyng his intent, cast coy countenances upon him to drive him to dispayre: so that where beefore his owne bashfulnesse kept him from discouverynge his purpose,

6 Alcathoé/Alcatho *DEF*

now her coynesse caused him to cover it. Yet extreme
love drave him to this extreeme shift, hee imparted his
purpose to an uncle of his, a noble man of great countenance in ye court, humbly desiryng him either by
counsayle, countenance, payne or policie to stande him
in some stead to the attaynyng of his purpose: his unckel
gravely advised him to avoyde sutch vanitie and not to
attempt any sutch enterprise whereby he should incur
the Kings displeasure, and *per consequens* his owne un-
doyng. But he tolde this tale to one that had no eares to   10
heare, for the deepnesse of his love caused deafnesse in
him to heare any thinge whiche might help to heale his
harebraind head, for forwarde he would with his folly
whatsoever came of it. The olde Gentleman seeing his
unadvisednes, tolde hym he would so far as he durst
feele the fancye of the younge Princesse, and therby he
should perceive how likely he were to prevaile in his purpose. And havinge convenient time he fel to sifting her
thoughts in this sort.

Fayre Lady, we have letters come to the Court con-   20
tayning this newes, that two or three younge Princes
have directed their course into this Country to see and
assay you in the way of marriage: wherein I doubt not
but you will deale to the Kinges majesties contentation,
and to our Countryes commodytie: and to consider that
the stay of the whole kingdome standeth upon your
marriage, for yt he whiche marrieth you must after the
kings decease succeede as lawfull heire unto the crowne.
Now if you match your selfe with a stranger, it is greatly
to be feared that we shall be greatly molested with   30
the fury of forraine force, for that the Kings garde and
court for the most part shalbe of his owne Country: and

1 cover/discover *EF*   2 drave/drove *CDEF*
10 this/his *CDEF*   20 to/from *BCDEF*

so strangers shal be preferred to offices, and we set besides our living, wheras if it shall please you to take to
husbande some of your owne country you shalbe as it
were King & Queene your selfe, and he as it were your
servante and subject. And so shal you raigne in great
soveraignitie and we live in great tranquillytie. His talke
beeing ended the Princesse made hym this prowde
answer.

My Lord, touching my marriage it toucheth me more
neerely then you, and my father the Kinges counsell I
meane cheefely to follow therin: neither will I so respect
your commoditie to neglect mine owne honour, neither
wil I have more consideration of the stay of my Countrie,
then of the state of my callinge, neither in that poynt by
your leave will I prefer the common wealth before mine
owne private will: for that it is onely I must marrie,
which if I doe to my liking, I am lyke to live pleasauntly, if otherwise I am sure to live sowerly all the
dayes of my life. And for marryinge any of mine country,
I promise you for my part I know never a Prince in all
this country my father excepted. Meaninge she would
matche with none under the degree of a Prince. Immediately after this the noble man called his nephew unto
him telling him he thought it as easy a matter to climbe
to heaven with ladders, as for so meane a man as he to
aspyre to the height of her haughtie minde. The younge
Gentleman thinking that his unkle for feare of displeasure durst not deale in so daungerous a matter, neither gave great credit to his wordes, neither yeelded him
any thankes for his paines, but determined notwithstanding of hymselfe to pursue his sute. And knowing that
proper Gentlewomen delight in pretty Jewels, and that the

2 shall *om. EF*   3 your/our *EF*   4 your selfe/of your selfe *EF*
19 mine/mine owne *BCD*, my *EF*   25 ladders/a Ladder *EF*

Goddes them selves are pleased with gifts, he gat the most precious Pearles & dearest Diamonds in the country, and caused them to be presented unto the Princesse from hym. But disdainfull rigour so ruled her, that she would not so mutch as looke upon them, saying she had no neede of his giftes, that he might better bestowe them on those who were not his betters, and that she thought it shame a Princes person should be purchased with perles. The Gentleman though greatly dismaide to see both his goodwill neclected [sic], and his giftes rejected, yet lyke a valiaunt Souldiour he gave a freshe onset uppon her with friendlye loving Letters whiche hee wrote in this wise.

Most peerelesse Princesse, though love hath almost blinded me in all thinges, yet I humbly beseeche you not to thinke me so forgetfull either of the meanesse of myne owne estate, either of the majestie of yours, as to pre- sume to practise you in the waye of mariage, for in my judgemente I thinke no man on earthe worthy that hon- our, but my pitifull petition is this, that you wyll accept mee for your slave and servant, and y^t what country so- ever you shall be married into, I may geve attendance upon you, to ye intent still to injoy the sight of your sweete face, & feede my fansy in ye contemplation of your beuty. For I am so vowed to your vertue, y^t onely the sweet remembrance of you shal mortifie in me ye mind to any other woman whatsoever. For I perswade my selfe to finde more felicity in one friendly looke of yours, then in any others faithfull love. And though these blotted wordes be to base an object for your heav- enly eyes, yet waighing the cause in the skales of curte- sye, I trust you will take them in good part. The cause of the blots was the teares whiche fell from my eyes at the

5 as/as to *EF*

making hereof, the cause of the words is the good will of the writer. Thus prayinge you to pittie the one and to accept the other, I leave, lyving onely to doe you duty and service.

Yours, though not yours: IPHIS.

The Princesse having this letter delivered unto her, by one of her waiting women, so soone as she knew from whence it came, floung it from her, sayinge shee had nothing to deale ether with him or his letters, and 10 straightlye charged her women not to salute her with any thing from him. But Fortune so framed that as she flung the letter from her, in came the king her father & caused the letter to be reacht unto him, and knowing the contentes therof, sent for my youth *Iphis*, shooke him up with sharp threatnings, and charged him upon paine of punishment never after to be seene at the Courte. The younge Gentleman seeing the ground which he tilled altogether barren, and that it yeelded him but care for Corne and griefe for graine, determined to bestowe no 20 more cost or labour thereon: and besides fearing the Kings fury and displeasure, with as convenient speede as he could co[n]veied hymselfe in to the countrie, and there asswaged his sadnesse with solitarinesse: & setting her crueltie towardes him against his curtesie towards her, her disdainfulnes, against his owne dutifulnes, he soone set himself free from his folly. This matter thus ended, greater stormes began to brue, & such a tempest arose that *Scilla* who beefore kept other in bandes, was now her selfe in the sandes, & where before 30 shee sailed in ship with top and top gallant, setting out flag of defiance, now she was driven to strik saile and vaile bonnet even to her fathers enemy. For it fell so out

18 for/of *B*   19 graine/gaine *BCDEF*
25 owne *om. EF*   30 in ship *om. EF*

that King *Minos*, moved justly therto for the murther
of his sonne, waged warre and came with a puisaunt
power against King *Nysus*, and layde so harde to his
charge that he made him keepe his Castle. Now while
Minos lay at the siege therof, it fortuned the younge
Princesse to have a sight of him out at the window of
the tower wherin shee lay: and now *Cupid* ment to
bee revenged on the crueltie which she used to his
Captaine *Iphis* who fought so faithfully under his
banner: and shot sutch darts of desyre into her towards   10
King *Minos*, that unlesse she might have him to husbande shee thought her selfe but a woman cast away:
and after a sobbinge sigh and tricklynge teare she fell
out with her self in this sorte.

Ah fond foolish girle, and canst thou finde in thine
hart to beare freindly affection to thy fathers feendly
foe? Can I love him kindly, who seekes to spoyle my
country cruelly[?] Coulde I valiauntly withstande the
assaultes of a flourishinge young man, and shall I
cowardly yeeld to a fadinge olde man without any   20
assault? O love without law, O rage without reason,
O will without wit, O fansy fraught full of fury and
frensy. Good God where are now beecome those lofty
lookes I was wonte to use to lovers? Where are the coy
countenances, the haughty wordes, the solemne salutacions, the dainty dealinges, the curious congies, and
sutch like? Alas now I am made to stoupe without
stale, to come without call or lure, yea to the empty
fist. But alas who is priviledged from the force of love,
no there are none so stout but love maketh them   30
stoupe, none so wise but love maketh them fooles,
none so shamefast but love maketh them bolde. And

3 Nysus/Nisus *DEF*   7 wherin/where *EF*
13 a/many a *BCDEF*   23 beecome *om. EF*

though I should first bewray my affection and make
love to kinge *Minos*, the offence is rather to bee pitied
then punished. Yea the more frankly I offer him my
goodwil, the more freindly no doubt but hee will accept
it: and the lesse hee hath deserved it, the more will hee
indevour himself to bee thankful for the same. Neither
can hee but take it as an undoubted signe of deepe
goodwill if I give the first onset in this skirmishe:
neither can it any way redound to my shame, the end
beeinge honest and my meaninge in the way of mariage.
And if it bee lawfull to follow the example of creatures
without reason, doth not the Cow loe to the Bull, doth
not the Mare neigh to the Horse, doth not the Yeaw
blea to the Ramme, doth not the Faulcon call to the
tossell gentle, the gerfaulcon to the Gerkin, the sparehauke to the Musket? And so of all other creatures the
females are more forward that way then the males.
Besides that by how mutch weaker women are then
men, by so mutch the more they are to bee borne with
all, if they bee lesse able to beare the heavy burthen
of love then men. Againe by how mutch more the love
of women is more fervent then of men, the more fiery
flames of force must fry within us, whiche without
great griefe cannot be concealed or covered. And
whereof springeth this errour that women may not first
make love but only of a precise and curious custome,
nay rather a prejudicall and carefull custome I may
tearme it to us women: for wherof commeth it that so
many of us are so evill matcht in mariage, but only
hereof, that wee are tyed to the hard cho[y]se of those
that offer their love unto us: whereas if it were lawfull
for us to make love where we lyked best, we woulde
never marry but to our minde and contentation.

14 blea to/blea for *EF*   17 the *om. EF*   30 the/that *EF*

Lastly I am not the first that have played the lyke parte, and that whiche is done by alowable example is lawfully done. For *Venus* her selfe yeelded her selfe to her darlinge *Adonis* withoute any sute made on his part: *Phaedra* made sute to *Hippolitus*: *Oenone* pleaded her right with *Paris*: *Dido* dyd *Æneas* to understande how deepely she desired him: *Bryses* besought the good-will of *Achilles*: *Adalesia* by her governesse made love to *Alerane*: the Dutchesse of *Savoy* went on pilgrimage to ye Knight *Mendoza*: infinit lyke exampl[e]s I could 10 alleage, and why is it not lawfull for me to do the lyke, and make love to King *Minos*, who perchance would first have sued to mee, if he had first seene mee? yes let the world judge what they will, I wyll doe what I shal judge best for my selfe, and with as convenient speede as I may I will either by letters or deedes do *Minos* to understand what minde I beare him. And as she was busely beating her braines here about, one of her most trusty and loving women came unto her, humbly requestinge her to make her privy to the cause of her 20 perplexitie. Alas good misteris (saith she) yf you want any thing, let your friends understand it, and it shal be provided. If my poore service may any way serve your turne, assure your selfe neither respect of honour, lyving or lyfe, shall let mee from doing any thing, which may deliver you out of distresse: if you have imprisoned your libertie any where, and gived your selfe in the fet-ters of fansy, I know a Gentlewoman, my familier freind, who can stand you in as much steed for ye obtaininge of your purpose as any gentlewoman in this Courte. 30

2 alowable/ a laudable *EF*   5 Phaedra/Phoedra *BCDE*
5 Oenone/Oenon *CDEF*   7 Bryses/Bryseis *EF*
20 the cause of *om. EF*   21 misteris/madame *BCDEF*
23 any way *om. CDEF*   27 gived/gyved *CD*, given *EF*

The princes desirous of aid in her distres, prayed her woman to procure the comminge of that Gentlewoman with all possible speede. Wherupon the wayting woman caused one of the princesses gentlemen to goe to this honest woman, and in her name to desire her to come to the princesse. You shall understande this gentle-womans name, who was sent for, was *Pandarina*, in her youth a servinge woman, and one which knewe more fashions then was fit for honest women. But nowe married to an honest Gentleman, shee entred into a newe religion seeming to renounce her olde fayth, & setling her selfe in sutch hiprocrysy, yᵗ she rather counter-faited cunningly then lived continently. But to paint her out more plainly she was more coy then cumly, more fine then wel favored, more loftly then lovely, more proud then proper, more precise then pure, more superstitious then religious, more of spighte then of the spirit, and yet nothing but honesty would downe *with* her, more Jelous then zelous, either judging her husband by her selfe, or judginge her selfe unworthy the severall use of so commodious a commen as her husband was. Well sutch as shee was this younge gentleman of the younge princesse was sent for her, & at yᵉ first comming according to the fashion hee kist her, and having done his message, with frowning face shee told him shee could not goe to the princesse, and though shee could yet would shee not goe with him. The Gentleman somwhat abashed hereat, returned to the gentlewoman that sent him, and told her what answere this honest woman made. Who mervailing mutch therat went presently her selfe unto her, desiring that gentleman to

4 princesses gentlemen/Princes Gentlemen *CD*, princes gentlewomen *EF*
18 honesty/divinitie *BCDEF*
23 princesse/princes *CDEF*   her *om. EF*

accompany her. Beeinge come to her lodging, after a
few salutacions, *Pandarina* prayed the gentlewoman
either to send unto her a more modest messenger then
the gentleman shee sent, or els to teache him to kisse
more continently. The gentlewoman blushinge for bashfulnes, told her she had not the skill to teache men to
kisse, shee thought that cunning concerned common
harlots, or at least married women rather then her, but,
sayth shee, I will tell him of it, that of him selfe hee
may amend his fault, and callinge the gentleman aside   10
unto her, shee asked him how hee had misused him
selfe towards Misteris *Pandarina* in kissinge her. No
way (sayth hee) that I knowe for, but if I kissed her
boldly, I trust shee wil attribute it to young mens
bashfulnesse, and if I kissed her kindly, I trust she wyll
impute it to good will. Yes marry (sayth the gentlewoman) it was more kindely then shee cared for or
liked of. Verily (sayth hee) if it were over kinde, it is
more then I know, or more then I ment for to speake
my fancy freely, I know never a gentlewoman in this   20
lande, that I like of worse: and if shee bee aferde I bee
to far in love with her, I will bee bound in what bond
shee will, to hate her no man more. But gentlewoman,
if you adhibite any credite to my counsayle, flie her
familiarity, eschew her company, sutch sayntes in shewe
are Satans in deede, sutch fayned holinesse is double
divelishnesse, sutch counterfayte continency I count
litle better then baudry. For sure this is a most sure
marke to knowe dissemblers by, that they will alwayes
far exceede the meane, for feare of beeing found in   30
their fayning. As those that fayne to weepe, houle out
right: those that fayne to bee freindly, shew them
selves plaine *Parasites*: as those that fayne to bee

14 boldly/coldly *BCDEF*   24 flie/flee *BCDEF*

valiant, brag most gloriously: and as shee counterfaytinge continency, sheweth her selfe altogether curious
and hipocritiall. But notwithstandinge I have had no
knowledge of her life and conversation, yet dare I lay
my life on it, that either shee hath bene naught, is
naught, or wilbe naught whensoever shee can get any
foule adultrour fit for so filthy an adultresse. The
Gentlewoman hearing him so ernest, prayed him to put
up the matter patiently, sayinge shee thought it was
but a shift to excuse her not comminge to the princesse:
and so went to *Pandarina* telling her the Gentleman
was sory hee had offended her, and so away they went
together to the princesse. I have wandred, Gentlewomen, somwhat beesides the path of my promised
purpose, but yet not cleane out of the way of mine owne
will and intent. For though this digression pertaine
litle to the history I have in hande, yet it may serve
to admonish you that you take not executions of
curiosyty against kisses which are given you of curtesy:
and if there chaunce to bee any fault in them, either
modesty to conceale it, or presently to returne the
kisses againe to him, which gave them. But in excusing
my former digression, I shall enter into another digression, therefore to the matter and purpose proposed.
Pandarina beeinge preferred to the presence of the
Princesse, havinge done dutifull reverence humblye
craved to knowe her pleasure. Nay rather answered the
princesse, it is my payne Gentlewoman which I meane
to make you privy to: and blushing either for giltinesse
or for bashfulnesse, shee unfolded ye secrets of her
thoughts to *Pandarina* in this sorte.

Gentlewoman, but that I know to whom I speake, I
shoulde perchaunce bee in doubt what to speake in
this matter, which is somewhat unmeete for my mayd-

enly estate. But considering you are a woman, and one who no doubt in your time have felt the force of love, I perswade my selfe I may boldly impart unto you the panges of my passion, as to one who (I hope) will rather seeke a salve for my sore, then thinke sinisterly of my dooinges. Therfore you shall understand that the sight of Kinge *Minos*, who layeth siege to our city, hath made sutch a breach into my heart, that I lie altogether open to his assaultes, and am fayne to yeeld my selfe his prisoner and captive. And though it may seeme straunge unto you that his forces beeinge not bent against mee, should have sutch force over mee, yet it is often seene that a dart leveled at one, lightes on another. And though you may mervayle to see mee yeelde beefore any onset bee given, yet no doubt that cittie merittes more mercy which yeeldeth without assault, then that which standeth to the doubtfull event of battayle, and after mutch effusion of bloud, yeldeth when it is able to stand no longer in defence. For here the losse in the siege, taketh away the gaine in the conquest, the paine in pursuing, taketh away the plesure in possessing, and the hardnesse in winning drowneth the happinesse in wearing. And surely if maides would follow my counsayle, I would not wish them to set sutch solemne lookes, to use sutch nice denials and dainty delayes to those, whom they thinke worthy of them, and whom they mean only shall injoy them. For they gaine nothing hereby but deferre their owne releife, and increase their lovers greife. Beesides that when they are so hardly wonne, it is a signe they yeeld rather by importunity of the wooer, then by any inclination of goodwill on their owne part. But what neede I use this defence, where no body chargeth mee

10

20

30

4 of my/of of *E, mispr.*, of *F*   8 into/in *EF*   32 of/to *EF*

with any offence? This rather lieth mee upon, ernestly
to crave your aide & assistance in this my distresse, and
that you will either by counsayle cure my disease,
either by paine or pollicy put mee in possession of my
desire. I am thus bolde to commit this matter unto
you, presuming of your good wit, and goodwill towardes
mee. And if you shew sutch faythfull freindlynesse
herein, as I verily looke for, assure your selfe I will
in sutch freindly manner requite it as you shall very
well like of. Misteris *Pandarina* having attentively
attended her talke, dutifully replied in this sorte.

Most excellent Princesse, I am humbly to thanke
you that it pleaseth you to repose sutch credite in mee
as to discloase your secretes to mee, and I shall thinke
myselfe most happy, if my duty may any way doe you
good, or my service satisfie your expectation. And
touching your love it is sutch that you neede not bee
ashamed to shew it, yea in my judgemente it is rather
to bee commended every way, then condemned any
way. For first in that your fancy is fixed on a prince,
you shew your princely minde in lyking your like: then
in that you seke to joyne your selfe to him in mariage,
you shew your godly disposition, in desiring to quenche
the desires of your harte by that godly meane which
god hath made and appointed. Thirdly in lovinge your
fathers foe, you followe gods commaundement, who
willeth you to requite good for evill. Yea and by this
meanes you may bee a meane to make peace and amity
betweene two enemies, and save your cittie from siege
and sacke. Lastly in that you yeeld so quickly to the
alarms of love, you shew your fine nature and wit which
are soonest subject to the impression of love. And for
your opinion touching the dealing of dainty damsels,

33 your/my *EF*

you are no doubt (Madame) in the right. For those
which are so coyishe & wilde, or so haggarde like, that
scarce in seven yeeres sute they will bee reclaimed, they
plainely shewe themselves either to bee of base mettal,
as not to bee capable of love, either of grose wittes
as not to understande when love is made unto them,
either of slender judgment as not to accept good offers,
either of incontinent conversation as beeing loth to bee
tied to one diet, either of inconstant conditions, as
judging men as light of love as themselves are leud of   10
life, or els some way imperfecte that they are not meet
for the holy state of matrimony. Now wheras you crave
my counsel and helpe to the bringing of your good
purpose to passe, good Madame would I were as well
able as willinge to doe you good: but so far as my
simple wits can see in the matter, I thinke this way the
best to worke your will: you knowe your father hath
on his head a golden haire whereon dependeth the stay of
his state and puissance of his power, no more but when
your father is a sleepe, pull of the the [*sic*] heire and   20
present kinge *Minos* therwith and no doubt but hee will
imbrace you as the autor of his victory, and receive you
for his lawful and loving wife, so shal you redresse your
own distres, and preserve the life of your father and
his people, who perchaunce by the continuance of this
warre, may come to confusion. The princesse likinge
reasonably well of this practise of *Pandarina*, gave her
thankes for her good counsayle, and departed into her
chamber by her selfe to thinke more of the matter,
where shee entred with her selfe into these contrarieties.   30
  I see there is no disease so desperate, but if it be

1 those/these *CDEF*   2 coyishe/ramage *BCDEF*
4 of base mettal/base of metal *C*, base mettall *EF*
20 the the/that *BCDEF*   22 his/this *EF*

taken in time phisick may help it: no matter so harde but polycie can prevaile in it, nor no policye so good but experyence will put into our heads: as may be seene by the sound advice and perfect polycie of *Pandarina*. I warrant I am not the first clyent that this counsellour hath had. I am not the first *Pupill* that she hath practised for, this is not the first sluttish sute that she hath bene Solicyter in, this is not the first honest match that she hath made. But stay, let me not commend her cunning and counsell to mutch, before I consider better of the goodnesse thereof. I must forsooth pull of my fathers golden haire and present *Minos* therwith: a light matter it seemeth to pul of a haire, but alas, that haire containeth my fathers helpe, his hope, his hap, his strength, his power, his conquest, and his kingdome. Shall I then so mutch transgresse the lawes of nature to bring him to a miserable plight, who was the cause that I came into this joyfull lighte? Who from my infancy carefully cherished, and fatherlye fostered mee up, whom by humaine and devine lawes I am bound to obey honor and love? No, avaunt unlawful love, thou art rated at to high a price to be reached: avaunte foule beastly baude, thy counsell is withoute conscience, thy advice without honesty: they which cleave to thy help shall bee served as he whiche ready to fall from a hedge, catcheth holde of a sharpe bryer to staye himselfe: they y^t follow thy phisick shal do as he which to heale his ague, slew himself: they which provide for their fathers peace and preservation as thou wouldest have mee to doe, shall with the Daughters of *Pelias* kill their father to make hym younge agayne: They which love their Father as thou wouldst have me to do, shall with *Thais* to her *Phaedria* shut hym out of the dores, and out of

27 y^t/that *C*, which *DEF*   33 Phaedria/Phoedria *BCDEF*

his kingdome for love. But what, doe floudes drowne
fieldes before they finde a brack? can one be exalted
without anothers wracke? Can I be preferred to pleasure
without some others paine[?] But it greeves mee my
father shoulde bee pinched for my pleasure. Why it is
reason the greife should be theirs, whose is the gaine.
But it is perilous for mee to enterprise so great a matter.
Why is it not reason the perill should be mine in pursuing, when the pleasure shall bee mine in possessing? but
alas it nippeth mee nere to lose my father the victory,   10
to winne my selfe my love. Why alas greevous woundes
must have smarting playsters, and those medicines ever
soonest heale us whiche most greeve us. And shall I
then preferre mine owne pleasure before my fathers
profit? why every one ought to be nerest to them selves,
and their wisdome is nothing worth which are not wise
for them selves. Nay rather shall I preferre the commodytie of King *Minos* before the commodytie of King
Nysus? why *Nysus* is my father: why *Minos* will be my
Phere: why *Nysus* gave me lyfe: Why *Minos* wyll yeelde   20
mee love: Why *Nysus* made mee a maide: Why *Minos*
wil make mee a mother: Why *Nysus* cherished mee
beeing young: Why *Minos* wyll make mutch of mee
beeinge olde: why nature bindeth mee to love my
father: why God commaundeth mee to love my husband: Ah foole, doe I call hym husbande who wyll not
have mee? doe I call him phere who forceth not of mee?
Is it lykely hee will receive a runnagate from her cittie, a
beetrayer of her Father? Can hee think to finde mee
faithfull towards him, that am faithlesse to mine owne   30
father? Tush hee will attribute all this to love, and love
mee ye better for it. He will excuse & beare with my
doings by the example of his owne daughter *Ariadne*,

32 ye/the *CF, om. DE*

who betraied him to her lover *Thesius*: by the example of
Medea, who betraied her father to *Jason*: by the example
of *Hyppodame*, who procured ye death of her father by
matching with *Pelops*. And therfore al doubtes done
away, I wil without delay put the policie of *Pandar*[ina]
in practise. The night following (sutch hast her hot love
required) she shewd her selfe Misteris of her word
though not of her selfe, and performed that which shee
sayde she would. For her father beeing a sleepe, shee
got softly to him and cut of his precious haire which
had in it sutch vertue. Which done, shee went to King
Minos and presented him therewith, who in most
reprochefull wordes reprehended her deede, and in
most disdainfull sort rejected her love. But she not
meaning to leave her love while shee had lyfe, leapt
into the sea to swim after him as hee sayled away. And
so quenched her desire in the bottome of the sea.

You see here, Gentlewomen, she yt would not looke
upon her *Iphis*, coulde not be looked upon by her
Minos. Shee that would make no account of her inferriour, could not be accounted of by her superiour. For
it is a plaine case, (and therfore looke to it) that they
which deale rigorously with other[s], shall bee rudely
dealt withal themselves. But I am by this story chiefely
to admonish you that you pull not of your fathers haire
that is, yt you pul not their harts out of their bodies,
by unadvisedly castinge your selves away in matching
in marriage with those who are not meet for you. That
is to pull of your fathers haire, when you shall cast of
the bridle of obedience, rashly run at randon [*sic*],
rudely neglect his precepts, and presumptuously place
your selves in marriage contrarie to his pleasure: that
is to pull of your Fathers haire. But (Soveraigne) now
your father is gone, I will give you more sound advice:

I will admonishe you all not to pull of your owne haire, that is not to binde your selves to the froward fansi of your politique parents, but to make your choice in marriage according to your owne mindes: [for parents usurpe that authoritie over their daughters, bicause it is in them to departe with their Dowryes *B–F*], for over widowes you see Fathers have no preheminence of power touching their marriages: and you are not to know that mariage is a contract consisting of the free consent of both the parties, and that onely is required in the consummation of marriages: and the *Rodians* have this law, that onely the mothers have rule over the Daughters. But mum, *lupus in fabula*. I must (I say) admonish you yt as your parents gave you your bodies, so they may dispose of them. That you requight all their love, care and cost, at least with obedience. I must tel you that if you honour not them your dayes will bee short on earth: I must tell you that Ravens will pull out the eye that blindeth the Father, and neglecteth the good instruction of the mother, as *Solomon* sayd.

Curiatius and Horatia.

[CURIATIUS a young Gentleman of the Citie of *Albania* in ITALY, fallinge into extreame love with *Horatia* a young Gentlewoman of the Cittie of Rome, after longe sute, and many delayes, obtaineth her graunt to bee his wife. But in the meane time, contention fallinge out beetwene the two Citties[,] *Curiatius* is slaine in the fielde by *Horatius*, brother to the said Gentlewoman, to whom hee was assured. Whose death *Horatia* most pittifully bewaylinge, her brother greatly disdayneth thereat, and cruelly thrusteth her to the harte with his Swoord.]

10   SURELY Gentlewomen, either according to *Ovid* his opinion *Forma numen habet*, Beutie hath some divinity or Godhead in it, or els contrary to the common opinion, love is some heavenly influence and no earthly accident. For of every earthly and mortall motion there may some probable reason or naturall cause bee given: as every lyving creature desireth that whiche is good and agreeable to it[s] nature, bicause every thinge is deere to it selfe, and desireth the conservation of it selfe in it[s] kinde. As the earth draweth downward, beecause
20   it is heavy, the fyre flyeth upward beecause it is light, the water contrarie to it[s] nature oftentimes ascendeth to the top of high hyls to avoyde vacantnesse. The aire for the same cause often times discendeth into the pores of the earth: as cholerike complexions are soonest incensed to anger, beecause they abound with heate, as women are not so subject to anger as men beecause they are more colde of nature. And so of all humaine actions & natural effectes, there may be some probable reason and naturall cause yeelded. But of love it is so

2 Albania/Albana *E*   21 it[s] *om. EF*
22 high/the high *EF*   29 so *om. EF*

farre without the compasse of reason and bounds of
nature, that there can no reason, no cause, no conjectur
bee given of it. Neither what it is, working sutch divers
effects, neither whence it is, proceedinge of so divers
causes, neither whether it will beeing never satisfied.
Therfore no earthly thing but some supernal power sure
it is, as your selves (I thinke) will say by that time you
have harde the History of *Curiatius* who was sodenly
strocken therewith as if it had beene with some thunder
or lightning from heaven. For you shall understande   10
this gentleman dwelling in a towne named *Albania*,
situate neere unto the Cittie of *Rome*, hee made dayly
repaire unto *Rome*, both in respect of profit, as to deale
with marchants in matters of waight, and in respect
of pleasure, as to frequent the felowship of lusty younge
Gentlemen whiche flourished in that Cittie. Now it was
his chaunce as hee strayed about the streetes, to see a
proper Gentlewoman named *Horatia*, sittinge at her
Fathers dore to take the aire, and to recreate her selfe
with the sighte of those that passed by: and notwith-   20
standinge he had never seene her before, yet through
the devine power of love, he was so blasted with her
beautie, that he presently proclamed her the soveraigne
of his thoughtes, and governesse of all his doinges. And
havinge passed by her twise or thrise with lookes
shewing his love, and salutations signifiyng his sute, he
could not be so satisfied but banishing bashfulnes, he
couragiously incountred her in this manner.

Gentlewoman, God save you, and send you that
which you wish, and to wish that which I would. Good   30
Misteris may it please you to know that though my
feete have force to cary my body from this place, yet
my harte will not suffer mee to turne my head from

12 unto/to *EF*

beholdinge your sweet face, whiche is the cause that
hath made mee thus boldly to intrude my selfe into
your company. But setting your goodnesse against my
rudenesse, I doubte not but you will attribute it rather
to abundaunce of goodwill, then to want of good
behaviour, and rather take it for good meaning then yll
manner. But if it please you not thus frindly to interpret
it, yet at least I beseech you not to impute it to my
boldnesse, but to your owne beautie: for as the Larke-
taker in his day net hath a glasse whereon while the
birdes sit and gaze they are taken in the net, so your
face hath sutch a glisteringe glasse of goodlynesse in
it, that while I gazed thereon I was caught in the
snares of *Cupid*. Or as the Spider in her webbe doth
fast winde the litle Flie, so your beauty doth so fast
binde mee in the beames thereof, that I am faine
presently to yeelde my selfe a pray to your good pleasure: humbly beeseeching you to account of mee, not
accordinge to my deserts which as yet are none, but
accordinge to the loyall service which I faithfully vow
hereafter to do unto you. Neither meane I to crave
other rewarde for my service, but onely that it will
please you in good parte to accept it. *Horatia* havinge
harkened to this talke with a certaine disdainfull and
solemne scilence made him this waspishe answer.

Gentleman, this libertie of speeche in you sheweth the
lightnesse of your love, for as I have harde those that
love most speak least, as hearing their cogitations con-
versant in the contemplation of the Saints whom they
serve, but your smooth tale and fine filed words shew
that your practise is rather fainedly to pretende love
then faithfully to love. And for my part I would not
you should think me either so simple as to beleeve your

19 as yet/yet *D, om. EF*　　33 as *om. EF*

coloured words, either so overgone in lykinge of my
selfe, but that I take the commendation which you
give mee, rather for triflinge mockinge then true meaninge, and I promise you I had rather you woulde use
some other to exercise your eloquence on then my selfe,
for that I neither like of your unlykely love, neither
meane to be framed to your folly. Your comming to mee
upon no acquaintaunce contenteth mee well inough for
that I may leave your company when I lyst, and so
turned in at the dore from him. The Gentleman seeing   10
her rigorousnesse to exceede his owne rudenesse, laying
aside a litle more good manner, tooke hir fast by the
arme desiringe her to stay a worde or twaine which he
uttered to this effect.

O good Misteris, goe not about to torment hym so
terribly whiche loveth you so intirely, deprive mee not
of that sight which doth onely work my delight, absent
not your selfe from him whom nothinge under the
Sunne pleaseth but your presence. And whereas you
chalenge my lybertie of speeche, may it like you to   20
understand that though this sodaine love hath made
me loose in a maner the remembraunce of my selfe, and
caused mee to bee carlesse and negligent in all other
affaires though of never so great importance, yet the
beeholdinge of your seemely selfe doth so revive my
sences and quicken my spirits that it maketh all my
partes to doe their part in praying for pittie and prays-
ing your person: wherein if I should bee speechelesse, I
might justly be thought to spare the trueth and spighte
your perfection. And that my love is modest without   30
mocking, true without triflynge, and vehement without
vanytie, I take the heavens to witnes: and beesid[e]s let
this be practised for proofe, that if it please you to imploy

15 hym/me *CDEF*   33 please/may please *CDEF*

mee, you shall finde mee as speedy to end my lyfe to
doe you good, as ready to spende my time to doe you
service. Mary (saith she) perchaunce so, for I thinke I
shall finde you neither speedy in the one, neither ready
in the other. But thei that have once passed the bounds
of shamefastnesse, may ever after lawfully bee impu-
dent, and you that have beegunne to scoffe and gybe,
thinke by authorytie you may continue in it: sutch a
one I count you to bee and so I account of you. And so
left my youth without dores. Who seeinge him selfe so
coursly accounted of, fell to raginge to him selfe in
this manner.

Ah the bravery of these fine girles, the more they are
courted the more they are coy, the more humbly they
are sued unto, the more loftyly they looke. And if a
man practise them in the way of marriage, good God
what shew of shamefastnesse will they make, what
visors of vyrginitie will they put on, what colours of
continencie wil they set foorth, what charinesse wil
they make of their chastitie? they never forsooth meane
to marrie, sayinge that single life is the only sweet life,
that marriage is invented rather for necessitie then for
any goodnesse that is in it, that their yeeres yet require
no hast of marriage, & that if God would give them
grace, & their freinds would not force them to the contrarie, they would never know what man meaneth while
they live. Whereas in very deede they desire nothyng
more then marriage, neither covet any thing more then
the company of men. Agayne if a man making love in
way of marriage do but so mutch as touche one of these
tender peeces, they crie phy away, away, but let one

9 count/deeme *CDEF*   17 shew/a shew *DEF*
22 is/was *CDEF*   24 of/to *CDEF*
26 man/a man *CDEF*   30 way/the way *DEF*

that is married, or one that meaneth not marriage dally
with them, why they are as lose of their lippes and as
free of their flesh as may bee: For let a man beehave
himselfe towardes them accordyng to the common
course of curtesie, hee shall obtayne any thyng of them,
for they know hee is soone lost if hee bee not soone
loved, but let one direct his doynges by the lyne of love,
and bee drawne into great depth of affection towardes
them, why they will raygne like princes over him: yea
they will make him glad of one glaunce of goodwill given
by the eye: for they know a litle thyng pleaseth a foole,
and they thinke him to fast hampred in folly to give
them the slip on the sodayne. And bicause they count
the number of suters a great testimony to their beutie
& proufe of theyr perfection, they use twentie shiftes to
have if it bee possible twentie suters, some they feede
with lookes, some with love, some with promises some
with practises, some with vowes some with vewes, some
with triflinge some with truth, some with woordes, some
with workes, some with kisses some with curtesy some
with witte some with wyles, some with fayth some with
fraude, some one way some another, so that by their
willes they will have as many suters as themselves have
sleightes to entertaine them. And yet these girles on
Gods name are to younge to have a husband, they are
loth to leave suckinge their dame [but if I durst say
my fancie, I am perswaded my dayntie dame which
sayth I do but dally and jest with her, yf one came [come
DEF] close to her in a corner, she would not refuse him
in good earnest. B–F] But ah blasphemous beast that I
am to cast sutch divelish doubtes of her honesty, whose
very countenance containeth continency in it, whose
visage seemes to bee without vice, and lookes without
lust. Is it likely shee will yeeld her body to bee abused

10

20

30

by any, who wil not suffer her selfe to bee used by any?
And she y^t will not enter into modest matrimony, is it
likely shee will fall into filthy fornication? No I thinke
her to bee as free from folly, as I thinke my selfe far
from wisdome who seeme to doubt of her honest dealing
bicause shee wil not yeelde consent to my hastie meaning. What know I whether shee be consecrated alreadie
to some other saint, which if it bee so, with what reason
can I looke to reape any thynge at her handes but a
repulse? For as gorged Hauks will stoupe to no lure, so
a woman vowed already to another man, the sickenesse
of other suters will not cure: or it may bee thus, that
as the Fauconer when hee first draweth his Hauke out
of the mew, giveth her washt and unpleasant meates to
make her after like better of better meates, so perchaunce her pollicie bee first to feede mee with bitter
brothes, that hereafter dayntie fare may more delight
mee: and now to tosse and torment me with the rigorous
stormes of repulse, that hereafter the caulme of her
consent may the better content mee. For springe time
would never seeme so pleasaunt unto us, but by reason
of the sharpe winter which went before: peace woald
not so mutch please us, but by reason that warre beefore
spoyled and wasted our country. So that if shee bee coy
of consent to make mee injoy the greater joy, may I
thynke my selfe misused? Againe would I have her so
light of love to yeelde to the firste onset? No shee
deserveth to bee pursued with endlesse paine, yea and
I will travayle in continuall toyle but her good will I
will attaine. Now as the good Spaniell having sprung
the partridge ceaseth not to raunge the fieldes and
beate the bushes untill hee have retrived it againe to
serve the Hauk which flew at it, so hee having once
seene this saint sought all occasions to come to the sight

of her againe, and if it were possible surely to seaze
upon her. Now it pleased fortune to bee thus frindly
to further his purpose with this oportunitie.

Ther was in the cittie a very solemne wedding
sumptuously celebrated, where hee by inquiry learned
that his Misteris was, whereupon hee assembled his
companyons together, and prepared themselves the
same night to goe thither in a maske: and beeing come
to the house, after they had marched up and downe
the great chamber, yᵉ first masker having taken the
bride, hee being the second addressed him selfe to his
Misteris with great devotion, and when the sownd of
the instrumentes ceased, hee entred into reasoning
with her in this sorte.

Good Misteris, you have allowed to your lot in steed
of a masker a mourner, and for one to delight you with
plesaunt discourse you shall have one to weary you
with rufull requestes: for you shall understande I am
your careful *Curiatius* whom nothing but the consent
of your good will can cure, and having no other way
to aspire to your speeche, I thought beste under this
disguised sorte to discipher plainly unto you the constancy of my good will towardes you. And if I could in
woordes set forth but halfe the heavinesse which since
the first sight of you hath sunke into my breast, I hope
your hart would not bee so hard frozen but that the
shininge sun of pity would thaw it againe. For if
plaintes may prove my paine, I have still continued in
carefull cries: if sighes may shewe my sorrow, the
smoake of them hath reached to the skies: if teares may
trie my truth, the water hath flowen as a floud from
my eyes. And as these thinges have passed heretofore
to my paine, so if hereafter the sheddinge of my bloud
may shew my constancy or woorke your contentation

any way, assure your selfe I will bee so prodigall therof, that your selfe shall have just cause to say I lived only to serve you, and died to doe you good. By this time the instrumentes sowned another measure, at the ende wherof shee began to reply in this sorte.

Sir, I am sory you have taken so great paine for so litle thanke, for if the end of your maske bee to make mee marche under *Venus* banner, yea or *Junoes* either, your successe wilbe sutch that you shall have cause to count this your labour lost, and that you have cast away so mutch cost. And for my part I promise you I had rather have bene matcht with a mery masker then a leude lover, for the one might delight mee, whereas the other doth but spight mee. And if (as you say) you maske without mirth so assure your selfe on the other side I daunce without delight: neither can it but greatly greive mee to bee troubled with so unreasonable a sutor, whom no reasonable answere will satisfie. This rigorous replie of his Misteris converted him from a masker to a Mummer, for hee was strooke so dead herewith that the use of his tounge utterly fayled him. But at length beeing come to himself againe, hee entred into this vehemency with her.

O Gentlewoman, suffer not the bright sunne of your beauty to bee eclipsed with cruelty: contaminate not your cumlinesse with coynesse: remember beauty and cumlinesse continue not, wheras curtesy and clemency remaine for ever. Consider that vertue is the true beauty which carrieth commendacion with it at al times, which maketh men love those whom they have never seene, and which supplieth all other wantes whatsoever. Did not *Antonius* that lusty gallant of this city prefer *Cleopatra* that blacke *Egiptian*, for her incomparable

29 it/you *EF*   33 Cleopatra/Cleopatria *E*

curtesy, before all the blasinge starres of this citty? and
did not the puisant knight *Persey*, in respect of her
vertue, fetch *Andromade* from the blacke *Indians*[?]
Wherby you see that bounty before beutie is alway to
be preferred. Whiche bounty I beseeche you imbrace
both to preserve my life and your owne good name.
Alas what renowme shall you reape by killinge cruelly
him that loved you intirely? What glory shall you get
by driving into dispaire him y^t was drawen into desire
towardes you? No, pitty is the onely patheway to   10
prayse, and mercy is the meane to make you immortall.
At the ende of the next measure shee replied in this
sorte.

Why Gentleman, doe you thinke it cruelty not to
condiscend to the requestes of every one that maketh
love? Doe you count it vice not to yeeld to the assaultes
of every lascivious young man? Doe you make so mean
a count of mariage that you thinke it meet for a maide
so rashly to enter into it, without sufficient knowledge
of your selfe, ignorante of your life and conversation,   20
not knowing your state, parentes, or freindes: againe
without the consent of my freindes, without their good
will and furtherance, and which is most of all, without
mine owne love and likinge? No, I will have more tryall
of him whom I meane to marry then I have had of you,
and I wil feele in my self more fervent affection towards
him, then as yet I doe beare you. You must consider
it is not for a day or a yeere that man and wife must
continue together, but even for the whole terme of their
life: and that they may not for any respecte chaunge,   30
beeinge once chayned together: but muste remaine content the one with the other in solace and in sorrowe,

2 puisant/pleasant *CDEF*
28 man/a man *CDEF*   wife/a wife *EF*

in sicknesse and in safenes, in plenty and in penury. Way againe that the happy life of the wife only consisteth in the loyall love of her husband, and that shee reposeth her selfe only in the pleasure shee hath in him. She for the most part sitteth still at home, shee hauketh not, shee hunteth not, shee diseth not, shee in a manner receiveth no other contentation but in his company. Hee is the only play which pleaseth her, hee is the only game which gladdeth her, hee is the field shee delighteth to walke in, hee is the forrest shee forceth to hunt in. So that in my judgement in takinge a husbande, no heede can bee to wary, no choyce to chary. And therefore you must make a count that mariage is a matter neither so rashly to bee required as you doe, neither so easely to bee graunted as you would have mee to doe. And if you adhibite any credite to my counsayle, I would wish you to sowe the seede of your sute in a more fertill soyle, for in mee no graftes of grauntes, or flowers of affirming will by any meanes growe, but only double denialles and ragged repulses. His replie hereto with divers other discourses whiche passed beetween them, I wil omit, lest I should weary you with the weary toyle whiche hee made of it. And besides I would not you should take example by her to hang of so straungly, when you are sued to so humbly: and not to faine dislikinge so deepely, when in deed you love intirely. For notwithstanding all his ernest sute hee could not receive so mutch as one good worde of good will. At length the dauncinge beeinge done, the banquet was beegunne whereuppon their talke ceased, but his love dayly increased: in so mutch that hee fully resolved with himselfe (hopinge thereby somewhat to bee eased of his greife) to forsake country, friendes,

16 to doe/doe *DEF*   27 his/this *DEF*

lyvinge and all that hee had. And there upon wrote a
letter unto her to this effect.

Seeinge (most mercylesse Misteris) neither my person
can please you, neither my lyvinge lyke you, neither
my calling content you, neither my singular affection
towards you cause you to requite it *with* lyke love, I
meane utterly to abandon the place of your abode, and
to bestow my selfe in some sutch fare country, whyther
not so much as ye report of your vertue and beuty
shall come: hopinge therby somwhat to appease my   10
paine, and to asswage the rygour of my raginge love.
For as the sence of seeinge is most sharp, so is that paine
most pinching, to see the thing one seeketh, and can
not possesse it. Lyke as the Greyhounde is greeved to
see the Hare if hee bee kept in slippe, and the Hauke
the Partridge if she bee tyed in lunes, and as the common saying is, y^t which the eye seeth, the hart g[r]eev-
eth. Likewise to heare of your happie marriage with
some other, would bee litle better then death unto mee,
to think any other should injoy that which by law of   20
love is proper to my selfe: and to heare of your unlucky
linking with any, would bee death it selfe unto mee, to
thinke that my only joy should live in annoy. Therfore
I thinke the best way to mitigate my martirdome, is to
absente my selfe from both hearing and seeing. I could
reave my self of life, and so rid my selfe of strife, but
alas to imbrue my hands with mine owne bloud, would
but bring to my body destruction, to my soule damnation, to my freindes desolation, and to your selfe
defamation. Where as by contynuinge my carefulll life,   30
I may at least or at laste make manifeste the constancy
of my love to the whole world, and some way imploy

11 to *om. CDEF*   15 slippe/the slippe *EF*
20 any/that any *EF*

my selfe to doe you service. For assure your selfe this,
that what land soever I shall lodge in, my hart and
body shall bee dedicated to doe you duty and service.
And thus ready to goe to seaward, I stay only to know
whether it stand with your good pleasure to commaund
mee any service.

yours while hee is, CURIATIUS.

Horatia having red this letter and thinking, shee had
sufficiently sounded ye depth of his devotion towards
her, returned him this comfortable answer.

Albeit sir, I nothinge doubt of your departure out
of your country, for that nothing is more deere to any
man then his owne native soyle, and besides I know
you use it only for a meane to move mee to mercy, yet
to confesse the truth the secret good will which longe
since I have borne you, will not suffer mee to conceale
from you any longer the secrets of my thoughtes.
Therfore you shall understand I have not used this
straungnesse towardes you for that my minde hath
bene enstraunged or alienated from you, but only to
try the truth of your good will towardes mee. For if for
one repulse or two (like an ill hound which for one losse
or twain giveth over the chase) you would have given
over your sute, I might have judged rightly that you
had loved but lightly. But now I see you continue to
the ende, there is no reason but you should bee saved,
if I may terme it saving, the having of so worthles a
wife as my selfe. But assure your selfe this, I have not
shewed my selfe heretofore in love so colde and fainte,
as hereafter you shall finde mee in affection fervent and
faithfull. I thinke your labour shalbe litle to get my
freindes good will, for if their judgment agree with
mine they will thinke you worthy of a worthier wife,

4 to seaward/seaward *BCDEF*

and rather thankefully accept you then daintily delay you. Thus ready to restoare the injury I have done you with any curtesy convenient to my maydenly estate, I cease, not ceasinge dayly to recorde the depthe of your goodwill in the bottome of my hart, and in devouring by all meanes possible to shewe my selfe thankefull for the same.

Yours, and her owne if yours: HORATIA.

This letter so lovinge, so unlooked for, so sweete, so sodaine, raised him from heavinesse to happinesse,   10 from hell to heaven, from death to life. And presently hereupon hee procured her parentes consent who were so willing thereto that they gave him great thankes that it would please him to match in their stocke and kinred, thinking perchance that hee had bene a man of a higher callinge then in deede hee was, and prayed to god that their daughter might become a wife worthy of sutch a husband. And hereupon the day of the solemniz- ing of the mariage was appointed, but many thinges (as the sayinge is) happen betweene the cup and the lip,   20 many thinges chaunce betweene the bourd and the bed: man purposeth and God disposeth, and it is the fashion of fortune commonly thus to frame, that when hope and hap, when health and wealth are highest, then woe and wracke, disease and death are nighest. For in this manner it happened this mariage to bee marred. There arose a quarrell beetween the towne [of *B–F*] *Albania* and the cittie of *Rome*, which not with wordes but onely with weapons must bee decided: great hurly burly there was in either towne, nothing but war, war, war, the   30 Cannons roard, the barbed horse neighed, the glitteringe armour shined, the boystrous billes and pearcing pikes pressed forward, the dartes were dressed, the bowes

18 hereupon/thereupon *CDEF*

were bent, the women wept, the children cryed, the Trumpets sowned Tan tara, tara the Drummes stroake up the mournfull marchinge forward, and the souldiours on both sides marched in battayle aray unto the field. Amongst whom *Curia[tius]* as one of the most couragious captaines and boldest blouds of the *Albanes,* was the formost. But to leave the battayle and come to the conflicte which *Horatia* had with her selfe when shee hearde that her beloved was in armes against her cittie. Shee fell forsooth to reasoninge with her selfe in this sorte.

O most doubtfull distres that ever poore damsell was driven to. For whom shall I offer uppe sacrifice, for whom shall I make my vowes? For whom shall I pray for victory, to whom shall I wishe the overthrowe? on the one side fighteth my freinde, on the other side my father: on the one side the cittie wherin I am is in daunger to bee sacked, on the other side the towne whither I must goe is in perill to bee spoyled, on the one side I am like to loose my love, on the other side mine owne life. So that I know not to whether part, I ought to incline in hart. No can? Why a woman ought to forsake father and mother and followe her husbande. But ought any thinge to bee more sweete unto mee, then the cittie [wherin I was borne? why, ought not his Citie *B–F*] to bee counted mine, wee beeing both one flesh? But life is sweet to every one: full sower God knoweth to mee without his love and life. So that if my will might worke effecte, I would rather wish that of the two, *Rome* might run to ruine. But alas, dareth hee lay siege to the cittie wherin I am? Is hee not affraide to overthrow the house that harboureth mee? Doubteth he not least some peece should perce my tender breast?

2 Tan tara, tara/Tantara *BCDEF*   9 that *om. CDEF*

Yes no doubt of it, hee deepely doubteth it: but alas, they that are bound must obey, hee must follow of force his general captayne, unlesse hee will incur the suspition of cowardlinesse, or treason, or both. Like as *Ulysses* was greatly defamed bicause hee faigned himself to be mad, for that he would not go to the siege of *Troy*. No god sheild my *Curiatius* from shame, god sende him either friendly to enter into the citie, all quarrels beeing ended and truce taken, either valiantly to venture into the cittie, and with triumphant armes to imbrace mee. By this time both the armies were met, and to avoyd the effusion of bloud, the general Captaines entred into this agreement. There were in either army three brothers of great courage and countenaunce, the *Romaines* were named *Horatii*, brothers to the Gentlewoman before spoken of, the *Albanes* were called *Curiatii*, wherof one was ye gentleman before mentioned. Now it was concluded that these brothers on both sides should by dint of sworde stint the strife betweene these townes: and if the *Hor[atii]* conquered the *Curiatii*, that then the *Albanes* should remain under the rule and empire of the *Romains*, if otherwise, then otherwise. Hereupon these sixe valiaunt champions at the sound of the Trumpets entred the listes, and fell to furious fight: within short time two of the *Horatii* were slayne, and al the three *Curiatii* wounded: the *Romaine* remaynynge alone to withstand three, retired somewhat backe, to the intente to single his enemies one from another, which done, hee slue them all one after another. This valiant victory atchived, *with* great joy & triumph he returned into ye citie, & amongst ye rest ready to receive him, was his sister *Horatia*, who knew nothing perticulerly of yt which was done in ye field, but only yt the

12 the effusion/effusion *EF*   21 and/of the *EF*

Romayns were victors. But seing a far of about her brothers shoulders yᵉ coate armour of her *Cur[iatius]* which she her selfe *with* needle work had curiously made, being therby fully assured of his death, she was driven into these dolefull plaints. Oh Heaveⁿs, what hellish sight doe I see, far more dolorous and dangerous then monstrous *Medusaes* head? And is my *Curiatius* slaine? then care come cut in sunder my corps, theⁿ dole deliver me to yᵉ dreadful darts of death. For what

10 lyfe (alas) in this lyfe is to bee counted lyfe, without his life and love? for so to live, as not to live: why should I long any longer to live? What joy in this commmon joy can I count joy, and not him injoy who was my only joy? No though the whole Cittie singe in triumphe, I must sorrow in torment: though the *Romanes* vaunt of victory, I must complaine of over-throwe: though they flourish in prosperytie, I must fade in adversitie: though they swimme in blisse, I must bath in bale: though they live in peace, I must lead

20 my lyfe in warre: though they possesse pleasure, I must pine away in paine. For my triumph, my victory, my prosperytie, my blisse, my peace, my pleasure, is perished. Yea now my marrying is turned to mourning, my wedding to weeping, my wealth by warre is wasted, my flowre of joy by the cold frost of cankred sight is defaced. Yea what flower can flourish where no Sun doth shine? what Sun can shine inclosed close in earth? My sun alas is dead, and downe for ever rysinge againe, and the worlde with mee is at an ende and done for

30 ever joying againe. Woe worth the cause, the quarrell, the conflict, that brought my *Curiatius* to this cureles case. O woulde to God my Citie had beene sacked, my friends spoyled, and my brothers brought to bane,

23 marrying/marriage *DEF*   to/into *EF*

rather then my *Curiatius* should have come to this
careful ende. O brother yᵘ hast not only slaine thy foes
but thy friends, thou hast not only killed *Curiatius* but
thou hast wounded thine owne Sister to death. Her
brother passinge by her and hearing her heavy plaints,
beeing therwith rapt into great rage, and with pride
of the victory almost beesides hymselfe, drew his sword
and forgetting al lawes of nature and humanytie thrust
his Sister therewith to the harte, saying: get thee hence
to thy kinde spouse with thy unkinde love, who forget-   10
test thy brothers that are dead, thy brother that is
alive, and the conquest of thy country. And so come
it to every *Romaine* that shall lament the death of an
enemy to the *Romaines*.

You have harde (Gentlewomen) that one harmefull
hand made a hand of two harmelesse wightes, and that
hand had hangd himself to, if his father by his pitiful
peticion had not purchased his pardon. Now I would
heare your judgementes to whom you thinke this
lamentable end of these lovers ought to be imputed.   20
Surely I think *Horatia* cheifly in fault for holding of so
longe beefore shee woulde accept and acknowledge the
love of her beloved. For if she would by any reasonable
sute have beene woon, they had bene married longe
time beefore this warre begunne. They had dwelled
quietly together in *Albania*, and *Curiatius* beeing a
married man should not have been prest to the warres,
but should have beene suffered to trye his manhood at
home with his wife. So that her lingring love hastened
her and his death, her selfewill wrought her selfe and   30
hym wracke. And for her Brother his offence was litle,
for in killing *Curiatius* hee procured conquest to his
Country and commendation to himselfe: and in killinge

13 an/any *EF*   14 to/of *DEF*

his Sister, hee eased her of so mutch labour, and saved her soule from damnation. For hee knew shee would desperately doe her selfe to death and considering the miserie shee was in, hee thought hee could not doe her a greater pleasure then to cause her to die for her *Curiatius* his cause.

[Now I am by this story to admonish you vertuous Virgins, which looke so loftily on them which serve you duetifully, whiche lyghtly account of those marriages, which your parentes (greatly tendering you) doo tender unto you, which drive of with delayes those which are drawen into deepe desire towardes you, to marke the ende of her finnesse, and see what was due to her daynty delayes. And if you repose any credit in my counsayle, I would never wish you to covet to continue maydes, or to keepe your virginitie too long. It is a Jewell hard to bee injoyed with joy, it is a pearle hard to bee preserved from peril. Therefore to avoyde inconveniences, take time in time, let not slip occasion, for it is baulde behynde, it cannot be pulled backe agayne by the heare. Marrye whyle you are young, that you may see your fruite florish before your selves fade, that you bee not in doubt or dispayre of having children, or in daunger of your lyves in having children, that you may have great tyme to rid a great many of husbandes, that no day may passe without dalliance, that you be not thought unwise in refusing good offers, that you be not judged disdainefull in contemning those which are woorthy of you, that with *Daphney* you be not turned to trees for nicenesse, with *Anaxarete* to stones for cruelnesse, and with *Horatia* hurte not your selves and your friendes with dayntynesse. *B–F*]

4 hee thought/thought *BCDEF*
6 his *om. EF*

Cephalus and Procris.

[CEPHALUS a lustye younge gallant, and PROCRIS a bewtifull girle, both
of the Duke of VENICE Courte, beecum eche amorous of other, and
notwithstandinge delayes procured, at length are matched in marriage,
Cephalus pretending a far journey and long absence, returneth beefore
appointed time, to trie his wives trustinesse. *Procris* falling into the folly
of extreme jelousie over her Husband, pursueth him prively into the
wooddes a hunting, to see his beehaviour: whom *Cephalus* heering to
russhell in a bushe wherein *shee* was shrowded, and thinking it had bin
some game, slayeth her unwares, and perceivinge the deede, consumeth   10
hymselfe to death for sorowe.]

IT is the provident policy of the devine power to the
intent wee shoulde not bee to proudly puft up with
prosperitie, most commonly to mix it with some sower
sops of adversitie, and to appointe the river of our
happinesse to runge [run(ne) *B–F*] in a streame of heavinesse, as by all his benefites bountifully beestowed on
us, may bee plainely perceived, whereof there is not
any one so absolutely good and perfect, but that there
bee inconveniences as well as commodyties incurred   20
thereby. The golden glisteringe sun which gladdeth all
earthly wightes, parcheth the Sommers greene, and
blasteth their bewtie which blaze their face therein:
The fire which is a most necessary element unto us,
consumeth most stately towres and sumptuous Cities:
the water which wee want in every thing we do,
devoureth infinit numbers of men and huge heapes of
treasure and ritches: the aire wherby we live, is death
to the diseased or wounded man, and beeinge infected

9 russhell/russhe *C*, rushe *DE*, rush *F*   12 the devine/divine *EF*
18 may bee/we may *EF*   perceived/perceive *EF*

it is ye cause of all our plagues and pestilences: the
earth which yeeldeth foode to sustaine our bodies,
yeeldeth poison also to [destroy] our bodies: the goodes
whiche doe us good, often times woorke our decay and
ruine: children which are our comforte, are also our
care: marriage which is a meane to make us immortall,
and by our renewing ofspring to reduce our name from
death, is accompanied with cares in number so endlesse
and in cumber so curelesse, that if the preservation of
mankinde, and the propagation of our selves in our
kinde, did not provoke us therto, wee should hardly be
allured to enter into it. And amongest all the miseries
that march under the ensigne of marriage, in my fancy
there is none that more torments us, then that hatefull
helhounde Jelousy, as the history which you shall heare
shall shew.

You shal understand in the Dukes Courte of *Venice*,
spent his time one *Cephalus*, a Gentleman of great
calling and good qualities, who at the first time hee
insinuated himselfe into the societie of the Ladies and
Gentlewomen, made no speciall or curious court to any
one, but generally used a dutifull regarde towards them
all, and shewed hymselfe in sport so pleasaunt, in talke
so wittie, in maners so modest, and in all his conversation so cumlye, that though he were not specially loved
of any, yet was hee generally lyked of all, and though
hee himselfe were not specially vowed to any, yet was
hee speciallye vewed of one, whose name was *Procris*,
a proper Gentlewoman, discended of noble parentage.
And though at the first her fancy towardes him were
not great, yet shee seemed to receive more contentation
in his company, then in any other Gentleman of the
troupe. But as materiall fyre in shorte time groweth

3 [destroy]/bane *BCDEF*

from glowinge coales to flashing flames, so the fyre of
love in her, in shorte time grew from flytting fancy to
firme affection, and she beegan to settle so surely in goodwil towardes him, that shee resolved with her selfe, hee
was the onely man she would be matched to, if shee
were ever married. And beeinge alone in her lodginge,
shee entred with her selfe into this reasoning.

How unequally is it provided that those which worst
may, are driven to holde the Candle? That we which
are in body tender, in wit weake, by reason of our youth   10
unskilfull, and in all thinges without experience, should
bee constrained to beare the loadsome burthen of love,
wheras ryper yeeres who have wisdome to wyeld it, and
reason to represse it, are seldome or never oppressed
with it? Good God what fiery flames of fancy doe frye
within mee? what desyre, what lust? what hope, what
trust? what care, what dispaire? what feare, what fury?
that for mee which have alwaies lyved free and in
pleasure, to be tormented therewith, seemeth litle better
then the bitter pangues of death. For as the colte the   20
first time he is ridden snuffeth at the snaffle, and thinketh the bit most bitter unto him: so the yoke of love
seemeth heavy unto me, beecause my neck never felte
the force thereof beefore, and now am I first taught to
drawe my daies in dolour and griefe. And so mutch the
lesse I lyke this lot, by how mutch the lesse I looked
for it, and so mutch the more sower it is, by howe mutch
the more soddaine it is. For as the Bird that hops from
bough to bough, and uttreth many a pleasant note, not
knowinge how neere her destruction draweth on, is   30
caught in snare before shee bee ware: so while I spent
my time in pleasure, assoone playing, assoone parling,

16 mee *om. EF*   20 bitter *om. EF*
26 looked/looked not *EF*

now dawncing, now dallying, sometime laughing, but always loytering and walking in the wide fields of free-dome, and large leas of lybertie, I was sodenly inclosed in ye strait bonds of bondage. But I se & I sigh, and sorow to see, that there is no clothe so fine but moathes will eate it, no yron so harde but rust will fret it, no wood so sounde but wormes will putrifie it, no mettall so course but fire will purifie it, nor no Maide so free but love will bring her into thraldome and bondage. But seeing the Goddes have so appointed it, why should I resist them? seeing the destinies have decreed it, why shuld I withstand them? seeing my Fortune hath framed it, why should I frowne at it? seeing my fancy is fast fixed, why should I alter it? seeing my bargaine is good, why should I repent it? seing I lose nothing by it, why should I complain of it? seing my choice is right worthy, why should I mislyke it? seeing *Cephalus* is my Saint, why should I not honour him? seeing hee is my joy, why shoulde I not injoy him? seeing I am his, why should not he be mine? yes *Cephalus* is mine, and *Cephalus* shall be mine, or els I protest by the Heavens, y^t never ani man shal be mine.

Ever after this shee observed all oportunities to give him intelligence, as modestly as shee might, of her good-will towards him. And as it happened a company of Gentlewomen to sit talkinge together, they entred into commendation of the histories whiche beefore had bene tolde them, some commending this Gentlemans stories, some that, according as their fancy forced them, but *Pro[cris]* seemed to preferre the histories of *Cephalus*, both for that (saith she) his discourses differ from the rest, and beesid[e]s, that mee thinkes the man amendeth the matter mutch. *Cephalus* though out of sight yet not

20 not he be/he be not *B*, he not be *CDEF*

out of hearing, replied in this sorte. And surely (Gentle-woman) the man thinketh himselfe much mended by your commendacion, and assure your selfe you shall as readily commaunde him, as you curteously commend him.

The Gentlewoman blushing hereat, saide she thought hee had not bene so neere, but touchinge your answere (saith she) I have not so good cause to commaunde you, as commend you: for as I thinke you well worthy of the one, so I thinke my selfe farre unworthy of the   10
other: but bee bolde of this, if at any time I commaunde you, it shall bee to your commodytie. I can not (sayth hee) but count your commaundment a commodytie, only in that you shall thinke mee worthy to doe you service: neither will I wish any longer to live, then I may be able, or at least willing, to doe you due and dutifull service. If sir (saith she softly unto hym) it were in my power to put you to sutch service as I thought you worthy of, you should not continue in the condition of a servant longe, but your estate should bee   20
altered, and you should commaunde another while, and I would obey. It shal bee (good misteris saith he) in your power to dispose of mee at your pleasure, for I wholy commit my selfe to your curtesy, thinking my estate more free to serve under you, then to raigne over any other whatsoever: and I should count my selfe most happy, if I might either by service, duty, or love, countervaile your continuall goodnesse towards mee. Upon this the companie brake of, and therewith their talke. But *Cephalus* seing her goodwil so great towards   30
him, began as fast to frame his fancy towardes her, so yᵗ love remained mutuall beetweene them. Which her father perceving, and not lyking very well of the match,

4 him *om. EF*   9 as/as to *EF*

for that hee thought his daughter not olde inough for a husbande, nor *Cephalus* ritch inough for sutch a wife, to breake the bond of this amitie went this way to worke. Hee wrought so with the Duke of *Venice*, that this *Cep[halus]* was sent post in ambassade to the Turk, hoping in his absence to alter his daughters affection. Which journy, as it was nothinge joyful to *Cephalus*, so was it painfull to *Procris*, that it had almost procured her death. For beeinge so warely wa[t]cht by her waspish parents, that shee coulde neither see him nor speake with him beefore his departure, shee got to her chaumber window, and there heavily behelde the Ship wherin hee was sorowfully sayling away. Yea shee bent her eyes with such force to beehold it, that shee saw the ship farther by a mile then any els could possibly ken it. But when it was cleane out of her sight, she sayd: Now farewell my sweete *Cephalus*, farewell my joy, farwell my life, ah if I might have but geven thee a carefull kisse and a faintinge farewell beefore thy departure, I should have bene the better able to abide thy aboad from mee, and perchaunce thou wouldest the better have mynded mee in thy absence, but nowe I knowe thy wyll, wyl waver with the windes, thy faith wil fleete, with the flouds, and thy poore *Procris*, shall bee put cleane out of thy rememberance. Ah why accuse I thee of inconstancy? No I knowe the seas will first be drie, beefore thy fayth from mee shall flye. But alas, what shal constancy prevayle, if thy lyfe doe faile? mee thinkes I see the hoysinge waves lyke a huge army to assaile ye sides of thy Ship: me thinkes I see the proulyng pirats which pursue thee: mee thinks I heare the roaring Cannons in mine eare, which are shot to sinke thee: mee thinkes I see the ragged rocks whiche

2 nor *om. EF*

stande ready to reave thy Ship in sunder: mee thinkes
I see the wilde beastes which ravenously runne with
open mouthes to devoure thee: mee thinkes I see the
theeves whiche rudely rushe out of the woods to robbe
thee: mee thinkes I heare the trothlesse *Turke* enter
into conspiracy to kill thee: mee thinks I feele the
furyous force of their wicked weapons, pitiously to
spoyle thee. These sights and thoughtes, deprived her
both of seeing, and thinkinge, for shee fell herewith
downe dead to the grounde: and when her wayting   10
woman could not by any meanes revive her, shee cryed
out for her mother to come help: who beeing come, and
havinge assayed all the meanes shee could for her
daughters recovery, and seeinge no signe of lyfe in her,
shee fell to outragious outcries, saiing: O unjust Gods,
why are you the authours of sutch unnatural and
untimely death? O furious feende, not god of love, why
dost thou thus divelishly deale *with* my daughter? O
ten times cursed bee the time, that ever *Cephalus* set
foote in this Court. At the name of *Cephalus* the maide 20
beegan to open her eies, which before [death B-F] had
dazeled, which her mother perceiving, saide, beeholde
daughter thy *Cephalus* is safely returned and come to
see thee. Wherewith shee start from the bed whereon
they had laied her, and staring wildly about the chamber, when shee coulde not see him, shee sunk downe
againe. Now her parents perceiving what possession
love had taken of her, thought it labour lost, to indevour
to alter her determination, but made her faithful promise shee should have their furtherance and consent to   30
have her *Cephalus* to husbande at his returne, wherewith shee was at length made stronge to indure the
annoy of his absence. It were tedious to tell the prayers,
the processions, the pilgrimages, the Sacrifices, the

vowes shee made for his safe returne, let this suffice to declare her rare good will towardes hym, that hearing of his happie comming towardes the courte, shee feared least his sodayne sight would bring her sutche excessive delight, that her sences shoulde not bee able to support it, and therfore got her into the highest place of the house, and beheld him comming a far of, and so by litle and litle, was partaker of his presence, and yet at the meetinge, shee was more free of her teares then of her tounge, for her greetinge was only weeping, word shee could say none.

Cephalus inflamed with this her unfaigned love, made all the freindes hee could to hasten the mariage bee-tweene them. But the olde saying is, hast maketh waste, and bargains made in speede, are commonly repented at leasure. For married they were, to both their inexplicable joy, which shortly after turned to both their unspeakable annoy. For the increase is small of seede to timely sowen, the whelpes are ever blinde that dogs in haste doe get, the fruites full sone doe rot, which gathered are to sone, the mault is never swete onlesse the fier bee softe, and hee that leapeth before hee looke, may hap to leape into the brooke. My mean-ing is this, that *Cephalus* his share must needes bee sorow, who would so rashly and unadvisedly, enter into so intricate an estate as wedlocke is.

The Philosophers will us to eate a bushell of salte with a man beefore we enter into strict familiarity with him, but I thinke a whole quarter litle inoughe to eate with her with whom wee enter into sutch a bond that only death must dissolve. Which rule if *Cephalus* had observed, hee had preserved him selfe from most irke-

5 support/suppresse *EF*
27 Philosophers/Philosopher *F*   will/willeth *EF*

some inconveniences. But hee at all adventures ventred uppon one of whom he had no trial, but of a litle triflynge love. I like but litle of those mariages which are made in respecte of ritches, lesse of those in respect of honours, but least of al, of those in respecte of hasty, foolish, and fond affection. For, soone hot soone colde, nothing violent is permanent, the cause taken away, the effecte vanisheth, and when beuty once fadeth (whereof this light love for the most part ariseth) good-will straight fayleth. Wel, this hot love she bare him,   10 was the only cause of his hasty and heavy bargaine, for womanlines she had none (her yeres were to young) vertue shee had litle (it was not used in the court) modesty shee had not mutch (it belongeth not to lovers) good government and stayed wit shee wanted (it is incident to few woomen) to bee shorte, his choyce was grounded rather upon her goodlinesse then godlinesse, rather uppon her beauty then vertue, rather uppon her affection then discretion. But sutch as hee sowed, hee reapte, sutch as hee sought hee founde, sutch   20 as hee bought, hee had, to wit, a witles wenche to his wife. Therefore I would wishe my freindes, ever to sow that, which is sound, to seeke that which is sure, to buie that which is pure. I meane I would have them in the choice of sutch choyce ware, cheifly to respect good conditions and vertue: that is the only seed which wil yeeld good increase, that is the onely thinge worthy to bee sought, that is the only thinge which can not bee too derely bought. And who soever he bee that, in any other respecte whatsoever, entreth into the holy state   30 of matrimony, let him looke for no better a penny-worth then *Cephalus* had, which was a lothsome life, and desolate death. For within a yeere or two after they had bene maried, his fancy was in a manner fully

fed, and his disordinate desire of her began to decay, so
that hee beegan plainly to see and rightly to judge of
her nature and disposition, which at first the parciality
of his love, or rather outrage of his lust, would not
permit him to perceive. And seeing her retchles regardes
and light lookes, which shee nowe used towardes al
men, rememberinge therewithall howe lightly hee him
selfe won her, hee began greatly to doubt of her honest
dealinge towardes him, and having occasion of far
journy and longe absence from her, hee wrought this
practise to try her truth. Hee told her his aboade from
her must of necessity bee fourty weekes: but at the halfe
yeeres end by that time his haire was wildly growen,
hee apparelled him self altogether contrary to his
wonted guise, and by reason of his haire so disguised
him selfe that hee was not knowen of any, which done,
his necessary affayres dispatched, he returned into his
owne country, and came to his owne house in manner
of a straunger which travayled the country, where hee
founde his wife in more sober sorte then hee looked for,
and received sutch courteous entertainment as was
convenient for a guest. Having sojourned there a day
or two, at convenient time hee attempted her chastity
in this sorte.

If (faire Gentlewoman) no acquaintance might justly
crave any credite, or litle merites great meed, I would
reporte unto you the cause of my repaire, and crave at
your handes the cure of my care: but seeinge there is
no likelyhoode that either my wordes shalbee beleeved,
or my woe releeved, I thinke better with paine to conceale my sorrow, then in vaine to reveale my sute. The
Gentlewoman somewhat tickled with these triflinge
woords, was rather desirous to have him manifest the
mistery of his meaning, then willing hee should desist

from his purpose, and therefore gave him this answere.

I am (Sir) of opinion, that credite may come divers wayes besides by acquaintance, & I my self have knowen mutch good done to many without desert: and therefore if your wordes bee true, and your desire due, doubte not, but you shal bee both credited, and cured.

For the truenesse of my wordes (sayth he) I appeale to the heavens for witnesse, for the duenesse of my desire I appeale to your curtesy for judgment. The wordes I have to utter are these.

There chaunced not longe since to traveile thorowe the countrie wherein lyeth my living, a Knighte named *Cephalus*, and though the report of the porte and house which I mayntaine be not greate, yet it is sutch, that it sendeth me many guestes in the yeere: it pleased this *Cephalus* to sojourne the space of three or foure dayes with mee, and in way of talke to pas away the time, hee made relation at large unto mee of his country, of his condition and state, of his speciall place of abode and dwelling, of his landes and living, and sutch like. I demaunded of him whether hee were married, saying, all those thinges beefore rehearsed, were not sufficient to the attaininge of a happy life, without a beutiful, faire, and loving wife. With that hee fetcht a deepe sigh, sayinge, I have (Sir) I would you knew, a wife, whose beuty resembleth ye brightnesse of the sunne, whose face doth disgrace all the ladies of *Venice*, yea *Venus* her selfe, whose love was so exceedinge great towardes mee, that beefore I was married unto her, havinge occasion to goe in Ambassage to the *Turke*, shee almost died at my departure, and never was rightly revived till my returne. Good God, sayd I, how canne you bee so longe absent from so lovinge a wife? How can any

3 by *om.* BCDEF   I *om.* EF   27 of/in CDEF

meate doe you good, which shee giveth you not? How can you sleepe out of her armes? It is not lawfull (sayth hee) for every man to doe as hee would, I must doe as my businesse bindeth mee to doe. Besides that, every man is not of like minde in like matters. Lastly, it is one thing to have bene happy, it is another thing to bee happy. For your businesse (sayd I) it seemeth not to bee great, by the good company, which I thanke you, you have kept mee this foure daies. For your minde, I know no man that would willingly bee out of the company of sutch a wife. For your present happinesse, in deed it may bee your wife is dead, or that her love is translated from you to some other. No (sayth hee) shee liveth, and I thinke loveth mee, but what good doth golde to him that careth not for it? And can you (sayd I) not care for sutch a golden girle? Then may I say you have a wife more faire then fortunate, and shee a husbande more fortunate then faythfull. Alas (sayth hee) with teares in his eyes, it is my great care that I doe so litle care, but no more hereof I beseech you. But my bloud beeing inflamed with the commendation which hee gave to your beuty, and pityinge your case to have so careles a husbande over you, I lay very importunately upon him to impart the whole matter unto mee, & with mutch adoe I wrung these wordes from him. Sir (sayth hee) I shall desire you to impute my doings not to my fault, but to the fates, and to thinke that whatsoever is done ill, it is done against my wil. It is so, that I remained married with my wife the terme of two whole yeeres, what time I did not only make of her, but I made a goddesse of her, and rather doltishly doated on her, then duely loved her: now whether it were the punishment of the

9 this/these *EF*   27 the/my *DEF*   28 it *om. EF*

gods for my fonde Idolatry committed unto her, or
whether they thought her to good for mee, or whether
the destinies had otherwise decreed it, or whether
love be lost when fancy is once fully fed, or whether
my nature bee to like nothing long, I know not, but
at the two yeeres ende I beegan sodainly in my harte
to hate her as deadly, as beefore I loved her deepely:
yea her very sight was so lothsome unto mee, that I
could not by any meanes indure it. And bicause her
freindes are of great countenance, and I had no
crime to charge her withal, I durst not seeke divorce-
ment, but privily parted from her, pretendinge urgent
affaires which constrained mee therto. Hereafter I
meane to beestow my self in the warres under the
Emperour, not minding to returne while shee liveth.
And for my maintenance there, I have taken order
secretly with my freinds, to conveigh unto mee yeerely
the revenewes of my lande. Thus craving your secrecy
herein, I have revealed unto you my carefull case. The
straungenesse of this tale made mee stand a while in
a maze, at length I greatly began to blame his disloy-
alty, to conceive without cause so great disliking,
where there was so great cause of good likinge. But
Gentlewoman, to confesse the truth unto you, my love
by this time was so great towardes you, that I never
perswaded him to returne unto you, meaning my selfe
to take that paine, and knowinge him better lost then
found, being no better unto you. Shortly after this hee
departed from mee towarde the Emperours courte, and
I tooke my journey hither as you see. And this is the
tale I had to tell you.

Procris havinge heard this forged tale, with divers
alterations and sundry imaginations with her selfe,

1 unto/uppon *BCDEF*   8 so *om. EF*   25 by *om. EF*

sometime fearing it was true, for that hee rightly hyt
divers pointes which had passed betweene her husband
and her, sometime thinkinge it false, for that shee had
firme confidence in her husbandes fayth and loyalty
towardes her, assoone castinge one likelyhoode one
way, assoone another another way, at length fully
resolving with her self that his wordes were utterly
untrue, she replied unto them in this sorte.

Good God, I see there is no wool so course but it will
take some colour, no matter so unlykely which with
wordes may not be made probable, nor nothinge so
false which dissembling men will not fayne and forge.
Shall it sinke into my head that *Cephalus* will forsake
mee, who did forsake all my freindes to take him? Is it
likely hee will leave country, kinsfolke, freindes, landes,
livinge, and (which is most of all) a most lovinge wife,
no cause constrayning him therto? But what use I
reasons to retell y^t which one without eyes may see is
but some coyned devise to cosen mee? No sir knight,
you must use some other practise to effect your purpose,
this is to broad to bee beleeved, this colour is so course
that every man may see it, and it is so blacke that it
will take no other colour to cloud it, the thread of your
hay is so big that the Connies see it before they come
at it, your hooke is so longe that the bayt can not hide
it, and your devise is to far fetcht to bring your purpose
neere to an ende. Gentlewoman (sayth *Cephalus*) I see
it is some mens fortune not [to *B–F*] be beleeved when
they speake truly, and others to bee well thought of
when they deale falsely: which you have verified in your
husbande and mee, who doubte of my wordes which are
true, and not of his deedes which are false. And this I
thought at the first, which made mee doubte to discloase
this matter unto you: for I knowe it commonly to bee

so, that travaylors wordes are not much trusted, neither great matters soone beleeved. But when the time of your husbandes returne is expired, and hee not come, then will you say that Sir *Sulahpec* (for so turning his name hee termed him selfe) tolde you true. For my part notwithstanding, the great good will I bare you, would not suffer mee to conceale this matter from you that you might provide for your selfe, yet I am very well content you should give no credite to my woordes, for I would not you should beleeve any thing which might greeve you any way, and I would wish you to thinke wel, till you see otherwise: for every evill bringeth greife inough with it when it commeth, though the feare before procure none. Therfore I crave no credite for my words, my desire is that you will beleeve that which you see, which is, that for your sake I have travayled with great perill and paine out of mine owne country hither, to your house, that uppon the reporte of your beauty I was so surprised therwith, that I thought every houre a yeere till I had seene you, that having seene you, I have resolved with my self to live and die in your service and sight. Now if in consideration hereof it shal please you to graunt mee sutch grace, as my goodwil deserveth, you shall finde mee so thankefull and grate-full for the same, that no future fortune shall force mee to forget the present benefite which you shall bestow upon mee, and if it chaunce that your husband returne, you shalbee sure alway to injoy mee as your faythful freind, and if hee never come again, you shall have mee if you please for your lovinge spouse for ever. Yea mary (sayth *Procris*) from hence came those teares, hereof proceeded your former fetche, this is it which hath seperated my husbande from mee, which hath sent him

31 those/these *EF*

to the warres, which will cause him never to returne, a
fine fetch forsooth, and cunningly contrived. Did that
report which blazed my beuty (which god knoweth is
none) blemish my name (which I would you knew is
good) in sutch sorte, that you conceived hope to win
mee to your wicked will? Were you so vaine to assure
your selfe so surely of my vanity, that only thereupon
you would undertake so great a journey? No, you are
conversaunt with no *Cressid*, you have no *Helen* in
hande, wee women will now learne to beeware of sutch
guyleful guestes. No, if you were as cunning as *Jove*,
yᵗ you could convert your self into yᵉ likenesse of mine
owne husband, (as *Jove* came to *Alcmena* in the likenes
of her husbande *Amphitrion*) I doubt how I should
receive you til, the prefixed time of my husbandes
comminge were come: mutch lesse shall your forged
tales or importunities constrayne mee to receive you
into that credite, and admit you into that place which
is and shalbe only proper to my husband. And this
answere I pray you let suffice you, otherwise you may
leave my house when you list. *Cephalus* liked this geare
reasonably wel, and perswaded him selfe, that though
hee had a wanton wife, yet hee had no wicked wife.
But knowing it the fashion of women at first to refuse,
& that what angry face soever they set on the matter
yet it doth them good to bee courted with offers of
curtesy, hee ment to prove her once againe, and went
more effectually to worke, to wit, from craft to coyne,
from guyles to giftes, from prayers to presentes. For
having received great store of golde and Jewels for
certaine lande, which hee solde there whyther hee
travayled, (the only cause in deede of his travayle) hee
presented it all unto her, sayinge, hee had sold al [that

9 Cressid/Cressed *BCDEF*   14 Amphitrion/Amphetrion *BCDEF*

B–F] hee had in his own country, minding to make his continuall aboade with her, and if shee ment so rigorously to reject his goodwill, hee willed her to take that in token therof, and for him self, hee would procure him self some desperat death or other, to avoid that death which her beuty and cruelty a thousand times a day drave him to.

The Gentlewoman heering those desperate words, and seeing that ritch sight, moved somewhat with pittie, but more with pencion, beegan to yeeld to his desyre,   10 & with *Danae* to holde up her lappe to receive the golden showre. O god golde, what canst thou not do? but O divel woman, that will doe more for golde then goodwill? O Gentlewomen, what shame is it to sell vily that which God hath geven freely, and to make a gaine of that whiche is more gratefull to women then men, as *Tyresias* gave judgement. Hereof came that odious name of whore, which in Latin is *Meretrix*, *a merendo*, of deserving or getting: a thing so unnatural, that very beasts abhorre it, so unreasonable, as if one should be   20 hyred to do ones selfe good, so unhonest that the common stewes thereof tooke first their beginning. But to returne to our story, *Cephalus* seeing the lewdnesse of his wife, bewrayed himselfe unto her who hee was, whereuppon shee was surprised with sutch shame, and hee with sutch sorow, that they could not long time speake ech to other: at length she fell downe upon her knees, humbly cravinge his pardon. *Cephalus* knowing women to bee to weake to withstand the might of mony, and thinkinge that her very nature violently   30 drew her to him, whom being her husband, though to her unknowne, shee loved intirely, hee thought best for

13 then/then for *EF*   17 Tyresias/Tiresias *BCDEF*
18 Meretrix/Meritrix|*DE*

his owne quiet, and to avoid infamy, to put up this presumption of this evill in his wife paciently, and to pardon her offence, and so they lyved quietly together a while. But within short time she, partly for want of government, & partly thinking her husband would reve*n*ge ye wro*n*g which she would have done to him, fel into such a furious gelosy over him, y^t it wroght her owne destructio*n* & his desolatio*n*. For this monstrous mischiefe was so merveilously crept into her harte, that shee beegan to have a very carefull and curious eye to the conversation of her husbande, and with her selfe sinesterly to examine all his wordes and works towardes her. For if he used her very familiarly, shee supposed that he flattered her, and did it but to coulour his falsho[o]d towardes her: if hee looked solemnely on her, she feared the alteration of his affections, and the alienation of his goodwill from her, and that hee rowed in some other streame: if hee used any company, and frequented any mans house, shee thought by and by that there dwelt the saint whom hee served: if he lived solytaryly, & avoyded company, she judged forthwith that hee was in love some where: if hee bid any of his neighbours to his house, why they were his goddesses: if hee invited none, shee thought hee durst not least she should spie some privie tricks beetweene them: if hee came home merely, hee had sped of his purpose: if sadly, hee had received some repulse: if hee talked pleasauntlye, his misteris had set him on his merry pinnes: if hee sayde nothinge, shee remembred it was one of the properties of love to bee silent: if hee laughed, it was to thinke of his love: if hee sighed, it was beecause hee was not with her: if hee kist her, it was to procure appetite against hee came to his misteris: if hee kist

2 this *om. BCDEF*

her not, hee cared not for her: if hee atchived any
valient enterprise at armes, it was done for his misteris
sake: yf not, hee was beecome a carpet Knight: if hee
fell out with any, it was some open enemie to his privye
friend: if hee were friendes with all men, hee durst
displease none, lest they should detect his doinges to
her: if hee went curiously in his apparel, it was to please
his misteries: if negligently, hee lived in absence: if hee
ware his haire longe, hee mourned beecause hee coulde
not bee admitted: if shorte, he was received into favour: 10
if he bought her any apparrell or any other prety trifling
trickes, it was to please her, and a bable for the foole
to play with: if hee bought her nothinge, hee had inough
to do to maintaine other[s] in bravery: if he entertained
any servant, hee was of his misteris preferment: if hee
put away any, hee had some way offended her: if hee
commended any man, hee was out of question his baude:
if hee praysed any woman, shee was no doubte his
whore: and so of all other his thoughtes, wordes, and
deedes, she made this suspicious suppose, and jelous   20
interpretation: and as the Spider out of most sweet
flowers sucketh poyson, so shee out of his most loving
and friendly deedes towards her, picked occasions of
quarrell, and conceyved causes of hate. And so long
shee continued in these carefull conjectures, that not
onely her body was brought low, by reason that her
appetite to meate failed her, but also she was so disquieted in minde, that she was in a manner beesides
her selfe, whereupon in great pensivenesse of hart, shee
fell to preaching to her selfe in this sorte.   30

Ah fonde foole, wilt thou thus wilfully woorke thine
owne wrack and ruine? if thy husbande commit treason
against thee, wilt thou commit murther upon thy selfe?

7 his *om.* DEF

if he consume himselfe away with whores, wilt yᵘ then consume thy selfe away with cares? wilt thou increase his mischief *with* thine owne misery? if he be so wickedly bent, it is not my care can cure him, for that whiche is bred in the bone will not out of the flesh. If hee bee disposed to deale falsly with mee, it is not my wary watching which wyll ward him from it, for love deceived *Argus* with his two hundred eies. If hee should bee forbidden to leave it, hee will use it the more, for our nature is to runne upon that which is forbidden us, vices the more prohibited, the more provoked, and a wilde coult the harder he is rained, the hotter he is. If I should take him tardy in it, it would but encrease his incontinent impudency, for beeing once knowne to have transgressed the lawefull limits of love and honesty, hee would ever after bee carelesse of his good name, which hee knew hee could never recover againe. And why should I seeke to take him in it? should I seeke to know yᵗ which I ought not to seeke, no not so mutch as to thinke on? was ever wight so bewitched to run headlong upon her owne ruine? So long as I know it not, it hurteth mee not, but if I once certainly knew it, God knoweth how sodainly it would abridge my dayes. And yet why should I take it so greevously, am I the first that have bene so served? Hath not *Juno* her selfe sustained the like injury? But I reason with my self, as if my husband were manifestly convicted of this crime, who perchaunce, good Gentleman, bee as innocent in thought, as I wrongfully thinke him to bee nocent in deede: for to consider advisedly of the matter, there is not so mutch as any likelyhood to lead mee to any sutch leud opinion of him, hee useth mee honestly, hee

19 I ought not to seeke, no not so mutch/I ought to seeke not so mutch
    BCDEF   32 leud *om. EF*

mantayneth mee honorably, hee loveth mee better then
my leude dealinge toward him hath deserved. No it is
mine owne unworthynesse that maketh mee thinke I
am not worthy the proper possession of so proper a
Gentleman: it is myne owne lustful desire that maketh
mee afrayde to loose any thing: it is myne owne weaknesse y^t maketh mee so suspicious of wronge: it is mine
owne incontinency which maketh mee judge him by my
selfe. Well, the price of my prejudiciall doings towardes
him is almost paide, and if paine be a punishment, then   10
have I indured a most painfull punishment, but let
this deere bought wit doe mee some good, let mee now
at length learne to bee wise, and not to thinke of evils
before they come, not to feare them beefore I have
cause, not to doubte of them in whom is no doublynge,
nor to mistruste them in whom is no treason, and faithfully to love him that unfainedly loveth mee. After
this shee indevoured to do sutch fonde toyes foorth of
her head, [and *B–F*] for a while shee lived lovingly and
quietly with her husband, but sodaynly by reason of   20
one looke which hee cast upon one of his neighbours,
shee fell into her olde vayne of vanitie agayne. And as
second fallynge into sicknesse is ever most daungerous,
so now her folly was growen to sutch furie, and her
disease so incurable, that shee could not conceale it any
longer, but flatly tolde her husbande to his teeth, that
she thought hee did misuse her. *Cephalus* knowyng his
owne innocencie, and seeyng her imbecillitie, gently
prayed her not to conceive any sutch evill opinion of
him, saying: If neither regarde of God, neither respect   30
of men, neither reverence of the reverent state of marriage could feare mee from sutch filthinesse, yet assure
your selfe the loyal love I beare you, would let mee
from sutch lasciviousnesse. For beeleeve me, your per-

son pleaseth mee so well, that I thinke my selfe sweetly
satisfied therewith. Yea if *Venus* her selfe should
chaunce unto my choice, I am perswaded I should not
prefer her beefore you. For as her beutie would intis-
ingly draw me to her, so my dutie wold necessarily
drive mee to you. Therefore (good wife) trouble not
your selfe *with* sutch toyes, which will but breede your
owne unrest and my disquiet, your torment & my
trouble, yea and in time perchance both our untimely
deaches. Let *Deinyra* bee a president for you, who sus-
pecting her husband *Hercules* of spouse breache, sent
him a shert died with the bloud of the *Centaure Messus*
[*Nessus B–F*], who tolde her that shert had vertue to
revive love almost mortified, but *Hercules* had no
sooner put it on, but it stocke fast to his flesh, & fried
him to death, as if it had been a furie of hell. Which
when shee knew, with her owne hands shee wrought
her owne destruction. See ye unworthy end which that
monster jelously brought this worthy couple too, &
foresee (sweet wife) that it bring not us to the like bane.
These wordes could worke no effect with her, but rather
increased her suspition, perswading her selfe, that as in
faire painted pots poyson ofte is put, and in goodly
sumptuous sepulchers rotten boanes are ryfe: so fairest
wordes are ever fullest of falshood. Yea, the more curteous hee shewed him selfe, the more culpable shee
thought him to bee. Which *Cephalus* seeing, bicause hee
would take away all causes of suspition, abandoned all
good company, and spent his time solytarily, hunting
in the wooddes, and seekinge the spoyle of spoylinge
savage beastes. But this helhounde Jelousy, did so
haunt and hunt her that shee could in no place bee in
rest, but made her plod from her Palaice to the wooddes,

10 Deinyra/Deianyra *EF*

to watche whether hee there hunted a chaste chase or
not. And one day as shee dogged him, where hee was
layde downe to rest amongest the greene leaves, shee
hearde him utter these woordes: Come gentle *Ayre* and
refresh my weried spirites, with sutch like woordes of
daliance, whiche hee beeing hot, spake to the gale of
Wynde whiche pleasauntly blew uppon him: but shee
thought hee had spoken of some woman with him,
whereupon she furiously fel to the ground, tearing her
haire and scratchinge her face, and though her greife   10
would not give her leave to speake, yet to her selfe shee
thought this: And can the traytor thus trecherously
deale with mee? Had the sorow which I sustayned only
for his absence beefore I was married to him, or any
way owed him any thing, almost cost mee my life, and
now shall his presence procure my death? Did I poure
out pensive prayers for his safe returne from the
Turkes, and doth his returne returne my good wil with
sutch dispight? Oh would to god the *Turkes* had torne
him in peeces, that hee had never come home to martir   20
mee in this manner. But Wolves never pray upon
wolves, his fraud was nothing inferiour to their falshood,
and therefore it had beene in vaine for them to have
haulted before a creeple: but me, beeing but a simple
sheepe, see how sone this subtill Foxe could deceive.
Is this the fruite of my fervente love? is this the felicitie
I expected in marriage? had I knowen this, I would
never have knowen what the subtill sexe of man had
ment: I would rather, as they say, have led apes in hell
after my death, then have felt all the torments of hell   30
in my life. But had I wyst, is ever had at the worst,
they that cast not of cares beefore they come, can not
cast them of when they doe come. It is to late to cast
Anchor when the ship is shaken to peeces against the

rockes, it booteth not to send for a phisition when the
sicke party is already departed. Well, I will yet goe see
the cursed cause of my carefull calamity, that I may
mitigate some part of my martirdome, by scratching
her incontynent eyes out of her whoorish head: and
therupon roused her selfe out of the shrub wherin shee
was shrouded. *Cephalus* hearing somwhat rush in the
bush, thought it had bene som wilde beast, and toke his
darte, and strooke the tame foole to the hart. But comming to the place, and seeing what hee had done, hee
fell downe in a sowne upon her, but with her striving
under him with the panges of death, hee was redused
to life, and sayd, Alas my *Procris* by my selfe is slayne.
Which she (not yet dead) hearinge, sayde, Alas your
Aire hath brought mee to this ende. With that hee
understood how the matter went, and sayd, Alas (sweete
wife) I used these wordes to the winde. Why then
(sayth she) not you, but that winde gave mee this
wound. And so joyninge her lippes to his, shee yeelded
up her breath into his mouth, and dyed. And he with
care consumed, taried not long behinde her, to beewayle
either his owne deed, or her death.

Now Gentlewomen, let the casuall end of this Gentlewoman bee a caveat to kepe you from sutch wary
watching of your husbandes, it is but a meane to make
them fall to folly the rather, as the thoughtful care of
the ritch man causeth the theefe the sooner too seeke
the spoyle of him. But if you will knowe the cheifest
way to keepe your husbandes continent, it is to keepe
your selves continent: for when they shall see you
which are the weaker vessels strong in vertue and
chastyty, they will bee ashamed to bee found faint in
fayth and loyalty, when they shall see you constant in

29 it *om. BCDEF*

good will towardes them, they wil feare to bee found fickle in fayth towardes you, when they shal see you love them faythfully, you shall bee sure to have them love you fervently. But if you shall once shake of the sheet of shame, and give your selves over to choyce of chaunge, then assuredly make accompt your husbandes will eschewe your companyes, loth your lips, abandon your beds, and frequent the familiarity of they care not who, if not of you.

Minos and Pasiphae.

[MINOS King of Creete, regarding the beautie of *Pasiphae*, a waiting gentle-woman in his Courte, falleth in love with her, and maketh her his Queene. Whom VERECUNDUS, a younge Gentleman also of the same Courte, having sollicited to lewdnesse, for feare of the Kings displesure, escapeth away by flight. MINOS entreth into sutch rage of gelousy over his wife, that in his absence hee setteth spies over her, to bewray her doynges. *Pasiphae* beecumminge unnaturally amorous of a Bull, by meanes of the Carpenter Dedalus, bringeth foorth a monstrous Childe, in parte re-semblynge the Sire, and in parte the Mother.]

OF all the ordinary accidentes incident to the lyfe of man, there is none of more moment to our prosperytie, or misery, then marriage: which estate if wee advisedly enter into, it maketh us in happinesse equall to Angels: but if wee rashly run into it, it prolongeth us in the paines of the furies of hel. And amongst all ye incon-veniences, which are to bee foreseene in this bargaine, there is none more daungerous, then inequalitie of estates beetweene the parties: for, what agreement of affections can there bee, when the one shall bee of a meane minde, the other hautie, the one lowly, the other loftie? how can there be one harte in two bodies, when the one wisheth one thinge, the other willeth another? When the one is disposed one way, the other inclined another way, accordinge to the secret instinct of their proper and peculier natures? For the nature of nothinge may bee altered: that whiche nature hath geven, connot bee taken away: and that whiche is bred in the boane, will not out of the flesh. So that for one of meane

4 same *om.* BCDEF   15 prolongeth/plungeth *BCDEF*

parentage, to bee marryed with one of princely race, I think as good a match, as beetweene Lions and Lambes. And as well they will agree together, as Dogs and Cats, and as the saying is, the Mastive never loveth the Greihounde. Besides, unequal Oxen draw not wel together in one yoke, Coks unequally matcht, make no good battaile in the pit, meats of contrary qualities, digest not well in the stomacke: and parties of contrary callinges, agree not well together in the bond of blessed matrimony: as the history I will tel you, shall shew you.   10

In the Country of *Creete*, raigned one *Minos*, a Kinge and Monarch of great might, to whom the blinde goddes Fortune assigned a wife of far more meanesse, then was meete for the majestie of his mightinesse. For there chanced to bee in his Court attendaunt upon a noble woman, a proper peece, named *Pasiphae*. Who by birth was but the daughter of a Knight, but by beauty seemed to bee a heavenly wight. On her cheekes, the Lilly and the Rose did strive for interchange of hew, her haire cumly curld, glistered lyke golde: her pierceinge eies,   20
twinckled like starres: her alabaster teeth stoode as a ranke of precious pearles: her ruddy lippes, were soft and sweete: her handes fine and white, yea all her partes so perfectly proportioned, that nature sought to winne great commendation in carving so cunningly so curious a carkas. But as a rusty Rapier is no trusty Rampier to defende a man, though the Scabbord bee of fine velvet: so a woman with foule conditions is coursly to bee accounted of, though her face bee faire, and body bewtifull. But destinies so drave, that this King by chaunce   30
cast a glaunce upon this gorgious goddes, and at the first view was so vanquished by vanitie, that hee thought his life no longer pleasaunt unto hym, then hee

1 with/to *CDE*   2 as/it as *DEF*   10 shew you/shewe *CDEF*

was in her sight: And fayled not dayly familierly to
frequent the misteris company, for the maides cause.
And having attempted her chastitie by shewing her his
great goodwyll, by beestowinge on her great giftes, by
large promises of preferment, and many other meanes,
and neverthelesse fayling of his purpose, in pensive
perplexitie fell to parley with himselfe, to this purpose.

I ever heretofore thought a Princes life to bee voyde
of strife, and that they had alwaies passed their time
in pleasure without paine: but now I see wee are subject
to sorow, so soone as the meanest subject we have.
Lykewise beefore this I was of opinion, that number
of frindes, aboundinge in wealth, abidinge in health, and
sutch lyke things which pertaine to the body, were
sufficient to attaine to a happy life in this lyfe: but now
I see, it is the minde whiche maketh mirth, and stirreth
strife, yea the contented minde is the onely ritches, the
onely quietnes, the onely happinesse. Good God, how
unsavery seeme those sweete meats unto mee, wherein
I was woont to delight? how unpleasant are ye sports,
wherin I was woont to take pleasure? how cumbersome
is ye company, which was woont to content mee? no
game glads mee, no daunsing delights mee, no justing
joyes mee, no playes please me, no triumphes, no
shewes, no hauking, no hunting, no nothing under the
Sunne doth solace mee. And would I know the cause?
why, I have not a contented minde: the perfect parts
of *Pasiphae* do so diversly distract my minde that only
her sight is sweete, onely her company is comfortable,
onely her presence is pleasaunt unto mee. And would
I know the cause? why, in her ye fates have fixed my
felicitie, in her the heavens have heaped my happinesse,
with her must I live, and without her must I die. Why,

4 great *om. DEF*   17 strife/griefe *CDEF*   20 are *om. EF*

I have pursued her goodwil with praiers and with presentes, with love and with liberalitie, with gifts and with
goodwill, and yet am never the neere. And would I
know the cause why? I sought not her goodwill in the
way of marriage. Only marriage is the meane, only wed-
lock must locke, and lincke us together. And shal I so
much debase the height of my estate, as to match in
mariage *with* so meane a mate? as though many princes
have not as meanely matcht themselves: as though the
Gods the*m*selves have not maried with earthly crea-   10
tures. And for my *Pasiphae*, though shee bee inferriour
to me in parentage, yet in personage, shee is good inough
for God himselfe. And for her dowry or wealth, what
neede I way [weigh *B–F*] it, who have the most part of
the world under my dominion? no, there shall no regard
of honour, or respecte of ritches, detaine mee from that
which doth only containe the contentment of my minde.
And in this minde ment to attempt her in the way of
marriage: but runninge fro*m Charibdis*, hee rusht uppon
Scilla: flying from one rocke, hee fell uppon another: 20
thinkinge to quench the coales of his desyre, hee fell
into hot flames of burninge fier: as hereafter you shall
heare.

Now so soone as hee had oportunitie offered him, hee
made *Pasiphae* partaker of his purpose in these termes.

Seeing the onely touchstone to trie true and loyall
love from lothsome lust, is marriage, I meane, if you
bee content, to consent therto, to seale the sincere
affectio*n* I beare you, with the sacred ceremonyes and
holly rites of matrimony: and as I have preferred your   30
love beefore all worldli respects, so I trust you wil
return my love *with* such loyalty, that I shall have cause

2 liberalitie/libertie *BCDEF*   13 God himselfe/the Goddes *EF*
13 or/and *DEF*   29 ceremonyes/testimonies *DEF*

to count my selfe as well matcht, as if I had married
with the greatest princesse in the world. *Pasiphae* hearing these wordes, was so ravished with joy, that shee
could not on the sodaine make the kinge an answere,
but having chaunged colour twice or thrise, from red
to white, and from white to red, in token of a minde
mooved with hope, assayled with feare, and passioned
with pleasure, at length shee sayd unto him. As (most
worthy prince) I ever thought my selfe far unworthy of
any sutch honour, so if it please your highnes plainly to
heare the truth, I ever thought my selfe far to worthy,
to yeeld to your desire in the way of wickednesse: which
was the cause I made so course account of your curtesy
heretofore. But seeinge it hath pleased you to lodge
your love thus low, and to thinke mee worthy the
honour of wedlocke with so worthy a wight: assure your
selfe your majesty shall finde mee in love so loyall, and
in obedience so dutifull towardes you: that in the one,
I wil supply the part of a loving wife: and in the other,
satisfie the duty of a diligent handmayd. Neither would
I you should thinke, that it is the name of a queene, or
estate of a prince, y^t winneth mee thus willingly to your
will, for I know that name to bee vaine, and that estate
full of paine: but it is your exceedinge love towardes
mee (O noble prince) that linketh my lykinge with
yours, it is your incomparable curtesy which forceth
mee to yeelde the forte of my fayth and virginity into
your handes. For as the sunne the higher it doth
ascende in the firmament, the more heate it doth extend
to the earth, so vertue and curtesy, in the more high
and princely person it is placed, the more force it hath
to win the wils, & binde the heartes of people to imbrace
it. And as my love is grounded upon your vertue, so I

32 people/the people *CDEF*

trust so to behave my selfe, that hereafter you shall have as great lyking to my conditions and vertue, as now you have love to my colour and beuty: that when yeeres shal take away the pleasure of ye one, you may take delight & solace in the other. The king was so deeply delighted with this dutifull discourse, that hee had not a woorde to reply, but satisfiyng him selfe for the time with a few sweete kisses, presently gave commanudement to his officers, to make preparation for the sumptuous celebrating of his mariage, which shortly after was consummated with sutch royalty, as is requisite in a matter of sutch majesty. So this married couple, consumed two or three yeres in the highest degree of happinesse. But the sunne beeinge at the highest, declineth: and the Sea beeinge at full tide, ebbeth: caulme continueth not longe without a storme, neither is happinesse had longe without heavinesse, as by this couple may bee seene. For when the kinges fancy had bene once fully fed, the vehemency of his desire beegan to vanish away, and hee began to love his new married wife rather with reason then with rage: by reason whereof with indifferency of judgement, hee could now note her naughty nature, which at first partialyty of love, would not permit him to perceive. For what Gentleman soever shee saw in the court, indued with a vertuous disposition and noble minde, shee would with the kinge hinder his preferment by all meanes possible, still advaunsing the vylest, to tipe of dignity. If any Gentlewoman were famous for her honesty and chastity, by some sluttish slights or other, shee sought to slaunder them. So that those in whom the kinge did only delight, shee indevoured with all dilygence to molest and spight. Which the king perceivinge, and

11 is/was *CDEF*   20 hee *om. EF*

consideringe how from low estate, hee had brought her
to heighth of honour, thought hee might more boldly
refourme her faultes, and began (with severity sufficient,
and in deede, more then was meete beetweene man and
wife,) to admonish her of her malitious disposition,
towardes those which were of vertuous inclination: and
made no curiosity though without curtesy, to tell her,
that shee beeinge ignoble her selfe, could not like of
those which were noble. But to mutch familiarity had
bred so mutch contempt in her, that shee beegan
impaciently to pout, to loure, to snuffe, to chafe, to
thinke her self mutch injuried by those wordes, and
sayd plainly shee would like of whom shee lyst, shewinge
her rude bringing up, her want of wit and government,
her currishe nature, her curst conditions, and howe
unfitte shee was for the place shee was in. Well, the
kinge was fayn to make a vertue of necessity, and to
take paciently, that which hee could not take away
easily. For shee still persevered in her perversenesse,
and hated those cheifly, whom her husband loved
especially. And amongst all other[s], there was one
proper young gentleman named *Verecundus*, attendant
upon the kinge, and in great favour and credit with
him, whom when shee could by no means bring into
displeasure or dislikinge, shee went about to intrap by
this traine of treason: shee began to cast glaunces of
good will towardes him, and by alluringe lookes to
thrall him in the thread of her beuty. The young gentleman beeing made of fine mettall, and therfore very apt
to receive the impression of love, in short time was so
framed to her fancy, that hee yeelded fayth to her fraud,
and requited her fayned lookes with unfayned love.
And as a pleasaunte praye soone intiseth a simple

4 was *om. BCDEF*   13 would/should *E*

theife: so hee thought her beuty sutch a booty, that in his opinion, no younge man in the world but would hazarde hanginge to have it. And hereupon fell to debatinge the matter with him selfe in this sorte.

It is a common opinion amongest men, that hee which is once chayned in the linkes of love, is foorthwith restrayned of his liberty and freedome, but if true lyberty bee to live as one list, I cannot but thinke my self to live in most large and licentious liberty, for that I lust not, or desire to lead any other life then that which I doe: which is, in the secret service and continuall contemplation of my princely *Pasiphae.* Yea I thinke every sorrow sweet, and every paine pleasure, which any passion proceeding of her beuty procureth mee: and I thinke my selfe more then happy, that the heavens thinke mee meete to suffer any martirdome for her sweet sake. And if I might ende my dayes in dooing her service, I should thinke it the only beginning of joy, the way to life, and the readie and perfect path wherby to passe to the pleasures of Paradise. Oh that fortune would minister some occasion wherby I might manifeste unto her the manifolde goodwill I beare her: and if without prejudice to her person it might bee done, would to god she were drowned in some sutch depth of daunger, that nothinge but the hazardinge of my life could preserve her from perill: then should shee see the service which I have sworne to doe her, then should shee see the duty which I have vowed to owe her, then should shee plainly perceive, that neither the pleasures of the world, neither the solace of freindes, neither the sweetnesse of life, neither the sowernesse of death should withdraw mee from sheadynge the deerest drop of bloud in mee to doe her good. And then woulde

27 doe *om. EF*

shee say (if any curtesy bee contained in her) that my
love is most loyal, and my freindship most faythfull,
then would shee paye (if any gratefulnesse bee grafted
in her) my daunger and perill with the price of her
person. But alas, how can she pay me with that which
is not in her own power? There is another only who
hath interest therin, she hath already payd her person
as a price of a prince & his whole kingdome: so that I
plough the barrein rockes, and set my share into the
shoare of the Sea: I till with toyle sutch a kinde of
soyle, whereof another by right must crop the corne.
But admit she were disposed to incroche somwhat upon
her husbandes right, [and for a common commoditie
would let the fielde lye open, which he for his private
pleasure, contrary to the lawes of nature would have
inclosed: B–F] yet is it likely shee will looke so low, as
let so meane a man as my selfe [enter common, or B–F]
growe into so great acquaintaunce with her? No, fortune denieth mee any sutch favour, my good will as
yet hath deserved no sutch gwerdon, my desire is far
above my desertes, my ambition above my condition.
Why, my birth is better then hers, why should shee
then neglecte mee? But her calling is better then mine,
why should shee then respect mee? My desire proceedes
of love, why should shee not then accept it? But alas,
it is contrary to law, why should shee not then rejecte
it? I am of noble bloud, why should shee refuse mee?
But shee hath a noble prince to her husband, why should
shee misuse him? Yea if I my self were not a villaine,
altogether devoyd of vertue, I would not suffer it so
mutch as enter into my thought to abuse him, who
hath alwayes used mee honourably, who hath sought
my prefermente by all meanes possyble, who from my
childhood hath brought mee up like a loving lord &

Maister. Shall I requite his liberalytie towards mee with sutch disloyaltie? shall I deceive the opinion whiche hee doeth conceive of mee, with sutche de[te]stable villany? shall I returne the trust which he reposeth in me, with sutch treson? shal I defile my faith towards him, by seeking to defile his bridly bed? But (alas) love is above lord or laws, above Prince or priviledge, above friend or faith. Where love leadeth no maister is made account of, no Kinge cared for, no friend forced of, no duty respected, no honestie regarded, but all thinges done   10 accordinge to the passion which prevaileth over us. And seeinge it is not in our power to prevent that passion, for it is either derived of our owne nature, or discended from the heavens, there is no reason I shoulde requier any proper or peculiar fortune to my selfe, and seeke to be dispensed withal from that which is common to all: and so mutche the rather I am induced to yeelde to the instinct of love, and to pursue my purpose, for that I perceive by the wanton lookes of the Queene, that she is determined to entertaine some secret friend, beesides   20 the King her husband, and if I flatter not my selfe, her very countinance towardes me imports some lykelyhood of love shee beares mee: therefore I think it wisdome to strike while the iron is hot, and if it bee posible to ease my hart of the greif, which her beuty hath bred mee. And if shee be disposed to arme her husband with horned harnesse, as good I be the instrument therof, as some other of meaner calling and countenance. After this, hee sought all meanes possible to insinuate him-selfe into her familiaritie, & courted her continually   30 with dutiful service and secret signes of sincere affection: hee so bribed her maides with benefits, & corrupted them with coyne, that they made him a God unto their

3 doeth conceive/hath conceived *DEF*   18 to *om. CDEF*

misteris: she could not looke out at her chamber window, but that she saw him walke solitarily under-
neath, casting up countenances which seemed to containe humble praiers for pitie and compassion, and
throwing up sutch sighes as might plainly signifie the
sorrow of his thoughtes. If she chaunced to walk
abroade, hee woulde meete her lyke a ghost in such
ghastly maner, with such a pale countenance, and pined
carkas, that it woulde have moved the stoany rocks to
10 ruth. But the Queene seeing him so fast fettered in
folly, had that she desired, and now she left her lovinge
lookes towardes him, and the more painfully shee perceived him tormented, the more disdainfully shee lokt
upon hym, and would not by any signes which hee did
shew of his affection, seeme to know it, to the intent
hee should by writing make manifest his meaninge unto
her. The yong Gentleman, seeing the hope which at the
first he conceived of her goodwill, altogether without
hap, and in a manner dispairing of his purpose, hee
20 coulde take no longer dayes with his desire, but that
hee must know a final resolution one way or other: And
beeing driven to carelesse desperatenesse, hee feared not
to commit his life to a tell tale peece of paper, and
beewrayed his miserie to his misteris in this manner.

Beecause (most soveraigne Lady) my duty and service heretofore hath beene nothinge acceptable to you,
I have devised a new way to woorke your contentation,
which is by writing to doe you to wit, that since it
liketh you not to geve mee lyfe, I meane to beestowe
30 uppon my selfe a desperate death, the only thing I
thinke which may procure you pleasure: and so long as
it may delight you, I way not how mutch it spight mee.
Yea love hath dealt so extreemly with mee, that though

8 ghastly/ghostly *BCDE*

I woulde my selfe, I cannot keep my corps from confusion. For as the frettinge *Fistula* past all cure, runneth
in the fleshe from place to place, and maketh the sound
flesh as rotten as the rest, so ye deadly poyson of love
first entred in at my eies, and after spred into every
part of mee, hath now dangerously infected my whole
body unto death. But yet my death will bee nothing
so greevous unto mee, as to thinke what a blemish it wil
bee to the brightnes of your beuty, when your tiranny
shal bee taken to bee the cause therof, yea and when   10
you shall have no cloude at all to colour your crueltie.
For if you alleage for your selfe, that you durst not
make so deepe a wounde in your honour, as to commit
your body to any, but to him who by marriage hath
merited it: why a lovely looke onely would have satisfied
mee, yea one glaunce of goodwill goyng from your eyes,
wil more content mee then all the actuall pleasure in
the world, receaved of any other woman in the worlde.
But seeing fortune doth wil, and you do wish my
destruction, I am content to obey the decree of the one,   20
and satisfie the desyre of the other: beeseechinge you
to take these witlesse wordes for a final fainting farewell, wishing you continuance of beautie, with increase
of bountie.

Nether yours, neither his owne: VERECUNDUS.

This Letter besprinckled with teares, he gave to one
of her maides of honour to geve her. But true the
proverbe is, that fish bred up in durtie pooles wil tast
of mud, one discended of meane race, cannot bee endued
with vertue fit for princely place: set a beggar on hors-   30
back and hee will never alight, extoll one of base stock
to degree of dignitie, and who is so haughtie? who is so
proude? for this crafty coy Queene having red his letter,

5 in at/into *EF*   11 colour/cover *EF*

though she were right glad thereof, for that thereby shee ment to purchase his utter discredit with the Kinge, yet shee seemed to bee in a great chafe, calling him traytor, that durst injury [*sic*] her eyes with sutch leude letters, with divers other imputations of reproche, and went presently to the Kinge and shewed him this letter: who in a great rage sent his guard to apprehende him, but hee having intelligence thereof, was faine to flye the country. See the force of fraude and the ende of lawles love, but marke moreover the reward of her trechery and tiranny. Her husbande ever after this, was so jelous over her, that hee woulde never suffer her to bee out of his sight, and doatinge somewhat of her beauty, but doubting more of her honesty, he never rode forth any journy, but that hee set wary watche and warde over her at home, yea this furious feende of hel did so torment him, that hee could take no rest day nor night, but his fancy still ran either uppon the Gentleman that would have done him that injurie, either uppon some other that shoulde be lyke to serve him in like sorte: so that the pleasure which her proper person procured him, was drowned with yᵉ doubt, lest she would not remaine proper unto him, and that she would bee as common in possession, as she was proper in personage. Alas, (saith hee) now my joy is at an end, yᵉ clouds of care have quight covered my sun and light, of solace & delight: yea the greater pleasure I take in practising *with* my *Pasiphae*, yᵉ greater feare I have yᵗ others deeply desyre to participate with yᵉ pleasure. And the more free she is in sutch freendship towards me, yᵉ more franck I doubt she will be towards other[s]. Ah, would to God I had never bene married, rather then to bee thus martired, or els would I had matcht with some

3 a *om. EF*   19 would/should *EF*   26 covered/severed *EF*

sutch, whose princely nature woulde have participated only with Princes, and whose royall bloude and birthe might have feared the baser sorte to presume to practise her to their purposes: but my chaunce was to chuse one, who if (as the sayinge is) like, like best of their likes, is like to like better of any other then of my selfe, for that in nature and conditions there is sutche difference beetweene us. But repentaunce now commeth to late, this only resteth to bee foreseene, that unto the greate greife which mine owne conceite procureth me, her abuse adde not infamy and dishonour. And if the heavens have assigned mee sutch heavy fate, as due to my doatinge desyre, yet this at least let mee take heede, that with the losse of her owne honour, shee procure not the losse of my lyfe. And hereupon appointed certaine of his assured friends, to have the custody and keeping of the queene: who seeinge her selfe thus disloyally without cause abridged of her liberty, beegan to curse the time that ever shee came to bee queene, wishing shee had continued in meaner callinge with fruition of liberty, rather then to sit in chayre of dignity, with suspicion of dishonesty. What pleasure, sayth shee, doth my princely estate procure mee, whiche must live as a prisoner? Who wil honour mee for queen, which am suspected for a queane and harlot? How shall I dare to shew my face in the Courte, when the kinge doubteth of my dealinge towardes him? My lookes have not bene so light, my curtesie hath not bene so common, my glaunces have not bene so garish, wherby hee shoulde enter into this sinister suspicion of mee. But love (they say) is light of beeleefe, and jelousy is grounded upon love. Avant fond foolish love, God send my husbande rather to hate me, then to beare mee any such

5 like, like/like *EF*   28 so light/light *EF*

love, which bereveth him of rest, and mee of renowme, which breaketh the bond of faythfull freindship and intire amity between us, which causeth him to doubt mee, and mee to dread him, which maketh both our lives so lothsome, that I wishe death to dispatch either the one of us or the other. But this froward fate, I must ascribe only to mine owne fault, and fraud towardes *Verecundus*, who hath now just cause to triumph that I my selfe am fallen into the pit I digged for him. Wel,

10 I must retire to patience perforce, and hange in hope of some good hap to redresse my woe and misery.

But you shall understand (Gentlewomen) this was not all her punnishment, nay this was but a trifle in respecte of that which after followed, a matter in haynousnesse so horrible, in desire so detestable, and in lust so lothsome, that it is no lesse strange to bee tolde, then hard to bee beleeved: so that I thinke my wordes will rather carry wonder then credite with you. For, whether it were gods plague for ye husbands jel-

20 ousy, or for her jolity, pride, and subtelty, I know not, but thus it pleased him to suffer the divell to deale with her. Beeing by her husbandes commaundement in his absence kept from company, her cheife solace was to walke in a pleasaunt grove joyned to her palaice, where used to feed a heard of beasts, amongest which was a goodly white bull. I dare not say shee fell in love with the bull, least I should drive you rather to laughinge at my story then listninge to it, but surely so it was. Yea shee was not only in love with the beast, and went

30 every morninge and with her owne hands brake downe boughes for him to brouse upon, but, which was more, shee was jelous over him: for what cow in all the herd shee saw hee liked best, shee caused to bee had from the heard and killed, as she pretended for sacrifice, but

in deed for satisfiyng her jelous minde. And as the
beast was opening, shee would take the inwardes in her
hand, saying, now goe thy way and please my love if
thou canst. And taking delight a while in this daliance,
at length her lust grew to sutch outrage, that shee felt
in her selfe an impossibility to continue her cursed life,
without the carnall company of the bull. And notwithstandinge shee assayed the assistaunce of reason, the
pollicy of perswations, the helpe of herbes, and the
meane of medicines, to mortyfy her beastly desire to   10
the beast, yet nothinge would prevayle, yea beeinge
often in minde to make her selfe away, her hart would
not suffer her hands to doe it: not that death feared
her, but that desyre forced her first to fulfil her filthy
lust, [and at length by the helpe of *Dedalus*, a cunning
Carpenter, shee was so cunningly conveyed into a Cowe
of wood, that shee had her beastly desire. *B–F*] But
Gentlewome*n*, because you shal not enter into colorick
conceites against me, for publishing in this presence, a
hystorie whiche seemeth so mutch to sounde to the   20
shame of your sexe, I meane not to justifie the truth
of it, but rather will prove it false by the opinio*n* of
one *Servius*, who writeth, that *Pasiphae* in deede played
false with one *Taurus* (which signifieth a Bul) secretary
to her husband in the house of *Dedalus*, and after being
delyvered, had two sonnes, the one lyke *Minos*, the
other lyke *Taurus*, and thereupon the Poets faigned
the fable aforesaide: but whether beeing a woman shee
used the carnall company of a beast, or whether lyke
a lewde wife shee gave her husbande the badge of a   30
beast, her offence was sutch, that I cannot (though
gladly I woulde) excuse it. Yet must I needes say that
in my fancy her husbande deserved some blame: for no

19 this/your *EF*

doubt his suspicion without cause, caused her in sutche
sorte to transgresse marriage lawes. For seeing her honestie doubted of, and her good name as good as loste,
shee thought as good to bee naught for somewhat as
to bee thought naught for nothing. And surely the
experience is to common, yᵗ suspicion and slaunder
maketh many to bee that which they never ment to bee.
But some are of this foolish opinion, that it is simple
and sottishe folly, for a woman to deale truly with
him, whiche dealeth jelously and cruelly with her:
some againe lewdly thinke, yᵗ if a woman cannot conceive by her husband yᵗ she may lawfully enter into conversation with some other: some wickedly weene, that
if the husbande bee not able to satisfie the insatiable
desyre of his wife, that to avoyde concupiscence, shee
may communicate with some other: but surely (Gentlewomen) I am setled in this opinion, that no suspicion
or jelousie ought to cause a woman to transgresse the
boundes of honesty: that chastitie is the only Jewell
which women ought to bee chary of, that women havinge lost their chastitie, are like broken glasses which are
good for nothing, that they make shipwrack of all, if
the cabels of constancie be once crakt, & the anchors
of honestie slipt: yᵗ it is better for them to be fooles
then false, to be simple then subtil, to be doves then
divels, to be abused then abuse: yᵗ it is better for them
to be barren then beastly, to bee without fruite then
faith, children then chastitie: that concupisence is only
to desire other[s] besides their husbandes, that they
which burne in sutch desire, shall burne in hell fire, yᵗ
no adultresse shall inherite the kingdome of heaven:
that all women ought to bee like yᵉ matronesse of *Rome*,

9 sottishe/foolish *EF*   11 yᵗ *om. DEF*
32 matronesse/Matrone *EF*

which knew ye favour of no mans breath but of her
husbandes, like the wife of *Fulvius Torquatus*, who died
with longinge, rather then shee would goe forth of her
chaumber in her husbandes absence, to see a wilde
Ægiption with one eye in his forehead, whom shee
longed to see: that women ought to spin with *Penelope*,
to spill with *Camma*, to kill with *Lucrece*, to bee slaun-
dred with *Susanna*, with *Savoy*, and with others, to
indure any torment, rather then to lose one jote of their
chastity and honesty.

10

1 of her/her *EF*   2 Torquatus/Torguatus *B*
3 would/should *E*   5 Ægiption/Ægiptian *BCD*, Ægyptian *EF*

Pigmalions friende, and his
Image.

[PIGMALION, a Gentleman of Piemount, continuing the space of certaine yeares, in honest affection, and vertuous love with PENTHEA, wife to Luciano a noble gentleman of the same country, is at length by her rejected, in respect of a base stranger. *Pigmalion*, abandoning the company of all women, and givinge himselfe to the arte of Carving, burneth in love with an Image, whiche himselfe had fashioned: whom, at his earnest sute *Venus* transformeth into a faire Mayde, and hee taketh her to Wife.]

10 To make the reckoning without the host, is the way soone to bee overshot in the shot: to resolve certenly upon incertenty, is the way never to be in any certenty: to looke for constancy, of those y^t lyke of inconstancy, or to determine of those things which are not in our powers to perfourme, is nothing els but to bee deceived of our expectation, and to be driven to alter our determination: as the History whiche you shall heare, shal yeelde example of both the one and the other.

In the country of *Piemount* had his beeinge one
20 *Pigmalion*, a gentleman discended of noble birth, indued with perfection of person, & perfectly pourtraied forth with ye lineaments of learning, so that it was dooubtful whether he were more indebted to fortune for his birth, to nature for his beauty, or to his parentes for his learninge. But as beautie, birth, ritches, and the rest must needes geve place to learninge, so no doubt but his parentes deserved the preheminence of prayse. For the other[s] are but dim starres, where learninge giveth

light. And as when the sunne shineth, the light of the
stars is not seene: so where learning appeareth, all other
giftes are nothing to be accounted of. Besides that,
beeside his learning, he was indued with a great dex-
teritie in all thinges, in so mutch as nothing came amisse
unto him, whiche was meete for a Gentleman: in feates
of armes no man more couragious, in exercises of the
body none more active, in game or play none more politike, amongst the auncient who more grave? amongst
the youthfull, who more merrie? so that there was no   10
time, no person, no place, wherto hee aptly applyed not
him self. By reson wherof, he was acceptable to all good
companies, & wel was he that might entertaine him in
his hous. But most of al he frequented ye hous of one
Luciano a noble Gentleman of the same countri, & in
continuance of time grew so farre in familiaritie with
his wife, that he reposed his onely pleasure in her presence. Yea shee had made sutch a stealth of his harte,
that neither Father nor Mother, Sister nor Brother,
nor all the friends he had in the country beside, could   20
keepe him one weeke together out of her compani. Yea
this faithful love hee bare her, seemed in a manner
to extinguish all naturall love towards his allies, and
kinsfolke: Who beeinge (as they were wont) desirous of
his company at hauking, hunting, and sutche like
pastimes, coulde not by any craving or importunity
obtayne it: but being ignorant of the cause, they
thought it had proceded of this, that his minde upon
some occasion had been alienated from them, which
caused them on the contrarie, somewhat to withdrawe   30
their goodwils from him. But hee forced litle thereof,
he cared not whom hee displeased, so he might worke
her contentation: shee was the starre by whose aspect

2 is/are *CDEF*   24 of/to have *EF*

he did direct his doynges, she was the haven wherein he sought to harborough, she was the heaven whyther he coveted to come, shee was the saint to whom hee did lend sutch devotion, that hee could finde in his heart to bend no liking to any other whatsoever. In so mutch, y^t having the profer of many ritch maryages, hee alway refused them, as having his hart so replenished *with* the love of her, y^t there was no roomth for the love of any other to remayn within him. Now shee, on the other side, whose name was *Penthea,* beeinge a curteous courtly wenche, gave him sutch freindly entertaynment, and used him so well in all respectes, that, her husband excepted, shee seemed to holde him most dere unto her of any wight in the whole world. Shee never made feast, but hee must bee her guest: shee never rode journey, but he must be her companion: shee never daunced, but hee must direct her: shee never dised, but hee must bee her partner: shee, in a manner, dyd nothing, wherin hee did not something. Her Husbande all this while beeinge fully assured of her vertue, and very well perswaded of the honesty of the Gentleman, suspected no evill beetweene them, but lyked very well of their love and familiarity together, neither in deede had hee any cause to the contrary. For *Pigmalion* knew her to bee indued with sutch constant vertue, that he thought it impossible to allure her to any folly: and besides that, his love was so exceedinge great towardes her, that hee would not by any meanes bee the cause to make her commit any thinge, which might make her lesse worthy of love then shee was. And if at any time (as the fleshe is frayle) the vehemency of his affection forced him to perswade her to folly, he did it so faintly, that it might plainly bee perceived hee was

4 lend/bend *BCDEF*   sutch/his *EF*   5 bend/lend *BCDEF*

not willing to overcome. For hee deepely doubted, that
if by the force of her love towardes him, or of his perswasions towardes her, shee should have yeelded the
forte of her fayth and chastity into his handes, his love
towards her (with the sun beinge at the highest) would
have declined and decreased, which would have bene
the greatest greife to him in the world. No, hee lived with
sutch delight in the contemplation of her chastity and
vertue, that hee was voyde not only of *Libidinous* lust
towardes her, but also towardes all other women what-   10
soever. Yea, hee received more pleasure of her by
imagination, then of any other woman by yᵉ acte of
generation. So that betweene these friends was no cause
of suspicion, no cause of jarre, no cause of jelousie: but
they lived together the space of three or foure yeares
in most heavenly haven of most happie lyfe. The floud
of their felicity flowed from the fountaine of most faithful friendship, the building of their bidinge together
was raised on the rock of vertu, so yᵗ it was to be
thought, no seas of subtiltie, or floudes of fickelnesse   20
coulde have undermined it. But what perpetuitie is to
bee looked for in mortall pretences? What constancy is
to bee hoped for in kytes of *Cressids* kinde? may one
gather Grapes of thornes, Suger of Thistels, or constancy
of women? Nay if a man sift the whole sexe thorowly,
hee shall finde their wordes to bee but winde, their
fayth forgery, and their deedes dissemblinge. You must
not (Gentlewomen) take these words to come from
mee, who dare not so mutch as thinke so mutch, mutch
lesse say so mutch, for that truth getteth hatred, I   30
meane sutch as tell not the truth, as hee in no wise
should not doe, which should blowe foorth any sutch

2 by *om. E*   of *om. F*   8 contemplation/company *EF*   11 Yea/Yet *EF*
19 was/is *EF*   23 kytes/kits *BCD*, kittes *EF*   32 foorth *om. EF*

blast of the most faythfull and constant feminine kinde.
But you must take these speeches to proceede from
Pigmalion, who, to speake uprightly, had some cause
to discommend some in particuler, though not to condemne all in generall, as you shall foorthwith heare. For
it fell so out that an Ambassadour came out of a
straunge country into *Piemount*, and was appointed to
lye at the house of *Luciano* the time of his aboade in
the country. Now amongest the company which came
with him, there was one young Gentleman, in whom
though there were nothing worthy of commendation
any way, yet whether it proceeded of the daintinesse
of women, who (as *Pigmalion* thought) wilbee soone
wery of one diet, or of their wavering (who are constant
in nothing) or of their imperfect nature (which tendeth
alway to the worst) I knowe not, but this lady began
to conceave a very good opinion of him, and in short
tyme in affection far to prefer hym beefore her old
faithful freind. Which *Pigmalion* perceiving, being in
their presence, drunke up his sorowe in scilence, but
having withdrawen hym self out of theyr companye,
into his solitarie chamber, he entred with hym self into
this raging rayling.

O faigned fawning, O counterfayt curtesy, O deepe
dissembling, O hony mixt with gall, O heaven turned
to hell. Now doe I perceive thy frendshyp heretofore
was nothing but flattery, thy love, leude thy curtesy of
course, nowe am I assured thou madest of me a vertue
of necessytye, to serve thy turne for lacke of other
company. Dyd I prefer thee before father and freend,
and canst thou preferre before me a straunger, whom
thou never sawest before, of no countenance, credite,

20 their/her *EF*   28 am I/I am *EF*
31 before me a straunger/a stranger before me *EF*

or constansy, but wavereth with the wynd? Dyd I beare
thee faythfull and intire affection, and canst thou beare
greater goodwill to hym, who careth not for thee? who
beareth stedfast affection to none, in whom is nothing
but flitting fantasy, and meere vanity? & canst thou
thus prefer leudnesse before learning, tryfling before
truth, clownishnes before courtlynesse, vanitie before
vertue? then farewel reason, thou resteth not in womans
head: then farewel wyt, thou wieldest not womens
doinges: then farewel fayth, thou art no womans pheare: 10
then farewel women, you are no mates for me. And here-
uppon verily determined with hym self utterly to abandon her company for ever: but reprehending his owne
rashnesse, he ment to have a further troyall of her
triflinge towardes him, and also to looke more narrowly
into the dooinges and behaviour of that other Gentleman, that if hee could see any thinge in him wherby
hee worthily deserved to bee preferred before him selfe,
hee might more patiently indure it. Wherupon dissembling his greife so well as hee could, hee made   20
repaire againe unto her house, and there noting her
love by her lookes, her fancy by her face, and her conceites by her countenance, hee easily perceived to whom
shee bent her best devotion, and who was her holiest
Idol. Likewise, diligently considering the conversation
of the gentleman, hee perswaded himselfe that in indif-
ferent judgment, where affection did not make blinde,
the best guiftes eyther of body or minde which were
in him, were not to be compared to the worst which
were in him self: the one being not perfect any way,   30
the other imperfect noway. So that seeing neither his
owne worthynes, neither the others unworthynes, could

14 a *om.* EF   further/farther D   16 that/the *EF*
19 more/the more *DEF*   30 being not/not being *EF*

settle her affection as it should be, he utterly apealed
from her unworthy & unequal judgme*n*t, and geving
her the *bezolas manos*, hee altogether estraunged hym-
self from her societie. See the mervaylous power of his
love, who notwithsta*n*ding he never injoyed ye use of
her body, and certaynly knewe that the other had not
won that poynt of her neither, yet he tooke it so
greevously, that she should seeme to beare greater goodwyll towardes the other then hym, that he fully resolved
with him selfe, to eschewe the company of all other
women for her sake, and never to suffer the love of any
to sinke again so deepely into his harte. And surely
(Gentlewomen) this *Pigmalion* may bee a presedent and
proofe to confute the errour of those, who thinke there
can bee no hot and fervent love betweene a man & a
woman, unlesse it proceede of some pleasant practise
between them. And if they see any freindly familiarity
betweene a younge Gentleman and Gentlewoman, they
forthwith conceive an evil opinion of their honest
affection. Which errour, as it is most grose, so may it
bee defaced by sundry reasons. For how it is possible
that of an il cause, can come a good effect? That firme
freindship can flow from fading fancy? That the heavenly consent of mindes, should proceed of the brutall
conjunction of bodies? Which, if it were so, those men
(if I may call them men) which dayly deale with common women, should bee very faythfully and freindly
affectioned towardes them: but it is so far of, that in
my fancy after the fact, they rather loth them, then
love them. Both for that a lothsome repentaunce followeth it, and also (as *Aristotle* saith) men therby are made

3 bezolas/bezelas *BCD*, bezelos *E*, baze los *F*   12 into/in *EF*
16 pleasant/fylthy *CDEF*   19 forthwith/forsooth *EF*
22 of an il cause, can come a/an ill cause can come to *BCDEF*

lesse perfect. So that I thinke the [unlawfull *B–F*] conjunction of bodies, rather a disjunction of minde then
otherwise. And true freindship beetweene man and man,
or man & woman, is grounded only on that which is
good and honest. Yea, I am perswaded, that the wanton
lover himselfe, is as well satisfied with the good countenaunce, loving lookes, and perfecte agreement of his
misteris minde with his, as with the use of her body.
Which, although hee oftentimes ernestly desire, yet I
thinke it bee as mutch to know therby her unfayned   10
goodwill towardes him, to confirme it with a naturall
bonde, and to procure her contentment, as for that hee
reposeth the fulnesse of his felicitie therein. So, if then
a lewd lover altogether vowed to vanitie, can love
without lust, how mutch more easily may a faithful
freind bee fervent in affection, and yet colde in desire?
And as *Pigmalion* may bee a playne president, that a
man may love loyally, and yet not desire lasciviously:
so may *Florinda* bee a fruitfull example to the feminine
sorte, to doe the like, who bearyng sutch fervent affec-   20
tion to her freinde *Amadour*, that shee helde him more
dere then her owne life, that shee received more contentacion in the companie of him, then of husband,
father, mother, [childe, *B–F*] freinde or whosoever: yet
shee was so far of from filthy affection towardes him,
that shee avoyded, so neare as shee could, all occasions
which might draw him into any disordinate desire
towardes her. In so mutch, that havyng occasion of
privie conference with him in a private place, beefore
shee came, shee fouly defaced her face, and bruised it   30
with a stoane, that hee might not bee inflamed with the

6 good *om. EF*   11–12 to confirme it with a naturall bonde, and to procure her contentment *om. CDEF*   23 husband *om. BCDEF*
24 whosoever/whatsoever *EF*   25 far of from/farre from *CDEF*

feature thereof, and divers other wayes at divers other
times, valiantly withstoode all alarms of lust. Therfore
they are no doubt deceived, which thinke that love
cannot bee without lust, neither fervent affection without fleshly fancie. And I would not wish any to judge
so injuriously of the familiaritie of freindes, sutch light
judgements, prove but a light judge: sutch suspicious
opinions, for the most part proceede from suspected
persons: and they are commonly sutche themselves as
they thinke other[s] to bee: for *mala mens, malus
animus*: an evil disposition breedeth an evill suspition.
But to returne to *Pigmalion*, who, for al his fervent
love, beyng frustrate of the fruites therof, and not
incountred with the like, got from the house of his fickle
freinde, and beeing alone in his owne lodginge, hee
entred with him selfe into this discourse. Notwith-
standynge my love hath been alway guided rather by
reason then rage, and my fancie never at any time
turned to furie, by reason wherof I have not been
greatly pinched with the panges therof, yet when I
consider the common course of lovers, and of love,
surely of all punishments inflicted on mankynde, there
is none that doth more afflict us, then the lewde lots
therof, and the firie dartes of *Cupid*. For all other evils
by nature we flie from, by reason we redresse, by
pollicie wee prevent, by pleasure wee mitigate, by
patience wee moderate, by labour wee lighten, by payne
we appeale, by counsayle wee cure, by time wee take
away, or by some meanes or other set our selves free
from. But this hatefull love by nature wee follow, it
bereeveth us of reason, pollicie hath no place in it,
pleasure doubleth our dolour, patience purchaseth no
ease, labour is lost, payne prevayleth not, counsayle

21 of love/love *EF*   31 it/us *DEF*

conduceth not, time tieth and intangleth us, no, nothyng is able to leade us out of this intricate Labyrinth: And though ye pleasures pertayning to love, seeme great: yet who so ever purposeth to purchase them, let him assure him selfe to but them at an unreasonable rate. Every pecke of pleasure shall cost him a quarter of care, for every pinte of hony hee shall taste a gallon of gall. Yea though the entry which leadeth to the lodginge of love seeme easy, & the porche paradise unto him, yet shall hee finde the hall a hell, and the whole house a hateful prison and place of bondage. For as Marriners yt under a shew of calme wether, commit them selves to the sea, are oftentimes with tempestes so tossed, that rushinge against the rockes, their ships are shaken to peeces, and they devoured in the depth of the sea: so hee that under the curteous countenance of a wavering woman yeeldeth himself to love, is commonly so wrapped in the waves of wiles, that hee is altogether drowned in the depth of deceit, and hardly escapeth with the losse of his liberty and lyvinge. Wee see the flie playeth so long with the flame, that hee is scourched therwith, and the experience is no lesse common then lamentable, that men dally so longe with dainty dames, that at length they are scorched in the flames of fancy, and the winges of their free will quight burned away. And then, good God it is strange to consider their case, how carelesly they deale in all thinges, how leudly they spend their time, how prodigally they consume their gooddes, how negligently they regard their freindes, how lothsomely they like good counsayle, how resolute they are in their owne fonde determinations, how dissolute in their beehaviour, howe solytaryly they sit in scilence, how secretly they

15 to/in *EF*

conceale their greife, how sorowfully they spend their
daies, how fantastically their mindes are troubled, how
feebly their bodies are weakned, what broken sleepes,
what doubtful dreams, what vaine visions they have.
And touching their beeloved, how curiously they commend them, howe partially they prayse them, how
doltishly they doate on them, how wilfully they are
blinded in them, how supersticiously they thinke of
them, how idolatrously they worship them, how zel-
ously they love them, how jelously they looke to them,
how warely they wa[t]ch them, how willingly they serve
them, how painfully they imploy themselves to pleasure
them, how readily they run under their commaundements, how obediently they bowe at their beck & cum
at their cal, how deadly thei hate their enemies, how
deeply thei love their freindes, how charily they seeke
their goodwill, how childishly they feare their ill will,
how gladly they take a good looke, how sadly they
receive a sower countenance, how foolishly they fulfil
their desires, how fondly thei frame them selves to their
fancies, how with lookes they shew their love, & with
signes signifie their goodwil, how it greeveth them to
have any other looked upon or spoken to, how in ye
presence of their ladies they frie as hotly as Mount
Ætna, how in their absence they frize as coldly as the
Hill Caucasus, how present they prefer sutes, how
absent they send salutations, how present they flourish,
how absent they fade: to conclude, how present they
live, how absent thei dy. But on the other side, to waigh
the dealings of their darlings towards them, it makes
my hart sore to think, that any man shoulde bee so
mad, as not utterly to abhorre them. For, first while
they see a man free from folly and without the com-

12 them/him E

passe of their cozenage, they fetch many a windlas to
drive him into the nets of naughtinesse, & to intrap him
in their trechery: and if they perceive him so strongly
armed with wisdome, that their bolstred beuty cannot
bleare his eyes, then foorthwith they goe about to compasse him with their counterfeit courtesye, then, forsooth, they frame sutch friendly countenaunces towards
him, and pretend to beare him so great goodwill, that
hee cannot (unlesse hee will shewe himselfe altogether
ungratefull and discourteous) but frame his fancy   10
towards them againe. Now, so soone as they see him
reasonably well reclaimed to the lure of their alluring
looks, they by and by stop the lure upon him, and cause
him to hover in hope and teach him to flie a high pitche,
for a pray of litle profit or pleasure. For then they cast
very coy countenances towards him, yea they will not
so mutch as with a glaunce give any signe of goodwil:
but when they have made him lie so long in the aire, that
he is redy either to take a stande, or soare away, they
flinge forth a traine of treason, and cast some flattringe 20
hope, and faigned fawning for him to feed on, lest his
kindnes by their coldnesse should quaile, and so he
retire his desyre. But if they see him to be so sharpe
set, y^t he will stoupe at every stale, or know him to be
an eyesse [a niesse *B-E*] which will never away, the*n*
they make him flye and never serve him, they bangle
him out and bob him as they list, then they keepe
themselves out of his sight to make him more sharp,
then in his presence they lend loving lookes to other[s],
then they make the matter so strange, that hee is driven   30
to beegin agayne, and to renew his sute afresh. And
the ende of all this is, to sport themselves in his paine,

16 yea/as *EF*   23 so *om. CDEF*
25 an eyesse/a Novice *F*   26 flye/flee *BCDEF*

to glory in his griefe, and to triumph in his tormentes. Sutch mallice they beare him that beareth them great goodwill. Yea hee whiche loveth them best is sure to be handled ye worst, for they know he is armed with love to indure the force of their fraude, & like an Asse to beare any burthen whiche they shal lay on his back. Yea they will not stick to yeelde their bodies to some course *quidem* in a corner, rather then they will bestow on him one courteous countinance, sutch is their ill nature to cleve to the worst, and proudly to disdaine him that humbly desireth them, and openly to reject all men though never so noble, and secretly to refuse no man though never so base. And as the Humblebee flieth all the day in the pleasaunt aire, and thinketh mutch to light even uppon the sweete flowers, but at night taketh no skorne to lodge in a Cowes foule sharde: so these dainty dames, in company think skorne to yeelde love to any, but in corners they care not to practise with some lothsome skullion, or horse boy. But if they think this lover, whom they have so daintily dealte withall, have oyle to coale their furious flames, and bee every way fit for theyr follye, he shall perchaunce, after this tedyous toyle, and long sute in the court of curtesy and conscience, be advised and admitted for a more speedy dispatch of his lyving, to enter his action in the common place: I meane, he shalbe receved into their good grace and favour, and be now and then feasted with the best banquets in their bodyes. But by that tyme the reckonnyng be payd, he shall finde his chere so chargable, that all thinges consydered, he might have fared better far better cheape, at the most cutthrote Inne in a country.

8 quidem/*Quidam BCDEF*   21 coale/coole *BCD*, cure *EF*
24 and conscience *om. CDEF*

Then must the Chaines, the Bracelets, the Jewels, the
Rings, the Diamonds, the Pearls, bee provided: then
must hee buie for every part a peece, for every finger a
fangle, for every toe a toy: then must their maides be
monied, their bauds bribed, their scouts considered,
their servaunts satisfied, and ever as they lye open to
him so his purse must lie open to them and theirs. And
hereof commeth the spoyle of a number of noble &
lustie younge Gentlemen: yea and the nobler bloude and
the franker hart they are of, the sooner & sorer is their   10
decay & confusion. For lyke as the fire having stones
cast into it doth onely alter their colour and make them
black, but cannot consume them, but having wood
thrown into it, it wasteth it cleane away: so these cous-
oning Curtizanes, if some hard mettald lover light unto
their lot, they onely alter his estate, and bringe him
from very wealthy to somewhat needy, but if a free
and franke childe chaunce uppon them, they wholy consume him body and goodes. A thing surely on our parte
rather to bee punnished then pittied, who being by   20
God endued with greater wits, should suffer our selves
so villanously to bee vanquished by the weaknesse of
women. But verely as Spiders convert to poison whatsoever they touche, so women infect with folly whom
so ever they deale withall. And I think them made of
God only for a plague and wo unto men, as their name
importeth. And as *Eve* caused *Adam* to bee deprived of
Paradise, so I think her sexe is ordained to deprive
Adams posterity of prosperiti. Yea in mariage it self
where only they are counted necessarie, I see not but   30
yᵗ they are accompanied with more care then commoditie, more cost then comforte, more paine then gaine,
more greife then good. Sutch falsenesse if they be faire,
sutch filthinesse if they bee foule, sutch wiles if they

bee wittie, sutch fondnesse if they be fooles, sutch
proudnesse if they bee noble, sutch rudenesse if they
be base, so nice if they bee vertuous, sutch vice if they
be vicious, sutch lustinesse if they bee young, sutch
lothsomnesse if they bee olde, sutch lightnes if they be
merrie, sutch sullennes if they be sad, sutch often desyre
of sport if they be healthy, sutch seldom quietnesse if
they bee sikly, sutch unholsomnesse if they be barren,
sutch quesinesse if they bee with childe, sutch longeing,
sutch daintinesse, sutch waiwardnesse: at all times in
fare sutch finenes, in apparrel sutch costlines, in hous-
holde stuffe sutch curiousnesse: at most times so immod-
est, sutch poutinge, sutch lowringe, sutch chidinge,
sutch chafing, that to conclude with scripture, I thinke
best for man not to touche a woman.

Gentlewomen, you must understande, this Gentleman was in a great heate, and therefore you must beare
with his bolde blasphemy against your noble sexe: for
my part, I am angry with my selfe to have uttred it,
& I shall like my lisping lippes the worse for that they
have bene the instrumentes of sutch evill, neither shall
I think them savory againe, untill it shall please some
of you to season them with the sweetenesse of yours.
But yet hee himselfe was so fully confirmed in this
fayth and beleife, touching the fraylty and fraud of
women, that I thinke no torment, no not the fury of
fire could have forced him to recant his opinion. For
ever after, hee fled al occasions of womens company,
perswading himselfe, that as hee which toucheth pitch
shalbee defiled therwith, so hee that useth womens
company shalbee beeguiled therwith. And as the mouse
having escaped out of the trap, will hardly bee allured

7–9 if they bee sikly . . . sutch quesinesse *om. EF*
15 man/a man *EF*

againe with the intising bayt, or as the Hauke having
been once canvassed in the nets, wil make it daungerous
to strike againe at the stale: so hee having beene caught
in the snares of crafty counterfaytinge, and now having
unwound him selfe thereout, and won the fieldes of
freedome, avoyded all occasions which might bringe
him eftsoones into bondage. But man purposeth, and
God disposeth, men determine, but the destinies doo:
for what shalbe, shalbe: no pollicy may prevent ye
power of the heavens, no dooinges of men can undoe the   10
destinies. For hee was so far of from beeing able to keepe
him self from beeinge in love with women, that hee
fell in love with a senceles thing, a stoane, an Image,
(a just punnishment for his rash rayling against the
florishinge feminine sexe [)]. For continuing (as I said
before) his solitarily [sic] life, seperated from ye society
of women, he consumed ye most part of his time in
carving & graving Images, & amongest all other his
workes, he made out of Marble ye likenesse of a proper
wench (as by like) notwithstanding ye new religion he   20
was entred into, having most fancy to a feminine forme,
& having fashioned and finished it in the finest maner,
he fel to looking on it: and as love first entreth in at
the eyes, and from thence discendeth to the hart, so
hee looked so longe theron, that at length hee fel in
love with it, yea he was so wonderfully bewitched with
it, that hee fell to imbrasing, kissinge, and dallyinge
with it. A monstrous miracle no doubt, and rather to
be wondred at then credited: And yet I have heard of
some that have beene so possest with melancholy pas-   30
sions, that they have thought themselves to bee made
of glasse, and if they had gone in any streete, they
would not come neere any wall or house, for feare of

7 into/in EF

breaking them selves: and so it may bee that this *Pigmalion* thought him selfe some stoane, and knowinge that like agree best with their like, hee thought he could make no better a match, then to match him self to a stone. Or it may bee hee was one of those, whom after the generall floud (as *Ovid* reporteth) *Ducalion* & his wife *Pirraha* made by casting stoanes at their backes: and then no mervaile though hee beare mervaylous affection to stones, beeing made of stoanes. Or whether his religion were to love images, I know not: neither is it any more to be mervayled at in him, then in an infinite number yt live at this day, which love images right well, & verely perswade themselves yt images have power to pray for them, & help them to heaven. Or whether it proceeded of this, that every one is lightly in love with that which is his owne, I knowe not: but this I read reported of him, that when neither by the feelinge of his sences, neither by the force of reason, neither by the assistance of time, neither by any other meane hee could rid his tender heart of this stoany love, hee tooke his image and layd it in his bed, as if it had bene his birde [*sic*—wife and bride *B–F*], which done, hee went to the temple of *Venus*, & there sendinge up sighes for sacrifices, and uttering his passions in steed of prayers, rufully repentinge his former rebellion against the majesty of the Goddesse *Venus*, for that hee had blasphemed wickedly against women, and neglected the lawes and lore of love, and sought to lodge himselfe in liberty, hee humbly requested her now to rue his ruthles case, and hee would remaine her thrall all the dayes of his life after. And that if it seemed good to her godhead to give him a wife, that shee might bee (hee durst not say his image) but like unto his

7 Pirraha/Pirrha *DE*, Pyrha *F*   20 of/from *CDEF*

image. *Venus* very wel knowing what he ment by this request, remembring also the wrong which *Penthea* beefore had profred him, for that hee loved her loyally the space of three or foure yeres with out any rewarde, except it were double dissembling for his singuler affection, & therfore had some reason to rage against women as he did, she thought her self bound in conscience to cure his calamity, and seeinge how Idolatrously hee was addicted to his Image, shee put life into it, and made it a perfect woman. The like miracles wee have had many wrought within these fewe yeres, when images have beene made to bow their heads, to holde out their handes, to weepe, to speake, &c. But to *Pigmalion*, who having done his devotions, returned to his lodging, and there according to custome fell to kissing his Image, which seemed unto him to blush thereat, and taking better taste of her lips, they began to waxe very soft and sweete, and entringe into deeper daliaunce with her, shee bad him leave for shame, and was presently turned to a perfecte proper maide. Which hee seeinge, magnified the might and power of *Venus*, joyfully tooke this maide unto his wife. And so they lived together long time in great joy and felicitie.

You have heard (Gentlewomen) what broad blasphemie ye ficklenes of *Penthea* caused unworthily to be blown forth against you all: wherefore to avoide the like, I am to admonish you that you prefer not new fangle freindes beefore olde faythfull freindes: that you neither lightly leave the one, neither lightly love the other, for it is great lightnesse to doe either the one or the other. And beesides the incurring of the blot of inconstancy and wavering, it is very perilous for you to commit your selves & your secrets to those, of whose trustines you have made no trial. For all is not golde

which glistereth, counterfayte coine sheweth more
goodly then the good: and it is most easy to deceive
under the name of a freind. The common saying is, the
chaunge is seldome made for the better, and your owne
sayinge is, that of your servauntes you had rather keepe
those whom you know, though with some faultes, then
take those whom you knowe not, perchaunce with moe
faultes. How mutch more then ought faythfull freindes
to bee kept and accounted of, whom you know to bee
perfectly good? They are not surely for any chance to
bee chaunged, they are not for any respect to bee
rejected, they are the only Jewels to bee joyed in, the
onely perles to bee preserved, the only pillers to bee
trusted to. Wee like a picture made in marble, better
then in waxe, bicause it will last longer: wee like the
ritch Diamonde cheifly bicause it lasteth longe, and
will not lightly lose it[s] bright hew: so likewise, you
ought to like those freindes best which last longest, &
have lived longest with you. For you must consider,
true freinds are not like new garments, which will be
the worse for wearing: they are rather like the stoane
of *Scilicia*, which the more it is beaten the harder it is:
or like spices, which the more they are pounded, the
sweeter they are, or like many wines, whiche the older
they are the better they are. But to leave true friendship, and come to trifling friendship, consisting in
pleasant privie practises, I would wish those women
which deale that way (although they bee no sheepe of
my flocke, yet for their sexe sake, I wish them wel) I
would, I say, advise them to use wary heed in ridding
away those freinds they are weary of. It is a daungerous
peece of worke, and importeth as mutch as their good

1 which/that *CDEF*   22 Scilicia/Scilitia *BCD*
24 sweeter/lesse sweeter *EF*   30 use wary/take *CDEF*

name commeth to, for if they shall, without discretion and great cause, disclaime a mans freindship, it is the next way (onlesse his government of himselfe bee very great) to make him proclayme what freindship hee hath had of them in times past. This was it whiche made *Faustine* so famous as shee was: this is it which blazed the bruite of *Blanch maria* thorowe out the world. And surely I know not well what counsayle to give in this case, it is a matter of harde digestion to a man to see her become straunge to him, who was wonte to bee   10 most familier with him, to have her his enemy, who was wont to be his freind. Therfore I would advise them to sticke to their old freindes still, if they cannot frame their fickle nature to sutch firmenes, the best way is, by litle and litle to estraunge them selves from their freindes, to pretend some ernest or honest cause, to professe that never any other shall possesse that place with the*m*, [and *B–F*] to promise that in hart they wilbe theirs during life.

4 what/that *EF*
6 is/was *EF*   7 Blanch maria/Blanca Maris *EF*
10 to him/unto him *EF*
10–11 who was wonte . . . his enemy *om. EF*
12–14 *CDE read* advise them, as they have wylyly caught them, waryly to cast them of. For the best waye is
17 that place/lyke friendship *CDEF*

l

Alexius.

[ALEXIUS given ernestly to follow the studie of his booke, and the knowledge of the liberall Sciences, is diligently exhorted by his father to take
a wife, whereunto though unwillinge, hee applyeth himselfe, and is
matched with sutch a one that in respect of her good graces, he ut-
tereth great commendation of woman kinde. But shortly after, fallinge
into lothinge of that which beefore hee most loved, hee repenteth himselfe of his bargaine, and forsaking both house, & wife, and all worldly
pleasures, consumeth the remainder of his life in Pilgrimage, and
traveile.]

10

Cicero was of this opinion, that the greatest doubt
which doth most deepely distresse a younge man, is to
determine with himselfe, what life in this life it bee
best to enter into: wherein no doubt hee had reason,
for beesides the diversitie of lives which are to bee
chosen, there is sutch a confused *Chaos* of conceits in
yong mens heads, that our wits are confounded with
them, [and *B–F*] are lost as it were in a *Labyrinth*, not
findinge any way out: so that if we chaunce to enter
20   into this deliberation, we are assone in one vaine, as
soone in another, and so many vaines so many vanities:
if vertue draweth us one way, vice driveth us another
way: if profite perswade one way, pleasure provoketh
us another way: if wit way one way, will wresteth
another way: if friends counsel one way, fancy forceth
us another way: yea some lyke *Horace* his guestes are
so daintily disposed, that no lyfe at al wil like them.
Kingdomes (they say) are but cares, in honour is envie,

no majestie in meane estate, penury in povertie, in single lyfe solitarinesse, in marriage troubles, and touching studies and faculties, divinitie is contemptuous, Phisick filthy, law laboursome, touchinge other trades of life, marchandise is but base, the country life is clownish, warfare is dangerous, in travaile is perrill, livinge at home is obscure, yea what life so ever it bee they count it lothsome: so that it is hard for them to resolve upon any one, who can frame them selves to fancy none. But for sutch as covet to bee of the corporation of the common wealth, and to bee profitable members thereof, I thinke these two points in this choice of our life chiefly to be considered. First, that we apply ourselves to that life wherto by nature we are chiefely inclined, for it is not possible well to goe forward in any thing, *Invita Minerva*, nature not consenting therto. Then, not so to addict our selves to any one lyfe, but that wee may adopt our selves to another, if neede shall require. For no man is so surely setled in any estate, but that fortune may frame alteration: like as no ship sayleth so directly to the wisshed haven, but that some contrary winde may convert her course against the wrackfull rocks. Which may bee justified by the example of a younge Gentleman named *Alexius*, who beeing setled in a stedfast state of lyfe, as was to bee thought, yet was hee driven to change, and change againe. For first beeing desirous to passe the pilgrimage of this short life in pleasure, hee avoyded (so neere as hee could) al worldly vanities, reposing his chiefe pleasure in serching out the sacred skill of learned books, so that studie was his only pleasure in prosperitie, his onely solace in adversitie, his only exercise beeing freshe, his only refreshing beeing wery, his only sport, his only play. And notwithstanding hee had good skill in hauking, huntinge, diceing, carding, with sutch lyke, and somtime for recreation sake used them, yet hee counted all those pastimes a paine, in the respect of the pleasure whiche study procured hym. His Father seeinge him setled in this solitary life, seemed to mislyke thereof, and disswaded hym from it, in this sorte.

I see, sonne, there is nothinge so good, but by il using may bee made naught, and true, that sayinge is, that every excesse is turned into vice. I meane your study, whiche of it selfe is lawdable, yet the immoderate use therof makeeth it rather to bee reprehended, then commended: and while you seeke your owne carelesse securitie, you neglect your countries commoditie, and live (lyke a drone by the hony) of other mens handes, and by the sweete of other mens swet. For you must know, al the praise of vertue consisteth in doing, from the which to be withdrawn with the doubt of daunger or trouble, is a signe of one which preferreth his owne private safetie, beefore the common societie. And yet he yᵗ wil not indevour to defend other[s], is commonly left destitute of help himselfe. What wonne *Archimedes* by his earnest study, who while *Marcellus* woonne his citie *Syracusis*, was so busily drawing figures of Geometry in the ground, that he knew not the citie was taken, and *Marcellus* sendinge for him to come unto him, hee answered hee woulde not come, untill hee had finished his figures, wherupon the messenger in a great rage finished his life: An ende fit for all sutch, who to satisfie their owne mindes, wyll not satisfie their duties to their rulers, Country and common wealth. Therefore I thinke good, you leave this labourlesse life, and to enter into the worlde, and take a wife, whereby you may beecome a profitable and fruitfull member of your country.

3 the *om. CDEF*   29–30 their rulers/the rulers *EF*

You knowe the law maker *Lycurgus* valued in a maner
with manslears, those which would of set purpose abide
barren, saying, that hee did in a maner deprive a man
of lyfe, which did not helpe to bringe a man into this
life, when hee might: and the difference is litle, beetweene doynge an injury, and sufferinge an injurie to
bee done, when one may prohibite it. You know also
the reproche which he suffered that ancient unmaried
captaine *Dercillidas* to receive, who passing by a yonge
princocks, had no reverence done unto him (whiche   10
amongst the *Lacedemonians* was the greatest dishonour
that might be) the Captaine complayning hereof, the
young man answered him, why sir, you have got none
which may do reverence to mee when I come to age,
and therefore it is no reason you receive that honour
at my handes: which answere *Lycurgus* allowed of,
thinkinge none worse Citizens then sutch as woulde not
marry. Wherefore if you will avoyde the like inconvenience, and frame your selfe to enter into that honorable state, I will depart with sutch part of my living   20
unto you, that you shalbe able to live in good credit
and countenance in your cuntry, and have cause to think
your life as pleasaunt as this you now leade.

Alexius havinge diligently given eare to his fathers
wordes, dutifully made answere in this sort.

Sir, if it please you, I am of this opinion, that a good
thinge, can not bee to mutch used, and that the more
common it is, the more commendable it is, neither is
it possible to seeke learning to mutch, whereof there
was never any man yet but had to litle: and I thinke   30
it shame to cease from seeking, when the thinge sought,
is the onely thing worthy to bee thought. For what
toyle can seeme tedious to finde the way to wit, and

9 Dercillidas/Darcillidas *CDEF*   32 thought/sought *BCDEF*

path to prudency, the line of life and vaine of vertue?
And for the commodity of my country, I doubt not,
but you know, that the studious stand the common
wealth in as great steed, as the industrious otherwise.
Yea who first brought men within the compasse of a
common wealth but only the learned? Who brought
them from savagenes to civilnes, was it not the learned?
Who reduced them from rage to reason, was it not the
learned? Who brought them into the society of a cittie,
who prescribed them lawes, who taught them religion,
who invented mariage it selfe, which you are so ernest
to have mee enter into, was it not the learned? Yes no
doubt, learning is the life of the common wealth, the
maker and mayntainer of it. I must confes that those
which use trades of travaile in the common wealth, doe
mutch good to the common wealth, but I must say,
the learned doe more good. I must confesse that souldiours often defend the common wealth: but I must say
that lerning must lead them, otherwise they will sooner
offend it, then defend it. I must confesse that souldiours
often win wealth to their country: but I must say that
Senatours must keepe it, and the cunning to keepe, is
no lesse commendable then the courage to get, and
courage god knoweth is litle worth abroade, unlesse
there bee good counsayle at home. For what worthy
exploytes did any captaine ever atchive abroad, but by
the advise of counsaylors at home? As the valiant victory which *Themistocles* had over *Salamis*, was atchived
by the counsayle of the *Senate* which *Solon* had constituted. The overthrow of *Carthage* was wrought by
the advise of *Cato* a counsailour. The distruction of
Troy was wrought not by lusty prowesse, but by learned
pollicie. The takinge of *Babilon* by *Darius*, was not

27 of/of yᵉ *E*, of the *F*

done by the strength of his army, but by the skilfull subtelty of his servaunt *Zopyrus*. And so almost in all notable victories, pollicy prevayleth above power. Which was the cause that *Agamemnon* in yᵉ siege of *Troy*, wished rather for ten sutch as *Nestor* (who was a grave counsaylour) then for ten sutch as *Ajax* (who was a valiant captayne): that *Trajanus* yᵉ Emperour, when hee went into the camp, ever had *Dion* the Philosopher with him in his owne chariote: that *Alexander* never went into the feelde without the philosopher *Calisthenes* with him: *Zerxes* never without *Damarathus*: that *Alexander* had evermore *Homer* his *Iliades* lyinge under his beds head: that *Julius Caesar* studyed in the night, and set downe in writinge, yᵗ which hee did in the day: that *Epaminondas*, *Mithridates*, *Themistocles*, *Adrian*, *Marcus Antonius*, *Marcus Aurelius*, *Alcibiades*, *Scipio*, *Brutus*, *Anniball*, *Alphonsus*, *Solomon*, *David*, with infinite other[s], who were couragious Capitans and Kinges, gave themselves most earnestly to study and learninge. For they very well knewe hee could not bee a perfect captaine, which was not perfectly seene in al sciences and learning. In *Grammer*, to attayn to the lattin tounge, and by it to the knowledge of other tounges, wherby hee may not bee deafe and dum amongst those with whome hee shall have to deale in warre. In *Rethoricke*, cherefully to perswade his souldiours to such enterprises as hee would have them attempt. In *Logike*, probably to reason with his souldiours in doubtfull matters, which are to be discussed amongst them. In *Arithmetick* to number his souldiours, to devide them into bands, as best may serve for the battell. In *Geometrie*, to measure the ground, to judge of the distance

10

20

30

11 Zerxes/Xerxes *EF*   17 Anniball/Annibal *BCD*
27 attempt/to attempt *DEF*

of places, wherby hee may cast his trenches, raise his
bulwarks, & place his ordinance and munition to most
advantage. In *Astronomy*, to know the course of the
starres, the place of the *Poles*, the sight of the *Zones*,
and sutch like, wherby hee may bee able to direct his
army by night (either on sea or land) into what coastes
hee shall have occasion. In *Musicke*, to recreat himselfe
beeing weary, to sing Psalmes [and *B–F*] prayses to God
for the victory. And as these seven liberal sciences are
shewed to be most necessary for a captaine: so is ther
no art or knowledge but ought to be knowen unto him.
Philosophy, to take away ye terror of death, to ease ye
evil of greif, to coole the heate of hate, to bridle rage
with reson, to turne rashnes to stayednes, as it did in
Fabius ye noble captayn *qui cunctando restituit rem*: to
mortify ye desires of ye flesh, as it did in *Alexa[nder]*
towards ye wife & daughters of *Darius*: to increase
abstinency, as it did in ye same *Alexa[nder]* who having
been three or foure daies without foode, would eate
nothinge him selfe till all his souldiours were satisfied:
to make pacient in paine as it made *Marius* abide
martiring without binding: to teach to indure hardnesse,
as it made *Agesilaus* to goe almost naked in the middest
of winter, that his souldiours by his example might doe
the like: to teach to set litle by ritches, to di[s]pise vaine
glory, to avoyd infamy, with infinite other commodities,
wherwith philosophy doth furnish us. *Cosmography*, to
know the situation of citties and countries, to take the
oportunity of mountaines, woods, and waters. *Surgery*,
to heale his wounds. Phisick, to cure his diseases, and
keepe himself in health. Law, to Minister justice to his
souldiours, to devide the booty indiff[er]ently amongest
them, to observe inviolably the law of armes. *Divinitie*,
to dehort his souldiours from swearing, from blasphem-

ing, from drinking, from whoring, and in the houre of death from dispairing. So that counsayle, learning and knowledge ought to bee the cheife weapons and complete harnesse of a captaine, yea knowledge is the armour of proofe which neither Cannon, Hargabus, nor Pistol can peerce. And what commodity is in courage without counsayle, may be seene by many rash conflictes of many rawe captaines. And not to touch any of fresh memory, it may please you onely to call to your remembraunce one *Callicratides*, who beeinge captaine of the *Lacedemonians*, in an expedition agaynst the *Athenians*, was advised by the *Senate* not to incounter with them, but to remove his navy from them, till more convenient oportunity might bee taken: but hee thinking it would have bene some derogation to his manhood sumwhat to have retired, at al adventure ventred upon them, to his owne utter overthrow, and to the great weakning of the wealth of his common weale and country. If then learninge bee so necessary to warre (whereto many thinke it rather a hinderance, as the french nobility forsooth at this day scarce dareth deale with it, for feare of marring their martiall feates) howe needfull must wee thinke it to other partes of the common wealth? Can the Prince set forth Gods glory, and see to the realmes safety? can the nobility provide for the preservation of their prince and countries commodity? can divines truly preach the gospel? can judges duely minister justice, can lawiers defend the innocent, can Phisitions heale the sicke, yea in warre can the surgions cure the wounded without learning? Can Merchaunts safely passe the daungerous seas without skilfull Pilotes? Can they mutually trafique and bring in necessaries into the realme without skilfull interpreters? To bee short, there is nothinge done to the coun-

tries commodity, wherto there is not had the help of
skill and learning. So that learning and wit is the only
wealth of ech country, the only conquerour in warre,
the only preserver of peace. Litigiousnes [*Lytae* the
goddesse of peace *B–F*] without learninge can doe no
good, *Mars* without *Minerva* can make no good mart.
Therfore (sir) well you may restraine mee from studye,
but you shall never diswade mee from it. And wheras
you perswade mee to enter into the state of matrimony,
I can not but thinke that the great desire you have to
do me good, doth so dim your understanding, that you
perfectly know not what will doe me good, otherwise
you would not goe about to bringe mee (as they say)
out of Gods blessing into a warme sunne. For if you
knew the commodities of this life, whiche I now leade,
& considered the discommodities of that life you would
have mee to leade, I knowe you woulde never counsayle
mee to cleave to the one and leave the other. In this
sutch quiet, in that sutch care, in this sutch puritie, in
that sutch pravitie, in this sutch vertue, in that
sutch vanytie, in this sutch contentation, in that sutch
vexation, in this sutch caulmes, in that sutch stormes,
in this sutch safetie, in that sutch jeopardie, in this
sutch felicytie, in that sutch miserie, that I mutch muse
that you your selfe murmur not at the miseries in
marriage, and seeke to bee setled in the sweete solace
of single life againe.

The people called *Massagetes* livinge in mountaines
without houses, enacted this law amongst them, that
everie inhabitant should have two tunnes, or fats, in
the one should lie the husband, sonnes, and men servants, in the other the wives, daughters, and maide
servants, they never eate together but on holy daies,
and may not lawfully lie together, but only once a

weeke. *Pompeius* having occasion to travell that way, demaunded of them, why they lived in y^t seperated sort? They answered him, The gods had geven them but short time to live on the earth, which they ment to spend quietly, which beeinge together with their wives, they saide they could never doe. And *Licurgus* himself, whom you alleage in commendation of marriage, was almost of the *Massagetes* minde, for hee willed men not to lie continually with their wives, but to use their company seldome and by stealth, whereby you may see   10 that marriage is a daungerous thinge, and daintely to be dealt with all, and that hee had neede to bee armed with more yeeres then I am, that shall venter uppon it. For my part, if you bee so content, I meane to continue as I am, and not to chaunge for the worse, and with *Glaucus* to give golden harnesse for *Diomedes* his brasen, or a precious stoane for a barley corne with *Æsops* cocke. His Father seeing how hee was bent, willed him to do as hee woulde, and halfe angrye, lefte him to his owne lykinge.   20

I have hytherto (Gentlewomen) done you some wronge in framinge my talke to the condition and capacitie of these Gentlemen, who, as you hard at dinner, helde so hotly that learning was not necessarie for a captaine, now I will perfourme my promise to you, and I will not onely pay you the principall, but beecause you have so quietly forborne your due so longe, you shal heare I wil yeelde you some interest besides.

May it please you then to knowe, that *Alexius* seeinge howe desirous his Father was to have him marrie,   30 thought it the part of an obedient child, to apply himself to the plesure of his parents, and to enter into that

6 Licurgus/Lycurgus *BCDEF*   21 hytherto/hereto *E*
32 that/the *EF*

trade of lyfe wherein his father beefore him had troden: whereupon hee somwhat intermitted his earnest study, and beegan to peruse those bookes, which treated but of litle learning, & in steed of schooles, frequented those places where at the first being a fresh man for the principles of his science, hee was taught with lookes, not with letters, and with the eyes, not with the mouth: well in short space it fortuned out of his good instructors, by lendinge him a looke to learne hym sutch a lesson (as best wits are soonest caught by *Cupid*) that hee could not bee quiet till he had gotten out alone by himself perfectly to con it: where he sayde it without booke in this sort.

I perceive now that saying is true, that the greatest clarks are not the wisest men, and that in respect of experience, learning is litle to bee accounted of. For I see the foolishnesse of my Father (if it were possible there shoulde be any in him) to bee far better then all my wisdome and learning. He only knoweth what is profitable, what is pleasant for mee. Hee knoweth and hee tolde mee, but I would not then beeleeve hym, that the marryed lyfe is the only life. Wel, now I se it to be so indeede. Good god what good did those loving looks only, which that lovely wench cast uppon me, doe mee? what then may I judge of the rest, if only lookes like mee so well? no never any woorke of other mens, or invention of mine owne, never any History, Commedie, Oration, or Verse, have procured mee halfe the pleasure, as this beautiful booke hath. Therfore now farewell *Minerva*, welcome *Venus*, farewell *Aristotle*, welcome *Ovid*, farewel *Muses*, welcome maydens, farewel learning, welcome Ladies. But what shall I thus neglect Gods commaundement, wisdomes lore, my fathers hestes, and

1 troden/traded *BCDEF*   18 all *om. EF*   26 any/any other *EF*

give my selfe over to fonde and foolish love? Why, as
though God allowed not of mariage, as though *Pallas*
her selfe were not subject to love, as though my father
him selfe did not in a manner force mee hereto? Yes I
wil evidently let this my goddesse understand my goodwil, I wil humbly crave her love agayn, I will make my
father privy to my practise, I will cause al yᵉ freinds I
have to further the mariage betweene us.

Now this younge *Punee* havinge perfectly learned his
first lesson, and liking it very wel, was taken forth   10
another lesson, hee was taught now forsooth his partes
of speeche, hee was driven to speake for himselfe, to
preferre many pitifull prayers, to feigne, to flatter, to
vow, to promise, to swere, to make verses, to write
letters, and to use all meanes to prove his owne love,
and to purchase hers, and this lecture also liked him wel
inough, for that in yᵗ hee was otherwise a good scholer,
& indued *with* a good wit, hee was well able every way
to discharge it, & besid[e]s that the gentlewoman
seemed at length almost willinge to bee woonne to his   20
wil. Then he proceeded further in his learning, and came
to [his *B–F*] numbers, hee was driven to number and
tell out his coyne, and to buie rings, tablets, chaines,
and sutch like, to sende to his misteris, as tokens of true
love, to linke liking, and to binde fast the bargaine.
After this, hee attained to the knowledge of the articles,
for now articles must bee drawen of their agreement,
her joynter must bee appoynted, all the conveiances
[*sic*] concerning this contract are concluded. This lesson
neither disliked hym, for that his father was able every   30
way to performe it. Immediately upon this, the mariage
day was appointed, and he must needs take foorth one

9 Punee/Punie *EF*   31ff. Immediately upon this . . . a thousand times
om. BCDEF, which read simply And thus the mariage is consumated.

lesson more, to bee fully instructed, and nowe forsooth hee is come to the conjunction of cases, and joyninge of genders together. And this was the lesson in deede that liked him, this hee thought ye lesson of al lesson[s], ye only lesson which led to perfect learning, ye only instruction which truly taught right construction, the onely lesson of lyfe, the only pathway to Paradise. This lesson hee soone had learned, and yet thought with himself that hee never had sufficiently learned it, which made him in short time make repetition of it a thousand times. And for recreation after his study, his exercise alwayes was either to triumph of his owne happinesse, either to trifle and talke with his misteris, either in verse curiously to commende her, or els in prose lively to paint foorth the praise of women, and amongst many other his frantick fancies, hee presented in writing to his wife, this mutch in effect.

As it somewhat easeth the afflicted to utter their annoy, so no doubt, it greatly increaseth our happinesse to expresse our joy. And I am perswaded that al the delightfull things we see, all the joyfull things we heare, and all the pleasaunt thinges we feele, woulde procure us litle pleasure, if we had no meanes to manifest them, or freinds to impart them to. Therefore I will unfolde my joyes to my joy, my pleasures to my *Peragon*, my mirth to my mistris. For who ever swamme in sutch seas of delight? who ever bathed in more perfect blis? for first, what could I have wished more of God then to have mine owne Father the author, the beeginner, the perswader, the practiser, the furtherer, and the finisher of my felicitie? to impart unto mee his counsayle, to depart with his coyne, to geve mee his goods, to leave me his lands, & to do more for me then I had ether reason to

11 And/¶Now *BCDEF*   25 Peragon/Paragon *BCDEF*

require, or so mutch as durst to desire? O Father, thou
only knowest how to blesse thy children? then what
more happines could happen unto me then to have a
wife, whose countenance coveteth only to content mee,
whose lookes are framed only to my lykinge, whose
wordes are only wrested to my wyll, whose deedes are
only directed to my delight, whose beautie then the sun
beames is more bright, whose bounty, wit and vertue
is more rare then to be comprehended in a mortal wight,
who in shape *Venus*, in wit passeth *Pallas* her selfe, who   10
is the only starre which giveth right light, who is the
only worship of the worlde, the only honour of her age,
the only *Phœnix* of the earth, whose government is
sutch, that she can guide her selfe wisely in all companies, in all causes, whose discretion is sutch, that shee
can applie herselfe fitly to all times, to all places, to all
persons, who loveth mee so loyally, that I cannot but
like it, who honoureth mee so dutifully, that I cannot
looke for more, who at all times entertaineth mee so
curteously, that I cannot but bee content with it, who   20
dayly filleth my eares with sutch sugred words, that
they can not but delight mee, who at borde feedeth mee
so daintily that a prince would bee pleased with it, who
at bed feasteth mee so delicately that *Cupid* him selfe
would bee glad of it? O Misteris, thou only knowest
how to make thy husband happy. But what mervayle
is it to see a good tree bring forth good fruite? what
wonder is it to see one woman good, when there are
none ill? And how is it possible [that *B–F*] there should
bee any ill, when yᵉ matter wherof they are made, &   30
causes wherof they come are right good? For first they

11 right/true *CDEF*   23 pleased with it/glad of it *EF*
24 at bed *om. BCD*   feasteth/comforteth *EF*   delicately/cheerfully *EF*
24 Cupid him selfe/the goddes themselves *BCDEF*   31 causes/the causes *EF*

are made of the purified mettall of man, wheras man was made of yᵉ grosse earth: And as in stils out of herbs is gotten pure water: so out of man was gotten yᵉ pure mettall of women, as may bee plainly perceived by the finenesse of their fourme, by the softnesse of their flesh, by the clerenesse of their colour & sutch like. Then for the constitution of their bodies, they are most commonly colde, by reason wherof they are most patient, modest, milde, and mercifull, most constant without lightnesse, most continent without leudnesse, neither offende, either in excesse of meate, either in fleshly heate, so often as men of firy and hot complexions doe. Besides that, the purity of their bodies may bee perceived by this, that no corruption comminge by the grosenesse of meat or otherwise, can continue long within them, but that they have continually evacuation of all yll humours: sutch force hath that which is fine, to expel that which is filthy. And as their bodies are most perfecte, so also their soules are most pure. For wheras men receive from *Adam* origynall sinne, women are altogether voide of that infection, which may be partly conjectured by the excellency of many of their complexions, & cleerenes of their skins: so that no man almost would think yᵗ there could lurke any lothsomnes to be misliked of, under so cumly a covert as their faire faces are, but only they yᵗ have proved the contrarie. But notwithstanding this perfection wherwith they are indued, yet (as things most excellent are ever most envied) their [there *B–F*] want not those which want so mutch governmente, that they will not sticke ernestly to inveigh against the noble feminine sexe, and amongest

13–18 Besides that . . . which is filthy *om. BCDEF*
21 altogether/altogether (if I be not deceived) *BCDEF*
21–26 which may be . . . the contrarie *om. BCDEF*   28 as/al *DEF*

the rest (as who is so bold as blind bayard.) *Mantuan* like a mad man, most rudely and rashly raveth and rayleth against them. But his wordes are so voyde of wit, and his railing so without reason, that if hee were alive, I thinke him rather with tormentes to bee confounded, then with argumentes to bee confuted. Before him *Aristotle*, as an Asse sotted with over mutch studdy maketh a great speake, sayinge: women are monsters in nature, and he alleageth a profound reason to prove it, for that nature, forsooth, always intendeth to bringe 10 forth that which is most perfect, and therfore would bring forth only men if shee might. A pythy argumente, hee reasoneth as though it were graunted him, that men were more perfecte then women, which with all his philosophy, hee shall never bee able to prove. And if hee make this reason, that the male is ever more perfect then the female, nature her selfe will quickly confute him, who in most of her creatures hath made the female far more perfect then the male. And not to use many instances, what need wee goe any farther then 20 consider the kinde of Hawkes, where wee shall see the Goshauke far better then the Tossell, the Gerfaulcon then the Gerkin, the Lanar then the Lanaret, the Sparehauke then the Musket, and so of all the rest. But *Aristotle* can make a better reason, for that women by mutuall conjunctions receive their perfection from men, a reason truely without all reason. What woman was ever more perfecte then the virgin Mary, who never knew man? Then the *Romaine* vestall virgins? Then our vowed virgins, who continued the whole course of their 30 life without the company of men? But *Ceny* forsooth beeinge a mayd desired to bee made a man. But will you know the cause? Not for that shee coveted to bee of the kinde of man, but that shee might bee free from

the filthinesse whiche men did force her to (for before
shee had bene ravished by *Neptune*) like as yᵉ litle
chicke being caught by the kyte, would wish with all
his heart hee were a Kite, and yet the kind of Kites is not
to be thought better then of the chicken. But to leave
Aristotle his railyng reasons, and to reason indifferently
of the matter, what one perfection any way are men
indued withall, that women want? Do men (I say)
either in natural wit, either in politike government,
either in valiant courage, either in skill and learnyng,
either in vertue and livyng, any thyng excell them?
And first for wit, *Aristotle* himselfe proveth them to
bee more apt in wit, for that they are more soft in
fleshe, and we our selves have a common sayinge
amongst us, that women are never without an excuse,
which is a sure signe of a most sharpe and readie wit.
And if I were driven to alledge examples of witty women,
I coulde recite whole countries, to wit, *Flaunders*,
Holland, *Zeland*, and most of the lowe countries, where
the women wittily deale in al thinges, discreetly order
their housholds, courteously entertayne straungers, and
wisely wield most waightie affayres, wheras the men
deale only with drinke, and like drunken doltes lie under
the bourde. In *Fraunce* also, the Gentlewomen generally
are more wittie in words, and eloquent in talke then
the men. The like no doubt may bee truly reported of
divers other nations. Then for politik government, is it
likely that they, who can governe them selves and their
affections discreetely, their families and housholdes
orderly, are to seeke in the polytike goverment of publike matters? For (no doubt) it is far more easy to see
wittily into other mens affaires then into our owne:
and *Solon* sayth, that they only are fit to governe

3 wish *om. CDEF*   5 of the/of *BCD*, the *EF*   20 in/with *EF*

other[s], who can well guide them selves, neither is the difference so great betweene a private family and publike society, but that they which can governe the one, may wyeld the other. Againe, seeinge in matters of love (which blinde the wisest men that are) women can deale so politikely, that though they themselves beare great affection to a man, yet they will so handle the matter that they shall humbly make sute unto them, and ernestly desire them to it, which thei of them selves most ernestly desire, seeinge in privy stealthes they can   10
practise so politikely y^t their husbands, though never so wary, shal never be ware of it, but rather the more they are deceived, doate ye more of them. Is it to be thought they are to learne of men, or any way inferiour to them, in the convaigh of ordinary accidents, and matters of common moment? But women are not admitted to the administration of the common wealth: but what forsooth is the cause? For sooth the malicious spite of men: and I may saye it to my self, it standeth us upon so to do, for if they should be allowed to execute publike   20
offices, whereby their discreet and good government might be generally known, it were greatly to bee feared that wee should be set to the clout and kitchin another while, and they placed in those offices, whiche wee now, not so worthy of them, wrongfully usurpe. And yet to the intent all sutch bright lights should not bee put under a bushell, it hath pleased god to set some of them on the hils of high estate, to give light of life and good government to the whole world: as namely the wife of Æneas, named *Lavinia*, after his death governed the   30
most turbulent state of *Italy*, with sutch policy and wisdome, that though the title of her husband to the

3 that *om. EF*   7 a man/men *EF*
9 it/that *BCDEF*   19 it *om. BCDEF*

kingdom were very tickle, beeinge a *Trojan* & straunger, though her neighbours on every side were given to spoylyng, incroching, oppressyng, and usurpynge, yet shee kept her people in peace, and her kingdome quiet, untill her sonne *Ascanius* came to ripe yeeres, & then safely set him in the regall seate and royall dignity of his father. As *Debora* for her wit and policy was appointed judge over the Israelits, by whose counsayle and courage that couragious captayne & capital enemy to the Israelits, named *Sysara* was subdued. [I could alleage most fruitfull examples of most freshe and famous memorie, of the noble government of women, if it were lawfull, *ludere cum sanctis. B–F*] But what should I rehearse examples of the politique government of women, whereas lawes (the only ground of all good government) were first invented and made by *Ceres*, a woman?

Therfore to the third point, which is valiaunt courage: wherin we our selves confesse them to be nothing inferriour unto us, in that wee say women are alwayes desirous of soveraintie, which evidently argueth a noble and haughty minde. Beesides that, howe mutch weaker their bodies are then mens, so mutch the more strength and vertue is contained in their mindes. For it is the justice of God commonly, to supply the debilitie of the body, with the might of the minde. Againe, how mutch shorter lyved are they then men, according to *Aristotle* his opinion, so mutch the more vertue of body and minde they are endued withall. Like as by dayly experience, wee see that those children which are destined to death in the prime time of their lyfe, are farre more wittie, discreete, & perfect every way, then those who have longe time graunted them to live on earth.

31 time *om. BCDEF*   their *om. DEF*

Lastly, if particularyties might prove a generality, what man was ever more couragious then *Semiramis*, who in the habite & apparell of a man governed yͤ *Assirians*, most couragiously? then *Tomiris*, who slue the mighty Kinge *Cyrus* most valiently? then the wives of the citie of *Scio*, who repulsed their enimies most reprochefully? with infinite other[s], who in stoutnes of stomack, and couragiousnes of minde, have ben equall to any man, that ever had any praise for his prowes and vertue. The fourth poynt is learninge, which to bee proper as it were   10 to women may bee proved by this, yͭ the *Muses* the authors of all lerning were wome*n*. It may be said that the people called the *Latines* lent us mutch learninge, but it must bee saide that a woman named *Nicostrata* first taught them their letters. It may be said that *Athens* hath bene the author of many arts, but it must be sayd yͭ *Aspasia* instructed *Pericles* the Duke thereof in learning. *Solomon* was most wise and learned, yet *Saba* was able to dispute with him. *Zenobia* had learned sonnes, but shee her selfe taught them. So that it is   20 evident that women are rather the author[s] of learninge, then any way inferiour to men in learning. The last poynt is vertuous life. Alas it greeveth mee to thinke how far we come behinde in this comparison. How straunge is it to heare a woman to bee a swearer, a stealer, a murtherer, a traytor, a rebel, an extorcioner, a perjurer, a cosener, or any sutch like? To our shame I speake it, we wallow in those wickednesses. How hard againe is it to finde a man of co*n*tinent co*n*versation, of modest manners, of milde minde, of gentle disposi-   30 tion, of curteous inclinatio*n*, of pitifull hart? To their praise I speake it, women abound in those vertues. So that to speake indifferently, beetweene the life of men

28 those wickednesses/wickednesse *EF*

and women, is as mutch difference as beetweene light
and darknesse, beetween vertue and vice, beetweene
God and the divell. Therfore, seeing women excell men
in perfection of body & soule, in wit and government,
in courage, in learning, in life & conversation, what
merveile is it if my misteris make mee happie? what
wonder is it if she winne mee to her wil? what meede
do I deserve, if I serve her all the daies of my life? For
duty no doubte is due unto her, and I thinke my service
not sufficient to shew the goodwil which I am bounde to
beare her.

You have harde (Gentlewomen) what praise *Alexius*
for his misteris sake hath bestowed uppon you all,
whiche I doubt wil drive you into so good an opinion
of your selves, that you will thinke so meane a man as
my selfe not worthy of your company: but I would wish
you to take heede, for in so doyng you might shew your
selves to want that wit and curtesie whiche *Alexius*
hath attributed unto you, and if you proove him false
in one poynte, it is as likely he hath lyed in all the rest.
But to speake my fancie freely of the praise which hee
hath geven you, though some particuler examples bee
so manifestly true, that all the world doth acknowledge
them, yet his general reasons are altogether sophisticall
and full of fallacies, set forth without any lively colour,
only with fayning & painting: and the fine Marble you
know needeth no painting, that is needfull only for
ragged walles. I meane not that hee ment women were
ragged walles, and therfore painted them out in sutch
sort, but surely the sequele of his dooings was sutch,
that it evidently appeared hee thought not so well of
women in deede as hee set foorth in wordes. For having
(as I sayd beefore) often saide his lesson of the con-

32ff. For having . . . no end in it *om. BCDEF*

junction of cases & genders together upon the booke, and either seeing it impossible to attaine it without the booke, either beeinge wery with the often repetition of it, either seing there was no end in it. [For now forsooth he is desirous to be further learned, and to take foorth a new lesson, he leaveth his former lessons with despayre, and proceedeth to declensions, he beginneth now to decline, which lesson he sayth to him selfe, in this sort. *B–F*]

Good God I see there is satietie of all thinges, & Hony   10 it selfe, if one have to mutch of it, seemeth nothing sweete unto him. How unpleasant now seemeth the pleasure of practising with my misteris, which but even now I thought heavenly happinesse? How are my firy flames vanished to dead coales? How is my lust turned to lothsomenesse? but what shoulde be the cause of this sodaine alteration? The beauty of my misteris blazeth as brightly as ever it did, her affection towards me is as fervent as ever it was, and my flesh as apt to follow folly as ever it was. The cause is this, I perceive   20 by this pleasure of the body my minde to be molested. I see that by this vanitie vice hath vanquished vertue in mee, I se hereby my wit dulled, my understanding blinded, my memorie weakned, my sences sotted, and all my parts able to play but one part, which is pleasantly to practise with my misteris. I see hereby all exercise of vertue, al respect of religion, all care of godlinesse utterly extinguished in mee. I see pleasure the very pathway to perdition, I see women the way to wrack and ruine. Which seeinge I see, shall I wilfully   30 woorke mine owne destruction? shal I greedely devoure

5 further/farther *DEF*   7 proceedeth/proceeding *F*
13 practising/dallying *CDEF*   23 hereby/thereby *E*
26 practise/dally *CDEF*

the baite, whiche I knowe hath a hooke hidden in it to
hurt mee? shal I frequent ye pleasure, which I know wil
turne to poyson? shal I continue her company, which
wil convert to my confusion? shal I with the Dog *redire
ad vomitum*? shall I with the divell, *dessendere ad infer-
num*? shal I preferre a faire wife before a vertuous life?
my goddesse before my God? transitory pleasure, beefore eternall blisse? No, let me first seeke my beloved,
who is gon downe into his garden to the beds of his
spicerie to gather up Lilies, and then shall I know how
to love my earthly beloved as I ought to doe. First let
mee lay up for my self treasure in heaven, and then
shall I injoy true pleasure in earth. First let mee seeke
the heavenly kingdom, and then shal I abound in
earthly blisse. First let me learne to serve my Lorde
aright, and then shall I serve my Lady without any
vayne delight.

Ever after this, this Gentleman gave himself to sutch
godlynesse, that he gave over all vaine delights of the
flesh, reposing his cheifest pleasure in divine contemplations: and seeing the sight of his sweet Misteris to be
a great hinderance to his heavenly cogitations, hee
altogether separated himself from her companie, left
freindes and country, and spent the remaindour of his
life in pilgrimage & travel.

You Gentlemen may learne hereby not to doate to
mutch of wives or women, but to use them as necessary
evils, and that if you be bidden to the heavenly banquet,
you ought not to returne answer that you have married
a wife, and therfore cannot come, but rather to forsake
wife and wealth, & take up the crosse of Christ and
follow him as *Alexius* did.

You Gentlewomen may also learne hereby, not to

5 *dessendere/discendere* BCDEF

repose any permanent pleasure in practising with your husbands, but only to use their companie as a solace, to sweeten yᵉ sowernesse of this life withal, and to thinke that sutch supersticious love towards your husbands, doth withdraw you from the true love which you ought to beare towards god. But I could preache better to you in a more pleasant matter, I wil leave this text to maister parson, who while he is unmaried I warrant you will disswade you so earnestly from sutch idolatrous doting on your husbands, that hee will not sticke to tell you   10 beesides [Scripture *B–F*] that you ought to have no respect of persons, but to love an other man or him selfe so well as your husbandes.

FINIS.

Printed at London, by R.W.

1 practising/dallying *CDEF*
7–8 maister parson/some odde mast person *BCD*, some odde mast Parson *EF*
FINIS *wanting in B*
Colophon same in BCD, wanting in EF

Notes

In the Notes which follow I hope to have suggested, with the aid of many reference works, some probable—and a few unmistakable—sources of the two hundred aphorisms, sententiae, and their like, in the *Petite Pallace*. Proverbs, of course, as Cervantes termed them, are 'short sentences drawn from long experience,' whose true origins must be sought among the nomads who furnished Adam's sons with wives. Occasionally Pettie acknowledges a debt to Aristotle or Ovid, or cites Scripture for his purpose. More generally, however, like most of his contemporaries, he starts a hare for source-hunters, whom Cowper might well have bracketed with his

> . . . *learn'd philologists, who chase*
> *A panting syllable through time and space,*
> *Start it at home, and hunt it in the dark,*
> *To Gaul, to Greece, and into Noah's ark.*

That chase, started from the thickets of any Elizabethan *omnium gatherum*, ends all too often beyond the cry of the hounds. At a time when proverbial wisdom was in the air, sitters in the sun bettered their grandsires' maxims and beldames quoted Seneca unwittingly. But with the *Petite Pallace*, as with *Euphues*, the scent frequently leads straight to Heywood's early garner of proverbs, or to the epigrams and adages of Erasmus. When these fail, the benighted annotator takes refuge behind an *et cetera* or a *confer*; but in each instance the problem remains. Such problems always remain until scholars with special focus find more cogent evidence of manifest parallels and actual pilfering. But the task, in the Augean stables of proverb lore, is endless.

The purpose of those Notes which deal with proverb lore is fourfold: to list first, whenever probable, Pettie's immediate 'source'—in Heywood, Erasmus, the Scriptures, or Latin authors; then to suggest either the apparent singularity of a given item or its wide currency, without specific citation, among the better known contemporaries in whose work it appears; thirdly, to reveal more specifically the manifest echoes, adaptations, and borrowings from Pettie in Lyly's *Euphues* and in Greene; and, finally, to list—for paroemiologists and special inquiries—references to the main channels of such investigation: by number in Tilley's *Elizabethan Proverb Lore*, and by page in Apperson's *English Proverbs and Proverbial Phrases* and Smith's (and Heseltine's) *Oxford Dictionary of English Proverbs*. Such a procedure can be but suggestive at best, never conclusive or exhaustive; and conversely, certain parallels turn up which seem worth listing, even though they betray the searcher's weariness rather than his conviction, where *cetera desunt* would better conclude the entry.

My indebtedness to the three primary source-books mentioned above is—without fussiness, I hope—everywhere apparent; and Professor Tilley's supplementary personal interest has been invaluable. Other reference books consulted include the anthologies by Bohn, Bartlett, and Burton Stevenson. Among the standard texts cited are Heywood's *Proverbs and Epigrams*, ed. Farmer; Painter's *Palace of Pleasure*, ed. Jacobs; Wilson's *Rhetorique*, ed. Mair; Guazzo's *Civile Conversation*, ed. Sullivan (Pettie's version); Lyly's *Euphues*, ed. Croll; *Tottel's Miscellany*, ed. Rollins; Marlowe's *Poems*, ed. Martin; Cunliffe's *Gascoigne*, and Grosart's *Greene*.

The Index of Proverbs, Maxims, and Sententiae combines an alphabetical arrangement by key-words (in which a certain amount of duplication is unavoidable) with a reference finding-list. An asterisk denotes that the particular item cannot be satisfactorily traced in earlier form through the usual channels; it may therefore, in style if not in content, be regarded as more or less 'original' with Pettie.

NOTES

Title-page. *comely colours.* The term, which is used in this sense as early as Chaucer, means 'Rhetorical modes or figures; ornaments of style or diction, embellishments'—*N.E.D.* Greene's *Euphues his censure to Philautus* (1587) is also 'figured forth in such comely colours.'

—, motto. *Omne tulit punctum, qui miscuit utile dulci.* Horace, *Ars Poetica,* 343. Greene used the same motto, 'occasionally from about 1584, and regularly from 1588 to 1590'—McKerrow, *Nashe,* iv.8. [It also appears written in an early hand in the margin of Wood's copy of Pettie's Guazzo (ii. 119v) against the phrase 'ioyning (if it may be) pleasure with profit.' The hand, however, is apparently not Wood's own.]

4,12. Comparisons are odious. Early French and Italian versions; *Toda comparacion es odiosa* appears twice in Cervantes. Found also in Lydgate, Fortescue, *Euphues* (52), Greene, Marlowe, etc. (Tilley, No.111; Apperson, 110; Smith, 79.)

4 and 5. '*R.B.*' By what seems more than mere coincidence the Harvard Library copy—formerly Sir Edward Sullivan's—of Pettie's Guazzo (1586 ed.) has these initials inked on the title-page. There are also scorings and sigla in the same hand throughout.

5,28. the Countess of Salisbury. Cf.27,*10* and 29,*3–4.* An allusion to the story in Painter, i.46, of the King of England's (Edward III's) courtship and marriage (origin in Froissart, through Bandello's *novella,* tr.Boaistuau).

6,1. the Duchess of Savoy. Cf.27,*17;* 29,*6;* 155,*9;* and 227,*8.* An allusion to the story in Painter, i.45, of the King of England's sister, who was saved from death after an unjust accusation, in the Duke's absence, of adultery, by Don John di Mendoza (source in Boaistuau, through Bandello's *novella,* tr. Belleforest).

—*,31. Terque quaterque beatum. Aeneid,* i.94.

7,1–2. Nunquam nimis cito est ad bonos mores via. Cf. Pub. Syrus: '*Non umquam sera est ad bonos mores via*'—cited by Greene, following 'Better late than never.' Cf. also Livy, IV.ii.11: '*Potius sero, quam numquam.*' Many early polyglot versions. (Tilley, No.377.)

—*,2–3. Qui non est hodie, cras minus aptus erit.* Ovid, *Rem. Amoris,* i.94. Cf. *Euphues,* 96, and n.7. (Tilley, No.5; Smith, 312, s.v. *never put off,* cites Pettie.)

—*,4–5. Principiis obsta, sero medicina paratur, Cum mala per longas convaluere moras.* Cf.82,*30–32.* Ovid, *Rem. Amoris,* 91–92. Appears also in Lyly,

Greene, Webster, etc.; adapted ('past cure is still past care') by Shakespeare, etc. (Tilley, No.133.)

7,6. Errare humanum est, in errore perseverare, belluinum. A sentiment proverbial in all tongues. Cf. Seneca, *Nat.Quest.*, iv.sec.2; also Cicero, *Ad Atticum*, xiii.21.5. Early Latin, German, Spanish, and Dutch versions. Appears variously in St. Chrysostom, Cognatus, St. Jerome, Polignac, etc. (The familiar modern form is from Pope, *Essay on Crit.*, ii.325.) Pettie's immediate source was probably Erasmus, *Adagia*: '*Errare humanum est, in errore perseverare diabolicum.*' (Tilley, No.192; Smith, 511.)

—,*7. Sins oft essayed are thought to be no sin.* Repeated 124,*24–5.* Cf. *Sententiae Pueriles* (1702), '*Assueta mala non offendunt.*' (Tilley, No.753.)

—,*12–16.* 'I meane, god willing . . .' Omitted in *BCDEF*. The Alexius is presumably the same friend 'darkely figured forth' in the last tale.

11. SINORIX AND CAMMA. Of this story there were three readily accessible versions, Plutarch's *De Claris Mulieribus* (probably in Ranutinus' popular translation), Castiglione's *Courtier* (tr.Hoby), and Guevara's *Diall*. All evidence points to the *Courtier* (cf. Bush, op.cit.,162). Pettie's Sinorix, like Castiglione's, is governor of the city; Plutarch's and Guevara's is but an ordinary citizen. Pettie makes Siena the setting; Plutarch and Guevara, Galatia; Castiglione names no city (cf. Koeppel, op.cit.,25). 'Other details peculiar to Pettie and the *Courtier* are the nature of the arguments used by those persuading Camma to marry, the effect of the poison on Sinorix, and the circumstantial conclusion in which Camma goes home, lies down on her bed, and cries to her dead husband to welcome her to the skies.'—Bush.

—,*2–10.* In *A* the Argument to 'Sinorix and Camma' is printed not as the first paragraph, but inserted in the preliminaries as though included as an afterthought. Apparently Watkins decided only after beginning the printing to include his Arguments.

—,*11–13. As amongst all the bonds . . . Marriage.* Later versions in Apperson, 404, s.v. *marriage* (5); Smith, 291, cites Pettie.

13,30–1. He which would reap should sow. Cf. Galatians, vi.7. Erasmus, *Adagia* (from Cicero, *De Oratore*, ii.sec.65), '*Ut sementem feceris, ita et metes.*' Found variously in Alfred, Cynewulf, Lydgate, etc. (Tilley, No.511A; Apperson, 591, s.v. *sow.*)

13,*31–2. He that would gather fruit should plant trees.* A common Biblical exhortation. Cf. Matthew, xii.33. (Tilley, No.524; Apperson, 645, s.v. *trees* (8); Smith, 30.)

—,*32–14,1. He that would reach the sweet rose should now and then be scratched with the sharp briars.* Cf. Ovid, *Rem. Amoris*, 46: 'Urticae proxima saepe rosa est,' etc. Images drawn from the rose and its thorns abound in all literatures. Among the Elizabethans, with whom it was a favourite, Lyly, Lodge, Shakespeare, Beaumont and Fletcher, etc., may be cited. Cf. Guazzo, *Civ.Con.* i.29: 'God hath given us Roses beset with thornes, the sweete with the sower.'

15,*17–22. he freely fed his eyes . . . the fever and disease.* Cf. Golding's *Ovid* (ed. Rouse), Preface, 169–170:

> 'Lyke as the fynest meates and drinkes that can be made by art,
> In sickly folkes too nourishment of sickness doo convert.'
> —Bush, 327.

17,*5–7.* The metaphor of the she-wolf (derived perhaps from the bestiaries) is closely copied by Lyly, in *Euphues* (82) and *Love's Met.*, III.i.45. Cf. Gascoigne, i.399:

> 'The fairest Woulf will choose the foulest for hir make,
> And why? because he doth indure most sorrow for hir sake.'
> —Bush, 327.

Apparently not recorded elsewhere. (Tilley, No.697.)

—,*30–1. If your sweet meat have such sour sauce.* Cf.106,*23–4* and 141,*22–3.* Heywood, *Proverbs*, I.viii, and *Epigrams*, No.197: 'Sweet meat will have sour sauce.' Appears variously in *Euphues* (172), Ben Jonson, Florio, etc. (Tilley, No.438; Apperson, 614; Smith, 408.)

—,*32–18,3. Such answer as was made to Cratorus . . . in all delicacy.* Originally from Diogenes Laertius' account of Diogenes of Sinope, in his *Lives and Opinions of Eminent Philosophers*, iii,sec.57—but Pettie's source is probably Erasmus. Cf. his *Apophthegmes*, tr.Udall, 1564 (ed. Roberts), 147, although instead of *salt* it is there *bread and cheese*. (Tilley, No.531.)

18,*30–1. Like purpose, like proof; like man, like matter.* Source unidentified, but a typical proverbial formula from earliest times, with an obvious appeal for Pettie.

19,*16–17. Chastity, which ought to be the joy, jewel and gem of all gentle women . . .* Cf.226,*19–20.* A favourite Elizabethan metaphor. Cf. Marlowe, *H.&L.*,ii.78, 'This inestimable gem'; *All's Well*, IV.ii.46; etc.

21,8ff. This is the first of nine letters used in the *Petite Pallace*. The convention was familiar from Painter following Bandello. The interchange of letters was a common device in the *novelle*, elaborated romantically by Boiastuau and Belleforest.—Bush, 168–9.

—,*16–17. The more hard the fight is, the more haughty is the conquest.* Cf.61, *29–30* for a more characteristic version. Cf. Cicero, *De Off.*, i.ch.19,sec.64: '*Quo difficilius, hoc praeclarius.*' Beaumont and Fletcher, *Rule a Wife &c.*, IV.i, cite the 'old Roman axiom'—'The more the danger, still more the honour.' (Tilley, No.139.)

—,*26–7. In all degrees of friendship equality is chiefly considered.* Cf.125,*1–2.* A popular Ciceronian concept. Erasmus, *Adagia*: '*Amicitia aequalitas.*' Also Pub. Syrus, '*Amicitia pares aut accipit, aut facit.*' The expression reappears in *Euphues* (372). (Tilley, No.278.)

—,*29–30. The haughty hawk will not prey on carrion.* Cf. Painter, *P. of P.*, 'A carrion kite will never make good hawk.' Also an early Scottish version: Henderson, 49. (Tilley, No.733; Apperson, 82.)

—,*30–1. —neither will courtly silks practise country sluts.* Unidentified in any early version. (Apperson, 571.)

22,24–5. the knight Virle . . . his lady Zilia. An allusion to the story in Painter, ii.27. (Source in Bandello.)

23,7–8. To hop against the hill and strive against the stream has ever been counted extreme folly. Heywood, *Proverbs*, II.v:

> 'Folly it is to spurn against a prick;
> To strive against the stream . . .'

Cf. Juvenal, *Satire IV*, 89: '*Dirigere bracchia contra torrentum*'; Erasmus, *Adagia*, '*Contra torrentum niti.*' Both parts appear in Gascoigne, Greene, etc.; the second in Alfred, *Tottel's Miscellany* (No.284), Shakespeare, etc. (Tilley, No.349; Apperson, 309, s.v. *hop*, cites Pettie; Smith, 236, s.v. *it is ill.*)

—,*12–13. The caterpillar . . . cleaveth only to good fruit.* An unidentified Plinian observation, repeated in *Euphues* (17). (Tilley, No.79.)

—,*13–14. The moth . . . most of all eateth the best cloth.* Cf.188,*5–6.*

—,*14–15. The canker . . . commonly breedeth in the fairest rose.* Cf.88,*22–3.* Specific 'source' unknown. A favourite figure with Shakespeare; cf. *Sonnets*, No.XXXV, etc. Found also *Euphues* (211), and Greene; *2 G of V*, I.i.42. (Tilley, No.70.)

—,*30–32. Adversity is ever most bitter to him who hath long time lived in prosperity.* Cf. Pub. Syrus, '*Bis ille miser est, ante qui felix fuit.*' (Tilley, No.318.)

24,6–8. For as a hawk . . . command it. Cf. Gascoigne, i.147:

'But the hawke which soareth in the skie,
And clymbes aloft for sollace of hir wing,
The greater gate she getteth up on highe,
The truer stoupe she makes at any thing.'
—Bush, 327.

26,3. with a flea in her ear. Cf. Fr. *puce à l'oreille.* A widely used phrase. *N.E.D.*'s earliest example c.1430. Found in Heywood, *Proverbs,* I.xi, *Euphues* (70), Nashe, Greene, etc.; also Bandello and Rabelais. (Tilley, No.245; Apperson, 219.)

—,13–14. Women always live chastely enough, so that they live charily enough. Cf. Lat. '*Nisi casta, saltem caute*' and '*Caute, si non caste*' (unidentified); also Sp. '*La mas cauta es tenida por mas casta.*' Appears variously in Castiglione, Greene, v.209, Marston, etc. (Tilley, No.87; Apperson, 92, cites Pettie; Smith, 207. Stevenson also cites Pettie.)

27,10. the Countess of Salisbury. Cf.*5,28.*

—,16–17. the Duchess of Savoy. Cf.*6,1.*

—,21. Of evils the least is to be chosen. Repeated at *67,13;68,18;123,11–12.* Heywood, *Proverbs,* I.v, and *Epigrams,* No.211: 'Of two ills, choose the least.' Cf. Cicero, *De Off.,* III.i: '*ex malis eligere minima*'; Erasmus, *Adagia*: '*E duobus malis minimum eligendum.*' Appears variously in Thomas à Kempis, Chaucer, *Euphues* (322), Greene (as from Aristotle), Nashe, Marlowe, Chapman, etc. (Tilley, No.195; Apperson, 654, s.v. *two evils*; Smith, 334.)

—,26. The sea hath fish for every man. This consoling, homely adage seems to have no discoverable earlier form. It appears verbatim in Camden's *Remains* (1614). 'There are as good fish in the sea as ever came out of it' dates from Scott. Cf. Ovid, *Ars Am.,* iii.425: '*Semper tibi pendeat hamus: Quo minime credas gurgite, piscis erit.*' (Tilley, No.537; Apperson, 555; Smith, 472, cites Pettie.)

29,1–2. Is not the loss of goods less than of one's good name? Cf.*18,12–13.* *Proverbs,* xxii.1: 'A good name is rather to be chosen than great riches.' Appears variously in Pub. Syrus, Erasmus, Cervantes, Barclay, etc. Cf. *Othello,* III,iii.157: 'Who steals my purse steals trash,' etc. (Tilley, No.292; early forms in Apperson, 261, s.v. *good name.*)

—,2–3. Is not an honourable death to be preferred before an infamous life? Repeated declaratively at *123,10–11.* Cf. Pub. Syrus: '*Honestam mortem vitae*

turpi praefero.' Pettie's identical phrasing reappears in Lyly's *Gallathea*; similar expressions in *Euphues* (409) and *Midas*. (Tilley, No.143.)

29 *3–4. the Countess before rehearsed.* i.e. the Countess of Salisbury. Cf. 5,*28* and 27,*10*.

—,*6. the Duchess of Savoy.* Cf.6,*1*.

—,*9–10. The more you stop* [*streams*], *the higher they flow.* Cf.75,*19–20*. Greene cites this among 'the aphorisms of the philosophers.' Found variously in *Euphues* (44), Deloney, Shakespeare, *Wit's Commonwealth*, etc. Unidentified in earlier form. Pettie's rhyming supplement appears to be original. (Tilley, No.592.)

—,*11–12. The more* [*spices*] *are beaten, the sweeter scent they send forth.* Cf. 246,*23–4*. Erasmus, *Similia*: '*Ut aromata tum vehementius fragrant, cum moventur ac teruntur frangunturve: Ita virtutis fama . . .*' Appears variously in *Euphues* (19), Greene, Webster, Bacon, etc. (Tilley, No.582; Apperson, s.v. *spice*, cites only Fuller.)

—,*12–14. The more* [*the herb camomile*] *is trodden down, the more it spreadeth abroad.* Cf. Pliny, *Hist.Nat.*, xxi.sec.6: '*Gaudet calcari et atteri, pereundoque melius provenit*' (of the crocus). Repeated by Erasmus, *Similia*. Used by Lyly in *Euphues* (27), Greene, iii.235;iv.183;xi.199, and—through Lyly—by Shakespeare, in the parody of euphuism, *I Henry IV*, II.iv.441. (Tilley, No.68; Smith, 452, cites Pettie.)

—,*15–17. Honour ever is the reward of virtue, and doth accompany it as duly as the shadow doth the body.* Cicero, *Philippicae*, iv.sec.81: '*Honor est praemium virtutis.*' Pettie's 'source' probably Erasmus, *Similia*: '*Ut umbra nos vel invitos comitatur: Ita gloria virtutem sequitur.*' Cf. Guazzo, *Civ.Con.* i.99: 'honour is the rewarde of vertue, and counted a divine thing.' The shadow simile reappears in *Euphues* (309). (Tilley, Nos.345,547.)

30,*1–2. The event of battle is always doubtful.* Cf.101,*33*. Versions in More's *Utopia*, *Euphues* (47), Shakespeare, Camden. Cf. *Sententiae Pueriles* (1702): 'Belli exitus incertus.' (Tilley, No.664.)

—,*4–5. People are ever prone to speak the worst.* Unidentified.

—,*15–16. There is no smoke but where there is some fire.* Cf. Plautus, *Curculio*, I.i.53: '*Flamma fumo est proxima*'—repeated by Erasmus; Pub. Syrus, '*nunquam ubi diu fuit ignis deficit vapor.*' Heywood, *Proverbs*, II,v: 'there is no fire without some smoke.' Early German and French versions. Also in Guazzo, *Euphues* (141), Florio, Nashe, etc. (Tilley, No.567; Apperson, 582, s.v. *smoke* (3); Smith, 316,323.)

31,33. swash buckler. The *N.E.D.*'s first citation of this phrase is from Pilkington, *Expos. Aggeus*, 1560.

32,9–10. I count any place my country where I may live well and wealthily. Cf. Cicero, *Tusc. Disp.*, v.37,108: '*Patria est, ubicumque est bene.*' Repeated by Erasmus, *Adagia.* Similar sentiments in Aristophanes, Pacuvius, etc. Versions in *Euphues* (173), Kyd, Jonson, Chapman, Massinger, etc. (Tilley, No.120; Apperson, 396, s.v. *Man* (43), cites Pettie—as does Stevenson.)

34,11–12. Did Julietta die upon the corpse of her Romeo? Cf.125,28. An allusion to the tragedy told in Painter, ii.25 (from Bandello's *novella*, tr. Boaistuau).

35,1–12. For as the bird that is bruised . . . every pleasant sight turns to bitter spite. Cf. Gascoigne, i.45:

'Or as the seely byrd, that with Bolte is *brusd*,
And *lieth aloofe among the leaves*, of al hir pheares refusd,
And *heares them sing* full shrill, yet cannot she rejoyce,
Nor frame *one warbling note* to passe, *out of hir mournful voyce,*
Even so I find by proofe, that pleasure *dubleth payne,*
Unto a *wretched wounded hart*, which doth in woe, remaine . . .'
—Bush, 326.

36,10–11. Vengeance asketh vengeance; and blood, blood. Cf. Genesis, ix.6; also *Gorboduc*: 'Blood asketh blood.' (Tilley, No.45; Smith, 69, s.v. *blood*.)

—,11–12. They that sow slaughter shall be sure to reap ruin and destruction. Cf.13,30–1. Like the preceding, unidentified in this form, although apparently a Biblical adaptation.

37,29–30. It is naturally incident to women to enter into extremities. Unidentified. (Tilley, No.701; Smith, 595.) Cf. the following:

38,1–2. The mean, [women] always meanly account of. Neither of these items of misogynist tirade is recorded elsewhere in comparable form. But cf. Pub. Syrus: '*Aut amat aut odit mulier: nihil est tertium.*'—which Nashe cites as from Seneca's proverbs (unidentified). Similar reflections appear in Castiglione and *Euphues* (81).

—,13. Lucrece. Cf.227,7. An allusion to the story in Painter, i.2 (source: Livy, i.57–60).

—,16. to gaze in every garish glass. Cf. Gascoigne, i.70: 'In everie gorgious garish glasse'—Bush, 326.

—,16–17. to have an oar stirring in every beautiful boat. Cf. Heywood, *Proverbs*, I.x, and *Epigrams*, No.189. The same metaphor appears in Cer-

vantes, Udall, *Tottel's Miscellany*, Nashe, Jonson, etc. (Tilley, No.466; Apperson, 461; Smith, 519.)

40. TEREUS AND PROGNE. The shortest of Pettie's twelve tales, based on Ovid, *Met.*, vi.424–674. Pettie's version adds a long and characteristic preamble on human frailties, develops at some length the courtship, and for the old female attendant substitutes a passing gentleman, who had lost his way by night, to carry the tell-tale web [embroidered cloth] to Progne. As usual, Pettie omits countless details and ramifications of the story, selecting only the dramatic features in outline, and adding his usual colloquies, tirades, etc. (The legend appears also in Hyginus, *Fables*, No.45, and Apollodorus.)

—,*24–6. The chameleon changeth himself into the colour and hue of everything he doth view.* Erasmus, *Similia*: '*Chamaeleon omnem imitatur colorem praeterquam album*' (from Pliny). A phenomenon referred to variously by Shakespeare. (Tilley, No.83.)

42,*25. Fame [is] a tattling goddess.* The form of this epigram may well be original with Pettie, although Virgil's Fama is conceivably the inspiration (*Aeneid*, iv.174ff.;viii,554;etc.).

47,*3. Tytus and Gysippus.* Cf.111,*4–5.* An allusion to the story in Boccaccio. —Koeppel, 23; retold in Elyot's *Governour.*

49,*27–8. We are born to die . . . even in our swathe-clouts death may ask his due.* Cf. Erasmus, *Adagia*: '*Mors omnibus communis*'; also Düringsfeld, ii.463: '*Nascentes morimur, finisque ab origine pendet.*' Similar reflections in Cervantes, Shakespeare, etc. (Tilley, Nos.152,728.)

51,*5–7. The just judgement of God, who will suffer no evil done secretly, but it shall be manifested openly.* Cf. Mark, iv.22. (Tilley, No.379.)

53,*32–54,1. Agave . . . Penthey.* The story of Agave and Pentheus is found in Ovid, *Met.*, iii.725ff.

55,*14. of the husband or the wife.* The *of . . . or* construction, now obsolete, appears to have been a normal English idiom in the sixteenth and seventeenth centuries (cf. Tilley, in *Mod. Lang. Notes*, XLI [Nov. 1926], 462–4).

56. GERMANICUS AND AGRIPPINA. The longest of Pettie's twelve tales, based upon Tacitus, *Ann.*, i.33,69;ii.43,73–75;iii.1–6 (and possibly Suetonius). Pettie's emphasis upon the courtship has no source in Tacitus, nor the long discourses on great place, with their *exempla*. 'Pettie's closing sermon exhorts women not to let their husbands be too ambitious, and not to

drive them to seek wealth for the gratification of feminine vanity. Tacitus might well have rubbed his eyes.'—Bush, 163. Among the anachronisms in Pettie's version are Germanicus' *exempla* from Painter (i.e. originally Bandello), quotations from Genesis, Hebrews, and I Corinthians. Renaissance ethics and Pauline doctrines proceed glibly enough from these pagan lovers' lips.

57,*14–15. Such as the cause of everything is, such will be the effect.* Cf.234, 21-2. Familiar scholastic philosophy. Cf. Erasmus, *Adagia*: '*Mali principii malus finis.*' (Tilley, No.28.)

58,*13. vi et armis.* Cf. Cicero, *Ad Pontifices*, xxiv.63.

—,*27–8.* [*to*] *promise golden hills and perform dirty dales.* Erasmus, *Adagia*: '*Aureos montes polliceri*'; also early German versions. The alliterative counter is typical of Pettie. (Tilley, No.508; cf. Apperson, 514, s.v. *promise* (2).)

59,*27–8. Every commodity hath a discommodity annexed unto it.* Unidentified early Lat., '*Omnis commoditas sua fert incommoda secum.*' Cf. Guazzo, *Civ.Con.*, i.29: 'this saying, That everie commoditie, bringeth with it a discommoditie.' (Tilley, No.107.)

61,*1–3. Alerane . . . Adalesia.* An allusion to the story in Painter, i.44 (from Bandello's *novella*, *tr.*Belleforest) of the Saxon lovers' flight into Italy.

—,*14–15. He is not worthy to suck the sweet who hath not first savoured the sour.* Cf. Erasmus, '*Dulcia non meruit qui non gustavit amara.*' Heywood, *Proverbs*, II.iv: 'Take the sweet with the sour.' Also an early Danish variant. (Tilley, No.147; Apperson, 613, s.v. *sweet* (2).)

—,*19–21.* The sole reference in the *Petite Pallace* to the story of Hero and Leander. 'Of English works published before Marlowe's career began Pettie's *A Petite Pallace* (1576) seems here to influence him more than any other.'— Marlowe's *Poems*, ed. L.C.Martin, 6 and n. The commentary cites seeming parallels: e.g., chastity as a jewel, etc.

—,*22–3. The remembrance of the peril past delighteth.* Cf. Cicero, *De Finibus*, ii.32,sec.105: '*Jucunda memoria est praeteritorum malorum.*' Also Pub. Syrus: '*Dulcis malorum praeteritorum memoria.*' Similar apophthegms are found in Euripides, Seneca, Erasmus, etc.; also polyglot versions. (Tilley, No.516; Apperson, 481,484; Smith, 458.)

—,*28. Fortune ever favoureth the valiant.* Cf.113,*26–7.* A common classical text. Cf. Terence, *Phorm.*, I.iv.26: '*Audentes fortuna iuvat*'; *Aeneid*, x.284; Cicero, Ovid, etc. Erasmus, *Adagia*: '*Fortes Fortuna adjuvat*;' Greene, etc. (Tilley, No.262; Apperson, 231; Smith, 112.)

61,29–30. Things the more hard, the more haughty, high, and heavenly. Cf. *21,16–17.*

62,13–14. Delay bred [breeds] danger. Cf. Livy, *Hist.*, xxxviii.25.sec.13: '*Periculum in mora.*' Also early Italian version. Appears variously in Cervantes, *Euphues* (49,68,96), Greene, Shakespeare, etc. (Tilley, No.145; Apperson, 141; Smith, 85.)

—,*15–16.* The more fire is kept down, the more it flameth up. Ovid, *Met.*, iv.64: '*Quoque magis tegitur, tectus magis aestuat ignis.*' Cf. Guazzo, *Civ.Con.*, i.18: 'as hidden flames by force kept downe are most ardent.' Appears variously in Chaucer, *Euphues* (46), Lodge, Shakespeare, etc. (Tilley, No.233; Apperson, 214, s.v. *fire* (15).)

63,13–14. It is better to be idle than ill employed. Erasmus, *Coll.* (from Pliny, *Epistles*, i.9): '*Otiosum esse quam nihil agere.*' Appears variously in *Euphues* (53,91) and almost verbatim in Lyly's *Love's Met.* (Tilley, No.352; Apperson, 45.)

—,*17.* the pilgrimage of this my short life. Cf.249,*27–8.* An ancient concept. Cf. Genesis, xlvii.9; Erasmus, *Adagia*: '*Vita hominis peregrinatio.—(Haec enim sententia frequenter in Sacris voluminibus, vitam hanc esse exilium, esse incolatum et peregrinationem).*' Appears in *Euphues* (100,166), Shakespeare, etc. (Tilley, No.385.)

—,*23.* (as Homer reporteth) . . . The Grecian ladies' custom of counting their age from their marriage, rather than from birth, is based on Homer's authority in the *Diall of Princes* (cf.1557 ed.,fol.253); but the reference in Homer remains unidentified.—Bush, 165, n.5. (Tilley, No.757.)

64,6. the opinion of Aristotle. The same doctrine reappears at 234,*31* and 263,*25–6.* Martin (Marlowe's *Poems*, 42,n.) traces it, not to Aristotle's *Physics*, but the *Problemata Aristotelis* (1501), iv.10: '*Nunc autem cum coniuguntur perfectum imperficitur et imperfectum perficitur.*' Cf. Marlowe's lines (*H.&L.*, 267–8)

> 'By which alone, our reverend fathers say,
> Women receive perfection every way.'

—also Castiglione.

—,*9–10.* Virginity, which you so highly esteem of. Cited in conjunction with Marlowe's 'Virginity, albeit some highly prize it' (*H.&L.*, 262)—Martin, 42,n.

65,4–5. God and Nature do nothing vainly or vilely. Cf. Wilson, *Arte of Rhetorique*, 49: 'a common Prouerbe, and almost in euery mans mouth, that neither GOD, nor yet Nature, did euer make any thing in vaine.' (Tilley, No.457; later versions in Smith, 307, s.v. *Nature*.)

68,*5–6*. *It is not good for man to live alone* . . . Genesis, ii.18.

—,*8–9*. *Marriage and the bed undefiled are honourable.* Cf.11,*12–13*. Hebrews, xiii,4. Cf. Wilson, *Arte of Rhetorique*, 42–43: 'The Apostle S. Paule in the thirteene chapter of his Epistle to the Hebrues, calleth Matrimonie honorable among all man, and the bed vndefiled.' (Tilley, No.750.)

—,*12–13*. *Doth not God say it is good for man not to touch a woman.* Cf.242, *14–15*. I Corinthians, vii.1. (Tilley, Nos.638,749.)

—,*15*. *It is better to marry than to burn.* Ibid., 9. (Tilley, No. 430.)

69,*12–13*. *As rare as the black swan* . . . *as common as the black crow.* The original 'rare bird' appears in Juvenal, *Satires*, vi.165: '*Rara avis in terris, nigroque simillima cygno.*' *Rara avis* reappears in Erasmus, Gosson, *Euphues* (209), etc.

—,*13–14*. *Of good things I think the more common the more commendable.* Cf. 251,*26–8*. Not listed in this form elsewhere except the early Lat., '*Bonum, quo communis eo melius.*' (Tilley, No.108.)

77,*30–1*. *Boistrous winds do most of all shake the highest towers.* Cf. Horace, *Odes*, II,x.9–12:

> *saepius ventis agitatur ingens*
> *pinus et celsae graviore casu*
> *decidunt turres feriuntque summos*
> *fulgura montis.*

A similar list of proverbs on the dangers of high estate is found in *Tottel's Miscellany*, No.194:

> 'The highest tree in all the woode is rifest rent with blustring windes:
> The higher hall the greater fall . . .' etc.

—,*32*. *The higher the place is, the sooner and sorer is the fall.* Various classical and polyglot versions. Quite similar expressions found in Gower, Guazzo, *Euphues* (17), etc. (Tilley, No.338; Apperson, 301, s.v. *higher*, etc.)

78,*1–2*. *In greatest charge are greatest cares.* Cf.248,*28*. An ancient universal proverb. Cf. early Lat., '*Curia curarum genetrix.*' (Tilley, No.346.)

—,*3*. *Envy always shooteth at high marks.* Cf.262,*28–9*. Cf. Ovid, *Rem. Amoris*, 369: '*Summa petit livor*'; also Livy, *Hist.*, viii.sec.31: '*Invidiam, tamquam ignem, summa petere.*' (Tilley, No.191.)

—,*3–6*. *A kingdom is more easily gotten than kept. For to get is the gift of fortune, but to keep is the power of prudence and wisdom.* Cf. Pub. Syrus:

'*Fortunam citius reperias quam retineas.*' Echoes in *Euphues* (177). (Tilley, No.281.)

78,*10*. *Euripides* . . . Cf. *Phoenissae*, 524–5. Suetonius cites Cicero as continuing the opinion through Caesar's repetition of Euripides' lines. The idea appears also in Guazzo, and, as from Euripides, in *Euphues*. Cf.82,*11–13*.

—,*14*. *Numitor and Amulius*. Cf. Ovid, *Met.*, xiv.772ff.

—,*22–3*. *Eteocles and Polinices*. Ibid.,ix.405ff.; also Seneca.

79,*4–5. as Adalesia did with her Alerane*. Cf.61,*1–3*; also 155,*8–9*.

—,*21*. *Honours change manners*. Cf. Polydore Vergil, *Prov. Libellus*, No.202: '*Honores mutant mores.*'—cited by Cervantes. Appears in Latimer, Greene, Chapman, etc. (Tilley, No.347; Apperson, 308; Smith, 192.)

80,*2–3*. *Freshest colours soonest fade*. Cf.148,*13–14*. Appears verbatim in *Euphues* (11). Erasmus, *Similia*: '*Ut in rerum natura spectatissime florent celerrime marcescunt.*' (Tilley, No.99.)

—,*3*. *Ripest fruit are rifest rotten*. Heywood, *Proverbs*, I,x: 'Soon ripe, soon rotten.' Appears variously in *Piers Plowman*, Erasmus' *Adagia*, Harman's *Caveat* (1567), Nashe, *Richard II*, etc. (Tilley, No.519; Smith, 398.)

81,*23–4. the whirling wheel of Fortune*. A common classical figure. Cf. Ovid, *Met.*, ii.72: '*et rapido contrarius evehor orbi*'; Seneca, *Agamemnon*, 71: '*Praecipites regum casus Fortuna rotat.*' Similar phrases in Cervantes, Lydgate, Shakespeare, etc.

83,*29–30. We must live by the living, not by the dead*. Luke, xxiv.5: 'Why seek ye the living among the dead?' No other 'source' discoverable. Cf. Florio, *First Fruites* (1578), fol.34: 'Quicke with the quicke and dead with the dead.' (Tilley, No.396; Apperson, 375, s.v. *live* (38).)

85. AMPHIARAUS AND ERIPHYLE. Source: Hyginus, *Fab.*, lxix–lxxiii. Pettie's version becomes rather a treatise on covetousness, involving a wordy courtship and a misogynist tirade. The character of Infortunio seems to be Pettie's invention, to heighten the effect of his concluding preachment.

86,*8. Fabritius/Valerius BCDEF*. The story of the incorruptible Roman consul Fabricius, who died poor, is told by Livy, *Epit.* 12; also Aulus Gellius, *Noct.Att.*, i.14. Painter (i.16), however, is probably Pettie's source. Pettie's spelling is like Painter's, and the latter's fourth sentence, 'Thus much is written in the historie of Valerius Antiates,' may have misled the editors or compositors of *B* into substituting the historically unaccountable 'Valerius' in the *exemplum*. (Neither, of course, occurs in Hyginus.)

88,*19–20*. *That which is mine should be yours, and yours your own.* (Tilley, No.445; Smith, 570, s.v. *what's mine*, cites Pettie.)

—,*22–3*. *In the fairest rose is soonest found a canker.* Cf.23,*14–15*.

—,*23–4*. *In fairest speech is falsehood and feigning rifest.* Cf.206,*24–5*. Cf. Erasmus, *Adagia*: '*Veritatis simplex oratio.*' Widely divergent variants appear in Heywood, Lyly, Shakespeare, etc. The highly alliterative form is characteristic of Pettie. (Tilley, No.650.)

—,*26–7*. *a fool's Paradise.* The phrase appears as early as the *Paston Letters* (1462); also in Mathew's Bible (1549): II Kings, iv; Guazzo, Bullein, Shakespeare, etc. (Tilley, No.252; Apperson, 225; Smith, 10.)

—,*28–9*. *He which knoweth not how to dissemble, knoweth not how to live.* Cf. *Sententiae Pueriles* (1702): '*Qui nescit dissimulare nescit imperare.*' An early Italian version. Appears variously in *Euphues* (79), Greene, etc. (Tilley, No.157.)

89,*26–7*. *The potter's clay being once hardened in the oven* . . . Images of the potter and his clay are found in Isaiah, xxix.16;xlv.9;lxiv.8; Jeremiah, xviii.4; Romans, ix.21. Cf. Erasmus, *Similia*: '*Ut gypsum, aut argilla dum est uda in quamvis imaginem facile sequitur fingentis manum: Ita rudes animi ad omnem disciplinam sunt idonei.*' The same figure reappears in *Euphues* (14). (Tilley, No.500.)

90,*19–22*. These three alliterative rhetorical questions, with their common cynical theme, seem to be of Pettie's own devising. Similar reflections, however, are found in the classics, e.g., Pub. Syrus: '*Pecunia una regimen est rerum omnium.*' Cf. Guazzo: 'the tongue hath no force when golde speaketh.'

—,*31*. *a fresh water soldier.* Cf. Guazzo, *Civ.Con.*, *i.7*: 'Those which mislyke studie or learnyng in Gentlemen, are some freshe water Souldiers'; the term is used again at ii.106.

91,*2–6*. *And as the North East wind* . . . *to drive him away.* Cf. Turberville, *Eclogues*, No.4:

> 'A Woman to the Northeast winde
>   may well compared bee,
> That gathers up the cloud and straight
>   doth force the same to flee
> Abrode by guileful puffe againe
>   and bitter windie blast.
> So she allures, and then she lowres
>   upon his Love at last.'

—Bush, 328. A translation from Mantuan, whom Pettie mentions at 263,*1*.

91,*12–16. And as a tree . . . wavered unconstantly.* Cf. Golding's *Ovid*, x.420–4:

> 'And like as when a myghtye tree with axes heawed rownd,
> Now reedye with a strype or twaine to lye uppon the ground,
> Uncerteine is which way to fall and tottreth every way:
> Even so her mynd with dowtfull wound effeebled then did stray
> Now heere now there uncerteinely, and tooke of both encrease.'
>
> —Bush, 328.

—,*20–1. as from most sharp thorns, to wit, the rose tree, spring most sweet flowers* . . . Cf. Ovid, *Epis. ex Ponto*, II.ii.34: '*Saepe creat molles aspera spina rosas*'; Pub. Syrus: '*Spina etiam grata est ex qua spectatur rosa*'; Erasmus, *Similia*: '*Ut rosa flos unus omnium longe gratissimus de spinis nascitur.*' The figure appears variously in Gower, Florio, etc. (Tilley, No.523; cf. Apperson, 539; Smith, 323, s.v. *no rose.*)

—,*30. Nothing venture, nothing have.* Heywood, *Proverbs*, I.xi, and *Epigrams*, No.77: 'Nought venture, nought have.' Variants in Chaucer, Tusser, Camden, etc. (Tilley, No. 657; Apperson, 454; Smith, 331.)

92,*11–12. The grass had been cut from under his feet.* A common French expression; 'to cut the earth from under my feet' appears also in Fenton's tr. of Bandello (1567). Pettie's version reappears several times in Greene. (Tilley, No.301; Apperson, 269; Smith, 508, cites Pettie—as does Stevenson.)

—,*18–20. hauled in the main sheet of her mind, and by the anchors of advice so stayed her course* . . . Cf. Gascoigne, i.110:

> 'Yet hauld I in, the mayne sheate of the minde,
>   And stayed thy course by ancors of advice.'   —Bush, 326.

93,*7–8. The disposition of the mind followeth the constitution of the body.* Cf.128,2–4. A Renaissance neo-Platonic and Erasmian doctrine; also elaborated by Plutarch, Seneca, etc. Cf. Guazzo, *Civ.Con.*, ii.47: 'The disposition of the mynd followeth the complexion of the body.' Appears twice, almost verbatim, in *Euphues* (50,389). Cf. Juvenal, *Sat.*, x.356: '*Mens sana in corpore sano.*' (Tilley, No.156; Smith, 28.)

—,*22–4.* The simile of the Panther appears twice in *Euphues* (36,138). Erasmus, *Similia* (from Pliny): '*Pardus odoris gratia allectas feras invadit, atque occidit.*' It was also a favourite figure with Greene. (Tilley, No. 472.)

—,*27. Anaxarete . . . Iphis.* Cf. Ovid, *Met.*, xiv.698ff.

93,*30*. *Angelica.* An allusion to the story told by Boiardo and Ariosto.— Koeppel.

94,*2*. *Marriages are guided by destiny.* Cf.126,*12*. Heywood, *Proverbs*, I.iii: 'Wedding is destiny, And hanging likewise'; also *Epigrams*, No.6: 'Wedding and hanging are destiny.' Cf. Guazzo, *Civ.Con.*, ii.77: 'Marriages (as they say) are made in heaven, and are guided by destiny.' Variants in Lyly, Greene, Shakespeare, etc. (A ballad licensed in 1558 [Hazlitt, 518] reads: 'The Proverbe is true y^t Weddynge is destinye.' Cf. also N.Ault, *Eliz. Lyrics*, 35–6.) (Tilley, No.428; Apperson, 403; Smith, 129,291.)

—,*2–4*. *God hath endued women with this property, to be wedded to their wills.* Cf. Heywood, *Proverbs*, II.xi; a similar reflection appears in Shakespeare, *L.L.L.*, II.i.211. (Tilley, No.675.)

—,*9–17*. *and as the bird enclosed in cage . . . vexation of mind.* Cf. *Tottel's Miscellany*, No.271:

> 'Lyke as the birde within the cage enclosed,
> The dore unsparred, her foe the hawke without,
> Twixt death and prison piteously oppressed,
> Whether for to chose standeth in doubt,
> Lo, so do I, which seke to bryng about,
> Which should be best by determinacion,
> By losse of life libertye, then lyfe by pryson.'
> —Bush, 327.

The same poem contains the maxim four times used by Pettie, in various forms, 'Of these two evyls let se now chuse the best.'

—,*28–9*. *The parish priest forgetteth that ever he was clerk.* Appears twice, almost verbatim, in Heywood, *Proverbs*, I.xi, and *Epigrams*, No.48; earlier in J.Heywood, *Tyb.*, 86 (1533):

> 'But now I see well the old proverb is true:
> That parish priest forgetteth that ever he was clerk!'

Also in Greene, iv.102. (Tilley, No.503; Apperson, 512; Smith, 456.)

95,*8–10*. An ancient paradox. Cf. Ovid, *Rem. Amoris*, 501–2; also Erasmus, *Adagia*: '*Suo ipsius laqueo captus est.*' Same figure found in Guazzo; Shakespeare uses it as applied to the woodcock's springe (*Hamlet*, V.ii.316). (Tilley, No.463.)

96,*14–15*. *Dropsy patients drink, and still be dry.* Cf. Guazzo, *Civ.Con.*, ii·100: 'it is as harde a matter to fynde servauntes without faultes, as Dropsye

Patients without thyrst.' Versions in *Euphues* (145), Greene, etc. (Tilley, No.170.)

96,23. Tarpeia. Cf. Ovid, *Met.*, xiv.776–7; also Livy, i.11.

97,23. [Women] are constant only in inconstancy. Cf. Ovid, *Tristia,* V.viii.18 (of Fortune): '*Et tantum constans in levitate sua est.*' Heywood, *Epigrams,* No.70, uses the expression applied to a man. The paradox appears variously (usually of Fortune) in Brooke, Barnfield, Marlowe, Sidney, etc. In *Euphues* (of wit, 303; of attire, 421). (Tilley, No.114.)

98,13. Dynira. Spelt *Deyanyre, Dyanyre* in Golding's Ovid, *Met.,* ix. For this list of proper names cf. Gascoigne, i.95.

—,16. Faustine. Cf.247.*6.* An allusion to the story in Painter, ii.10 (source in Bandello).

—,29. the fifty daughters of Danaus. The legend of Hypermnestra (referred to also in *Euphues,* 87) has its origin in Ovid, *Heroides,* xiv.

—,31–99,1. Candaules . . . Gyges. An allusion to the story in Painter, i.6 (source and origin in Herodotus, i.7–13). (Croll, p.46,n.3, confuses Pettie with Painter in his note to a similar allusion in *Euphues*).

100,3. A [the] virtue of necessity. Repeated at 216,*17* and 232,*28–9.* Cf. Quintilian, *Inst.Orat.* I.viii.14: '*Laudem virtutis necessitati damus.*' Erasmus, *Adagia:* '*Necessitatem in virtutem commutare.*' An adage common to all literatures; old French and Dutch versions; found in Chaucer, Rabelais. Greene, Shakespeare, etc. (Tilley, No.462; Apperson, 663; Smith, 282, s.v, *make.*)

101,33. the doubtful event of battle. Cf.30,*1–2.*

102,12–13. Cf. Matthew, vii.2. Pettie echoes the Mosaic doctrine at 164, *22–4.* It appears variously in Guazzo, *Euphues* (77), etc. (Tilley, No.437.)

—,27–8. Rather weigh the will of the speaker, than the worth of the words. (Tilley, No.433; Apperson, 687, s.v. *will* (2); Smith, 410, s.v. *Take the will,* cites Pettie.)

103. ICILIUS AND VIRGINIA. Source:Livy,III, xliv–lviii (also Painter, i.5). Livy's account has Verginia betrothed at once to Icilius, and makes much of the political aftermath of the slaying: the rebellion, the rights of the plebs, Appius' exile, trial by Verginius, appeal, and death. Pettie adds a long preamble on the origin of love, develops Icilius' suit and its vicissitudes (with soliloquies, discourses on friendship, exchange of letters, etc.), and ends with counsel on the evils of tyranny and senile lust and remarks on the rewards of chastity (Livy: *pudicitiae praemia*).

103,*23–4. I am as bad troubled as Simonides was* . . . Cicero, *De Nat. Deorum*, i.22, Quintilian, and others, tell of the poet-philosopher of Ceos. Appears in extended form in *Euphues* (432).

—,*27–8. I think love chiefly to be grounded upon the similitude of manners.* This platitude, which reappears four times in *Euphues* (29,78,274,372), is typical of the casuistry found in Guazzo and all courtesy books of the time. (Tilley, No.277.)

104,*13. One swallow makes not summer.* Heywood, *Proverbs*, II.v: 'One swallow maketh not summer, (said I), men say.' Also Erasmus, *Adagia*: '*Una hirundo non facit ver.*' Found in early Italian, Dutch, Danish, and French versions; in Aristotle (*Nicomachean Ethics*, I.vii.16), Cervantes, Greene, Nashe, etc. (Tilley, No.610; Apperson, 612; Smith, 346.)

—,*13–14. One particularity concludeth no generality.* Cf.232,*3–5* and 267,*1.* Unidentified in this form. Gosson's *School of Abuse* (1579) repeats the statement, coupled, as in Pettie, with 'one swallow brings (Pettie: makes) not summer.' (Tilley, No.473.)

105,*28. in the dumps.* Cf.133,7. The *N.E.D.* cites earlier instances in Skelton, More, and W.Waterman. In the sense of perplexity, melancholy, low spirits, the phrase is 'first found early in 16th c.; derivation obscure.' Cf. Guazzo, *Civ.Con.*, i.22; also Greene.

106,*31–2. Every dram of delight hath a pound of spite. Every inch of joy hath an ell of annoy.* Cf.237,*6–8.* Rhymed antiphonal epigrams of this sort appear frequently in Heywood. Cf. *Euphues*, 93—a passage of which, Tilley remarks, the comparison 'reveals the care with which Lyly studied the proverbs in Pettie's work.' 'A dram of sweet is worth a pound of sour' appears in the *Faerie Queene*, iii.30. Cf. Greene, ii.115 and iv.147. (Tilley, No.166; Smith, 318.)

107,*15–16. Fine gold must be purified in the flaming fire.* Cf. Seneca, *De Prov.*, V.ix: '*Ignis aurum probat*'; also Pub. Syrus. (Tilley, No.630.)

—,*18. Pleasure must be purchased with the price of pain.* Cf.142,*6–7.* A highly alliterated version of a universal epigram probably classical in origin. It appears variously in *A Paradise of Dainty Devices* (1576), Chapman, Camden, etc. *Tottel's Miscellany* No.267 is entitled 'That pleasure is mixed with every paine.' Unidentified in earlier form. (Tilley, No.493; Apperson, 502; Smith, 322, s.v. *no pleasure*, cites Pettie.)

110,*23. Syrinx . . . Pan.* Cf. Ovid, *Met.*, i.689ff.

—,*33. Two wits are better than one.* Heywood, *Proverbs*, I.ix: 'two heads are better than one.' Also early Italian and Portuguese versions (of two eyes). Variants in Homer, Gower, Palsgrave (1530), etc. (Tilley, No.332; Apperson, 655; Smith, 557.)

111,*4–5*. *Gysippus to his Titus*. Cf.47,*3*.

—,*32–3*. *as coals of fire covered close with ashes keep their heat long time* . . . Cf. Gascoigne, i.114. (Tilley, No.730.)

113,*26–7*. *Fortune, you know, favoureth not the faint-hearted*. Cf.61,*28*.

—,*30–1*. *No hawk soareth so high but she will stoop to some prey*. Cf.172.*10*. Cf. Guazzo, *Civ.Con.*, ii.76: 'like haukes, for feare least they should stoupe at some pray.' Versions in Kyd, Gascoigne, Watson (who cites Serafino), *Euphues* (12), etc. (Tilley, No.330.)

115,*25–6*. *But as the smith his forge* . . . Cf. *Euphues* (44): 'Hast thou not read . . . that he that casteth water on the fire in the smith's forge maketh it to flame fiercer?' Same simile in the *Diall of Princes*. (Tilley, No.667.)

116,*2–5*. *The horse now and then* . . . *never at rest*. Cf. *Tottel's Miscellany*, No.265:

> 'For all thynges having life sometime have quiet rest.
>
> The bering asse, the drawing oxe, and every other beast . . .
>
> Save I alas whom care of force doth so constraine
>
> To waile the day and wake the night continually in paine.'
>
> —Bush, 327.

117,*20–1*. *And as the laurel or bay tree ceaseth not to be green* . . . Cf. Psalms, xxxvii,35; also Erasmus, *Similia*: '*Ut laurus tota viret perpetuo*.' Found also in Pliny. The figure reappears in *Euphues* (67). (Tilley, No.379.)

122,*31–3*. *The greatest felicity is never to be born; and the second, soon to die.* Erasmus, *Adagia* (from Cicero, *Tusc. Disp.*, i.38.14): '*Optimum non nasci*.' A sentiment found also in Plutarch and Pliny. Verbatim in *Euphues* (168–9): 'The philosophers accounted it . . .' (Tilley, 222.)

123,*10–11*. *An honourable death is always to be preferred before an infamous life.* Cf.29,*2–3*.

124,*17–18*. *ravening wolves in sheep's clothing*. From the familiar charge against false prophets, Matthew, vii.27. Appears variously in Barclay, Heywood, *Proverbs*, I.x, Shakespeare, etc. (Tilley, No.698; Apperson, 701; Smith, 31.)

—,*19*. *Old dogs ever bite sorest*. Heywood, *Proverbs*, II.vi: 'It is said of old: an old dog biteth sore.' (Tilley, No.158; Apperson, 157; Smith, 42.)

124,24. Use of evil maketh us think it no abuse. Cf.7,7. (Tilley, No.753; later versions in Apperson, 468, and Smith, 339: '*Once a use and ever a custom.*')

—,*32*-125,*1. Perfect love can never be without equality* . . . Cf.21,*26*-7.

125,*28. Romeo and Julietta.* Cf.34,*11*-*12*.

126. ADMETUS AND ALCEST. Source: Hyginus, *Fab.*, l-li (cf. Euripides' *Alcestis*). In the Greek legend Admetus is the son of Pheres, king of Pherae in Thessaly; Alcestis the daughter of Pelias, king of Iolcus. Pettie transforms the story into an allegory of marriage.

—,*12. Marriages are guided by destiny*, etc. Cf.94,*2*. Martin (Marlowe's *Poems*, 36,n.) links this passage with 103,*21*-*3* as worthy of comparison with Marlowe's lines (*H.&L.*, 167-8):

'It lies not in our power to love, or hate,
For will in us is over-rul'd by fate!'

—'almost certainly a reminiscence of Castiglione's *Il Cortegiano*.'

127,*26. Of little seeds grow great trees.* Cf. Matthew, xiii.31-32; Erasmus, *Similia*: '*Cupressi semina adeo minuta sunt; ut quaedam oculis cerni non possint, et tamen in eo tanta est arbor tam procera*'; also Pliny: '*Et maioris cedri duo genera* . . . *Semen eius cupresso simile.*' Versions in Pub. Syrus, Gosson, Lyly, etc. 'Tall oaks from little acorns grow' is a modern rendering. (Tilley, No.541; Apperson, 461, s.v. *oak* (5).)

128,*3*-*4. Nothing breedeth bane to the body sooner than trouble of mind.* Cf.93, *7*-*8*. Cf. Guazzo, *Civ.Con.*, ii.113: 'our Galen sayth, The disquiet of the minde breedeth the disease of the bodye.'

—,*13. at their wit's end.* Cf.135,*12*. An expression found in Psalms, cvii.27; also Chaucer, Lydgate, Heywood, Lyly, etc. (Tilley, No.695; Apperson, 699, and Smith, 142, cite Pettie.)

—,*25*-7. *The sight of meat is very loathsome to him whose stomach is ill or hath already eaten his fill.* Cf. Erasmus, *Similia*: '*Sicuti qui morbo laborant regio, iis mel caeteris dulcissimum, amarum est.*' Early Spanish and German versions. Several variants in *Euphues*.

130,*31*-*2. Salves seldom help an overlong suffered sore.* A highly alliterated version of an ancient maxim. Appears in Draxe. Cf. Turberville, *Tragical Tales* (Roxburghe Club ed.), 283: 'Too late com salves to cure confirmed sores.'—Bush, 329. (Tilley, No.741.)

—,*32*-131,*1. It is too late to shut the stable door when the steed is stolen.* Heywood, *Proverbs*, I.x: 'When the steed is stolen shut the stable durre.'

Earlier versions in Plautus, Vilain, Gower, Caxton, Barclay, etc. Early polyglot versions. Pettie's form appears verbatim in *Euphues* (15). Cf. also Turberville, *Tragical Tales*, 282: 'When steedes are stolne tys bootles doores to barre.'—Bush, 329; and Greene, vii.245. (Tilley, No.378; Apperson, 598; Smith, 241.)

131,*5–6. As poison pierceth every vein, so love* . . . This adaptation of a 'commonplace of mediaeval science' appears in *Euphues* (57,277), Gosson, Shakespeare, etc. (Tilley, No.497.)

—,*25. If* [*necessity or*] *love had law.* Heywood, *Proverbs*, I.x, and *Epigrams*, No.20: 'Need hath no law.' A universal maxim; polyglot versions. Found in Chaucer (through Boethius), Langland, Gower, *Euphues* (of love: 69,78,378), etc. Cf. St. Augustine: '*Legem non habet necessitas.*' (Tilley, No.411; Apperson, 438; Smith, 308.)

133,*12–13. Cupid's carpet captains.* Cf.203,*3.* The *N.E.D.*'s earliest citation is Whetstone's *Rock of Regard* (1576). Cf. Guazzo, *Civ.Con.*, i.44: 'a Carpet knight corrupteth and effeminateth a valiant man.' The phrase appears in Montaigne, Du Bartas, Greene, Nashe, Shakespeare, etc.

—,*29–31. And as a boat* . . . *wind and wave.* Cf. Golding's *Ovid*, viii. 614–16:

'And as a Boate which tide contrarie beares

Against the winde, feeles double force, and is compeld to yeelde

To both . . .' —Bush, 328.

136,*25–6. Tantalus, Tytius* (= Tityos), *Sisiphus.* Cf. Ovid, *Met.*, iv. 456ff.

139,*29–30. Why hath not nature caused love to ascend as well as descend?* A figure found also in *Euphues* (87) and Greene. (Tilley, No.409.)

—,*30–3. Why hath* [*nature*] *endued the stork* . . . Versions in Pliny, Wilson's *Rhetorique*, *Euphues* (325–6), Greene, etc. (Tilley, No.590.)

140,*11–12. Love hath no respect of persons.* Cf. Romans, ii.11; Acts, x.34; also Ecclesiasticus, xxxv.12. (Tilley, No.756.)

141,*22–3. Sharp sauce gives a good taste to sweet meat.* Cf.17,*30–1*; also 106, *23–4.*

—,*23–5. Trouble and adversity makes quiet and prosperity far more pleasant.* Erasmus, *Adagia*: '*Discordia fit carior concordia.*' Identical form in Pub. Syrus.

—,*27–8. He careth not for ease who was never troubled with any disease.* Apparently a rhymed adaptation of the foregoing. (Tilley, No.729.)

142,6–7. No state so plentiful in pleasure but that it is mixed with pain. Cf.107,*18*.

—,*21. Philemon and Laucis* (= Baucis). Cf. Ovid, *Met.*, viii,631ff.

144,4–5. Death is but a fleeting from one life into another. Unidentified in this specific form. Cf. Guazzo, *Civ.Con.*, ii.128 (Book IV, tr.Young): 'Plato was wont to say, that during this present life, we are as dead men, and that our bodies are our owne sepulchres, meaning to inferre thereby, that we begin to live, when we dye.'

—,*9. Cleobis and Bito*[*n*]. An allusion found also in Painter, i.7: Solon answering Croesus' question as to the second happiest person in the world.

145,1–2. Nothing can be uneasy or hard unto a willing heart. Heywood, *Proverbs*, I.iv: 'Nothing is impossible to a willing heart.' Cf. Cicero, *Orator*: '*Nihil difficile amanti puto*'; also Wilson's *Rhetorique*, 30: 'For vnto a willing heart, nothing can be hard.' Early Italian and French versions. (Tilley, No.354; Apperson, 454, s.v. *nothing* (16).)

146,27–8. Hylonomo . . . Cyllar. The story of the female centaur Hylonome beloved by Cyllarus is told by Ovid, *Met.*, xii.405ff.

147. SCILLA AND MINOS. Source: Ovid, *Met.*, viii.1–151; xiv, 698–764. Iphis the lowly suitor and Pandarina the prurient go-between are Pettie's own creations. In addition to ranting speeches not found in Ovid, Pettie adds a preamble on the mischiefs of love, a digression on hypocrisy and kissing, and concluding injunctions to maidens on their choice of suitable mates, and obedience to parents. Ovid's Iphis (*Met.*, xiv.698ff.) is a humble Cyprian youth who, languishing for unrequited love of Anaxarete, hangs himself.

148,13–14. The freshest colours soonest fade the hue. Cf.80,*2–3*.

—,*14–15. The finest metals soonest break.* Variants (i.e. of glass) in *Euphues* (302), Greene, etc. (Tilley, No.283.)

—,*22–3. Under most green grass lie most great snakes.* Cf. Vergil, *Eclogues*, iii.93: '*latet anguis in herba*'; *Tottel's Miscellany*, No.4: 'I know under the grene the serpent how he lurkes'; also Guazzo, *Civ.Con.*, i.137: 'the verse of the Poet, That in the fayrest flowers and grasse, the serpent most doeth lurke.' Versions in *Euphues* (35), Lodge, Shakespeare, etc. (Tilley, Nos.348, 570; Apperson, 583; Smith, 395.)

—,*23–4. Under enticing baits* [*lie*] *entangling hooks.* Cf. *Tottel's Miscellany*, No.261:

> 'To view the limed bushe, to loke afore we light,
> To shunne the perilous bayted hoke, and use a further sight;'

also Guazzo, *Civ.Con.*, i.82: 'as the hooke is hidden under the bayte, or the serpent amongest the flowers.' Versions in *Euphues* (36,62), Greene, Dekker, etc. (Tilley, No.348; Apperson, 23; Smith, 417.)

151,1. The gods themselves are pleased with gifts. Cf. Ovid, *Ars Am.*, iii.654: '*Placatur donis Iuppiter ipse datis.*'

154,26 and 32. make love. Cf. *Euphues* (271): 'A phrase now there is which belongeth to your shopboard, that is "to make love" . . . '—the earliest citation in the *N.E.D.* Ascham's *Scholemaster* (written 1563–8) refers to travellers returned from Italy as 'the greatest *makers of love*.' Cf. Fr., *faire l'amour*; Ital., *far l'amore*. Pettie seems to have assisted in introducing the idiom into English.

155,8–9. Adalesia . . . Alerane. Cf.61,*1–3*; 79,*4–5*.

—,9–10. the Duchess of Savoy . . . Mendoza. Cf.5,*28*.

157,33–158,1. Those that feign to be valiant, brag most gloriously. This charge against the *miles gloriosus* appears variously and widely, in Barclay, Middleton, Marston, etc. Unidentified in its—probably classical—origin. (Tilley, No.620; cf. Apperson, 63: Deloney's 'old saying'—*They brag most that can do least.*)

163,2–4. Can one be exalted without another's wrack? Can I be preferred to pleasure without some other's pain? The doctrine of compensation is one of the oldest. Cf. Pub. Syrus: '*Lucrum sine damno alterius fieri non potest*'; Seneca: *Nullum sine auctoramento malum est*'; Erasmus, *Adagia*: '*Bona nemini hora est, ut non alicui sit mala;*' etc. (Tilley, No.738.)

—,11–12. Grievous wounds must have smarting plasters, etc. Cf. Hippocrates: 'Extreme remedies are very appropriate for extreme diseases.' Early Italian and French variants. Versions in Lyly, Shakespeare, Chapman, etc. (Tilley, No.574.)

—,16–17. Their wisdom is nothing worth which are not wise for themselves. Cf. Cicero, *De Off.*, iii.15.sec.62: '*Nequiquam sapere sapientem, qui ipse sibi prodesse non quiret.*' Also Pub. Syrus: '*Sapit nequicquam, qui sibi ipsi non sapit.*' Versions in Lodge, Shakespeare, etc. (Tilley, No.693; Apperson, 696, cites Pettie.)

165,13. Lupus in fabula. A common phrase appearing in Cicero, *Ad Atticum*, xiii.33.4; Terence, *Adelphi*, 537. The Latin equivalent of 'Speak of the devil and he will appear.' Holland's *Pliny*, viii.c.22, cites the Italian adage of wolves' eyes striking a man dumb if they see him first. Cited by Lyly, Chapman, etc. Found also in Erasmus. (Tilley, No.422.)

166. CURIATIUS AND HORATIA. Source: Livy, I.xxiv–xxvi. (Cf. Painter, i.1). Livy's account focuses on the engagement of the triplet brothers,

and Horatius' strategy in slaying the Curiatii, concluding with the trial of Horatius. Pettie adds a preamble on the supernal power of love, makes much of the courtship (including an exchange of letters and soliloquies on women), whereas Livy wrote simply, *'soror virgo, quae desponsa uni ex Curiatiis fuerat.'*

168,*27–8. Those that love most speak least.* (Tilley, No.419; Smith, 589, s.v. *Whom we love best,* cites Pettie.)

171,*11. A little thing pleaseth a fool.* Cf.203,*12–13.* Unidentified earlier in this form. Cf. Ovid, *Ars Am.,* i.159: *'Parva leves capiunt animos.'* (Tilley, No.394; Smith, 274.)

172,*30–3. Now as the good Spaniel . . . the Hawk which flew at it.* Cf. Gascoigne, i.109:

> 'Or as the kindly Spaniell which hath sprong
> The prety Partriche, for the Falcons flight,
> Doth never spare but thrusts the thornes among,
> To bring this byrd yet once againe to sight . . .'
> —Bush, 326.

176,*5–8. She for the most part sitteth still at home . . .* A passage which clearly reflects Ovid, *Heroides,* xix.9ff.

177,*14–16. Like as the Greyhound . . . in lunes.* Cf. Gascoigne, i.335–6:

> 'And as the hooded Hauke, which heares the Partrich spring,
> Who though she feele hir self fast tied, yet beats her bating wing . . .
> The Greyhound is agreev'd, although he see his game,
> If stil in slippe he must be stayde, when he would chase the same.'
> —Bush, 327.

—,*17–18. That which the eye seeth, the heart grieveth.* Heywood, *Proverbs,* II,vii: 'that the eye seeth not, the heart reweth not.' A 'common saying' (Pettie) found in early French, Scots, and Spanish versions. Also Greene, xi.140. (Tilley, No.203; Apperson, 196; Smith, 569.)

179,*19–20. Many things . . . happen between the cup and the lip.* Erasmus, *Adagia:* '*Multa cadunt inter calicem supremaque labra.*' 'A very ancient proverb, sometimes attributed to Homer, and frequently quoted'—Stevenson, who cites Palladas (Greek *Anthol.,* X, epig. 32), Aulus Gellius, Cato, etc. Found later in *Euphues* (455), Greene, Jonson, etc. Pettie appears to have added the alliterative sequel, *Many things chance between the board and the bed.* (Tilley, No.564; Apperson, 129, s.v. *cup* (4); Smith, 290.)

179,*22. Man purposeth and God disposeth.* Cf.243,*7–8.* Langland's *Piers Plowman* quotes '*Homo proponit at Deus disponit*' as from Plato. But cf.

Thomas à Kempis, *De Im.*, i.ch.19; also Proverbs, xvi.19. Versions in French literature, and in Ariosto, Cervantes, Bishop Fisher, etc. (Tilley, No.424; Apperson, 397, cites Pettie; Smith, 285.)

180,*22*. *No can?* A fairly common Elizabethan construction. Cf. Schmidt, *Shakespeare-Lexicon*, 774, s.v. *No.*

—,*27*. *Life is sweet to everyone.* Cf. Euripides, 'Life is short but sweet.' Versions in *Patience*, Gower, *York Plays*, *Wit's Commonwealth*, etc. (Tilley, No.387; Apperson, 363, cites Pettie; Smith, 262.)

181,*2*. *They that are bound must obey.* Verbatim in Heywood, *Proverbs*, II.v. (Tilley, No.53; Apperson, 62; Smith, 485, cites Pettie.)

184,*19–21*. *BCDEF Occasion . . . is bald behind, it cannot be pulled back again by the hair.* Cf. Dionysius Cato, *Disticha*, ii.26: '*Fronte capillata, post est Occasio calva.*' Versions in Phaedrus, Rabelais, Thales of Miletus, Erasmus, Painter (i.226), Marlowe, Greene, Spenser, Bacon, etc. Early French and Italian versions. (Tilley, No.468; Apperson, 462; Smith, 411.)

185. CEPHALUS AND PROCRIS. Source: Ovid, *Met.*, vii.690–752, 796–862; also *Ars Am.*, iii.707–8,731–2,737–44. Ovid's Cephalus is an Athenian prince, Pettie's a lusty young gallant of the court of the Duke of Venice (sent as ambassador to 'the Turk'). Pettie's version, as usual, stresses the elements of courtship and fidelity. He has his Cephalus return disguised as Sir Sulahpec (the anagram is not in Ovid) to test his wife's faithfulness. His conclusion is a caveat on the subject of continence. Also, Ovid's hunting scene is cut to its bare essentials.

—,*28–9*. *The air whereby we live is death to the diseased or wounded man* . . . (Tilley, No.751; Smith, s.v. *ill air*, cites Pettie.)

186,*1–3*. *The earth which yieldeth food to sustain our bodies yieldeth poison also to destroy our bodies.* Cf. Ovid, *Rem. Amoris*, 45–46: '*Terra salutares herbas, eademque nocentes, Nutrit . . .*' A version appears in *Euphues* (93). Cf. *Rom. & Jul.*, II.iii.9–12. (Tilley, No.178.)

187,*8–9*. *Those which worst may, are driven to hold the candle.* Heywood, *Proverbs*, II.11: 'Who that worst may shall hold the candle.' Old English and French versions. Appears in *Euphues* (34), Greene, Camden, etc. (Tilley, No.719; Apperson, 713, cites Pettie; Smith, 175.)

188,*5–6*. *No cloth so fine but moths will eat it.* Cf.23,*13–14* (Tilley, No.451.) Early Italian version. Adapted interrogatively in *Euphues* (98), along with the following:

—,*6*. *No iron so hard but rust will fret it.* Cf. Erasmus, *Similia*: '*Ut ferrum si non utaris, obducitur rubigine.'* Early German, Scotch, and Portuguese versions. Appears in *Euphues* (58,98). (Tilley, No.357.)

188,*6–7. No wood so sound but worms will putrefy it.* Appears in *Euphues* (58) along with the foregoing. Versions in Gosson, Greene, Florio, etc. (usually *oak*; probably alliterated by Pettie). (Tilley, No.748.)

192,*14–15. Haste maketh waste.* Heywood, *Proverbs*, I.ii, and *Epigrams*, No.15. The 'old saying,' inevitable as rhyme, appears in Gascoigne, *Tottel's Miscellany*, Greene, etc. (Tilley, No.327; Apperson, 228; Smith, 132.)

—,*15–16. Bargains made in speed are commonly repented at leisure.* Unidentified in this form. Early French, Italian, German, and Dutch versions. Variants in Painter, Greene, Lodge, Shakespeare, etc. (Tilley, No.429; Apperson, 404, s.v. *marry* (12); Smith, 292, cites Pettie.)

—,*18–19. The increase is small of seed too timely sown.* Not recorded elsewhere. Cf. Greene, *Mamillia*, 121: 'The seed too timely sown hath ever small increase'—which may be borrowed from Pettie. (Tilley, No.540.)

—,*19–20. Whelps are ever blind that dogs in haste do get.* Erasmus, *Adagia* and *Similia*: '*Canis festinans caecos parit catulos.'* Cf. More, *Utopia*: 'The hasty bitch brings forth blind whelps.' Found also in Gascoigne and Greene. (Tilley, No.39; Apperson, 289; Smith, 443.)

—,*21–2. The malt is never sweet unless the fire be soft.* Heywood, *Proverbs*, I.ii, and *Epigrams*, No.16: 'Soft fire maketh sweet malt.' Versions in Udall, Greene, Camden, etc. (Tilley, No.231; Smith, 396.)

—,*22–3. He that leapeth before he look may hap to leap into the brook.* Heywood, *Proverbs*, I.ii: 'ye may learn good cheap In wedding and all thing to look or ye leap'; also *Epigrams*, No.5: 'Look ere thou leap: nay thou canst in no wise brook To look ere thou leap, for thou leapest ere thou look.' Early Italian and German versions. Variants in Cervantes, Tusser, *Euphues* (178–9), Florio, etc. Cf. Painter, iii.53: 'According to the common saying: He that loketh not before he leapeth, may chaunce to stumble before he sleepeth.' (Tilley, No.400; Apperson, 380; Smith, 276.)

—,*27–9. The Philosophers will us to eat a bushel of salt with a man before we enter into strict familiarity with him.* Cicero, *De Am.*, xix.sec.67, refers to this as a well known adage. Erasmus, *Adagia*: '*Nemini fidas, nisi cum quo prius modium salis absumpseris.'* Erasmus traces the saying through Cicero back to Theophrastus and other Greek sources. It appears later in Pub. Syrus, Cervantes (as a 'true saying'), *Euphues* (29,92–3), Greene, and an early Scottish version.

193,6. Soon hot, soon cold. Identical form in Heywood, *Proverbs*, I.ii. Variations in *Euphues* (29,57) and Greene. Appears as early as Burgh (and Lydgate), Malory, etc. (Tilley, No.573; Apperson, 588; Smith, 132,193,398.)

—*,7. Nothing violent is permanent.* Cf. Aristotle, *Sententiae . . . Selectissimae* (1556): '*Nullum violentum est perpetuum.*'—cited by Greene. Variants in Erasmus, Heywood, *Euphues* (45,363), Marlowe, Shakespeare, etc. (Tilley, No.660; Smith, 331, cites Pettie.)

—*,19–20. But such as he sowed, he reaped.* Galatians, vi.7. Cf. Erasmus, *Adagia*: '*Ut sementem feceris, ita et metes.*' Similar expressions in Alfred, Cynewulf, Gower, Lydgate, etc. (Tilley, No.577; Apperson, 591.)

196,4–5. Every man is not of like mind in like matters. Cf.248,21. Terence, *Phormio*, II. 454, and Cicero, *De Fin.*, I.v.15; also Erasmus, *Adagia*: '*Quot homines, tot sententiae.*' Appears variously in Chaucer, Heywood, *Euphues*, etc. (Tilley, No.331.)

—*,15. What good doth gold to him that careth not for it?* Cf. Pub. Syrus: '*Quid tibi pecunia opus est, si uti non potes?*'

198,9–10. No wool [is] so coarse but it will take some colour. Cf. *Euphues* (314): 'There is no wool so white but the dyer can make black.' Variant in Heywood, *Proverbs*, II.ix. (Tilley, Nos.98 and 709; Apperson, 709, cites Pettie; Smith, 225.)

199,1. Travellers' words are not much trusted. A maxim appearing variously in Barclay, Deloney, *Euphues* (61), Dekker, etc.; also foreign versions. (Tilley, No.639; Apperson, 643.)

200,13–14. Alcmena . . . Amphitrion. Cf. Ovid, *Met.*, ix.23ff.

203,3. a carpet Knight. Cf.133,12–13.

—*,12–13. a bauble for the fool to play with.* Cf.171,11.

—*,21–2. The spider out of most sweet flowers sucketh poison.* Cf. Gascoigne, i.6; appears variously in *Euphues* (12,85,345). (Tilley, No.24.)

204,4–5. That which is bred in the bone will not out of the flesh. Repeated at 210,28–9. Heywood, *Proverbs*, II.viii: 'It will not out of the flesh that is bred in the bone.' Early polyglot forms. Appears variously in Caxton, Malory, Erasmus, *Euphues* (310), Greene, etc. (Tilley, No.49; Apperson, 66; Smith, 567.)

—*,8ff. Argus.* Much of this passage (the reined-in colt, Argus, hoarding, etc.) is an adaptation of Ovid, *Amores*, iii.4. (Tilley, 402.)

—*,11. Vices the more prohibited, the more provoked.* Cf. Pub. Syrus: '*Nihil magis amat cupiditas quam quod non licet.*' Variants of the Ovidian concept that 'Stolen fruit is sweetest' are quite common. Versions in Kyd, Marston, etc. (Tilley, No.258.)

206,22–3. In fair painted pots poison oft is put. Versions in *Euphues* (35,36, 62), Greene, Nashe, etc. Unidentified earlier. (Tilley, No.499.) (Bond cites Pettie as Lyly's source, for in *Euphues*, 35, the apophthegm is combined with the one which here follows:)

—*,23–4. In goodly sumptuous sepulchres rotten bones are rife.* Unidentified earlier. Variants in *Euphues* (35), Greene, etc. Cf. Shakespeare, *M. of V.*, 'Gilded tombs do worms enfold.' Also Matthew, xxiii.27. (Tilley, No.546.)

—*,24–5. Fairest words are ever fullest of falsehood.* Cf.88,*23–4*.

207,21–2. Wolves never prey upon wolves. Early German, French, and Italian versions. Bebel, *Prov. Germanica*: '*Lupus non mordet lupum.*' (Tilley,No.700; Apperson, 703, cites Pettie.)

—*,23–4. to have halted before a cripple.* A proverbial phrase found also in Chaucer, Gascoigne, Heywood, *Euphues* (71), etc. (Tilley, No.310; Apperson, 122; Smith, 234.)

—*,29. I would rather, as they say, have led apes in hell* . . . Called 'an old proverb' in *The London Prodigal* (1605), but unidentified. The expression appears in Gascoigne, *Euphues* (60,72,263), Shakespeare, etc. (Cf. *Studies in Philology*, xxii. No.4,453–66.) (Tilley, No.470; Apperson, 13; Smith, 336.)

—*,31. 'Had I wist' is ever had at the worst.* Heywood, *Proverbs*, I.ii, and *Epigrams*, No.256: 'Beware of, Had I wist.' Versions in Gower, Beryn (c. 1400), Skelton, *Towneley Mysteries*, *Tottel's Miscellany*, No.284, Greene, etc. (Tilley, No.35; Apperson, 277; Smith, 67, s.v. *beware*, and 128.)

208,1–2. It booteth not to send for a physician when the sick party is already departed. Cf. Smith, 34: '*After death the doctor* (Fr. *physician*).'

—*,31. the weaker vessels.* I Peter, iii.7. The phrase appears also in Guazzo, *Euphues*, Greene, Shakespeare, etc. (Tilley, No.702.)

210. MINOS AND PASIPHAE. Source: Ovid, *Ars Am.*, i.289–326 (also Servius' commentary on Vergil, *Eclogues*, vi.46—Thilo and Hagen ed., iii.74.) Pettie adds the introductory paragraph on inequality in marriage, Minos' soliloquies, and the pre-marital business; also Verecundus and his role, with his soliloquy on illicit love (and a letter); and the exhortations on continence.

—*,28–9. That which is bred in the bone* . . . Cf.204,*4–5*.

211,4–5. The mastiff never loveth the greyhound. Unidentified except in an old French form, '*Oncques mâtin n'aima levrier.*' (Tilley, No.432; Apperson, 406, cites Pettie.)

211,*18–27. On her cheeks . . . fine velvet.* Cf. Gascoigne, i.97–98:

> '. . . the heeres were not of Gold . . .
> Like glistring wiers against the Sunne that shine,
> And therewithall the blazing of hir eyne . . .
> Upon his cheekes the Lillie and the Rose
> Did entremeete, with equall change of hewe . . .
> That ruddy lippe wherein was pleasure plast,
> Those well shapt hands . . .
> I may no prayse unto a knife bequeath,
> With rust yfret, though paynted be the sheath.'
>
> —Bush, 326.

212,*17. The contented mind is the only riches.* Echoed from Erasmus, *Coll.*, 576. Cf. Apperson, 112: '*A contented mind is a continual feast.*'

213,*19–20. running from Charybdis, he rushed upon Scilla. Aeneid,* iii.420. Cf. Erasmus, *Adagia*: '*Evitata Charybdi, in Scyllam incidi*'; also '*Incidis in Scyllam, cupiens vitare Charybdim.*' A common allusion in various later forms. (Tilley, No.536.)

—,*21–2. thinking to quench . . . of burning fire.* Seemingly a rhymed couplet variant of Erasmus, *Adagia*: '*Fumum fugiens, in ignem incidit.*' 'From the frying pan into the fire' appears in Cervantes, Heywood, etc. (Tilley, No. 565.)

215,*14–15. The sun being at the highest, declineth.* Cf.231,*5–6.* The figure, here used for love, is adapted in *Euphues* (56) to the praises of women. (Tilley, No.602.)

—,*15–16. Calm continueth not long without a storm.* Early Italian version. Appears variously in *Euphues* (452), Greene, Shakespeare, etc. (Tilley, No. 67; cf. Apperson, 604, s.v. *storm* (1,2).)

216,*9–10. Familiarity had bred . . . contempt.* Cf. Pub. Syrus: '*Nimia familiaritas parit contemptum.*' Also Guazzo, *Civ.Con.*, ii.105; 'too muche familiaritie would breede contempte.' Versions appear in Alanus de Insulis (c.1160), Cervantes, Harvey, Greene, Shakespeare, etc. (Tilley, No.211; Apperson, 203; Smith, 103.)

—,*33–217,1. A pleasant prey soon enticeth a simple thief.* (Tilley, No.502; Apperson, 475; Smith, 349, cites Pettie, s.v. *Opportunity makes the thief.*)

219,*24. Strike while the iron is hot.* Heywood, *Proverbs*, I.iii, and *Epigrams*, No.268. Cf. Erasmus, *Adagia*: '*Ferrum tuum nunc in igni est.*' Found in

Greek Anthol., Pub. Syrus, Chaucer, Lydgate, Rabelais, *Euphues* (14,352, 367–8,450), Lodge, Greene, Shakespeare, etc. (Tilley, No.594; Apperson, 605; Smith, 405.)

221,*2–3*. *For as the fretting Fistula past all cure* . . . Cf. Golding's *Ovid*, ii.1033ff.: 'And as the freting Fistula forgrowne and past all cure . . .'— Bush, 328.

—,*28–9*. *Fish bred up in dirty pools will taste of mud.* Same in Googe, *Eglogs &c.* (1563), with *stynke* for *taste.* (Apperson, 215, s.v. *fish* (3), cites Pettie.)

—,*30–1*. *Set a beggar on horseback and he will never alight.* No earlier English form recorded. Early German and Dutch versions. Appears later in Greene, Shakespeare, Camden, Burton, etc. (Tilley, No.27; Apperson, 35, cites Pettie; Smith, 384.)

223,*5*. *Like like the best of their likes.* Cf.244,*3*. Heywood, *Proverbs*: 'Like will to like.' Cf. Cicero, *De Sen.* iii.7; Erasmus, *Adagia*: '*Simile gaudet simili*' and '*Aequalis aequalem delectat.*' A proverb of wide currency in all languages. Versions in Taverner, Guazzo, *Euphues* (29: a 'byword'), Shakespeare, etc. (Tilley, No.390; cf. Apperson, 367, '*Like will to like.*')

224,*9*. *I myself am fallen into the pit I digged for him.* Cf. Psalms, vii.15; ix.15; Proverbs, xxvi.27; Ecclesiastes, x.8. Also Erasmus, *Adagia*: '*Incidit in foveam, quam fecit.*' (Tilley, No.489.)

225,*23*. *Servius.* A reference to Servius' *Commentarius* on Vergil's *Eclogues*, vi.46. The note on *Pasiphae* reads, '*quae tauri amore flagravit* . . .' (Thilo and Hagen ed.,iii.74).

226,*19–20*. *Chastity is the only jewel which women ought to be chary of.* Cf.19, *16–17*. Cf. Marlowe, *H.&L.*, ii.85–86.

> 'Jewels being lost are found again, this never,
> 'Tis lost but once, and once lost, lost for ever.'

—Martin, 55,n. Somewhat the same metaphor appears in *All's Well*, IV.ii.46. Cf. also Proverbs, xxxi.10.

—,*20–2*. *Women having lost their chastity are like broken glasses which are good for nothing.* Early Spanish, Portuguese, and Italian versions. Variants in Lyly, Shakespeare, etc. (Tilley, No. 284.)

227,*2*. *like the wife of Fulvius Torquatus.* An anecdote found in Guevara's *Diall*, 1557 ed., fol.108.—Bush, 165,n.5.

—,*7*. *Lucrece.* Cf.38,*13*.

—,*8*. [*the Duchess of*] *Savoy.* Cf.6,*1*.

228. PYGMALION'S FRIEND. Source: Ovid, *Met.*, x.243–97. Ovid's Pygmalion is a Cyprian, Pettie's a Piedmontese. Pettie introduces Penthea, a 'courteous courtly wench,' wife of Luciano. Ovid's well-known story is quickly told. To Pettie it provides opportunity for his most elaborate misogynist tirades and 'blasphemies,' padded with proverbs and *exempla*, and leading to a long piece of concluding homily.

—,*10. reckoning without the host.* A proverbial phrase found in Caxton, Rabelais, Heywood, *Euphues* (69,253), etc. (Tilley, No.513; Apperson, 525.)

229,*1–2. When the sun shineth, the light of the stars is not seen.* Cf. Erasmus, *Similia*: 'Luna cum soli conjungitur, tum obscuratur, et occultatur: cum abest, lucet.' (Tilley, No.605; Smith, s.v. *the moon's not seen*, cites Pettie.)

231,*23. kytes of Cressids kind.* Cf. Gascoigne, i.98: 'kits of Cressides kind.' —Bush, 326; also *Hy. V*, II.i.78.

—,*23–5. May one gather grapes of thorns, sugar of thistles, or constancy of women?* Cf. Matthew, vii.16. Versions in *Euphues* (20) and Florio. (Tilley, No.299.)

232,*25–6. O honey mixt with gall, O heaven turned to hell.* Cf. Gascoigne, i.107:

> 'The costlye tast, of hony mixt with gall:
> The painted heaven, which turnde to hell at last.'
> —Bush, 326.

233,*10. then farewel fayth, thou art no womans pheare.* Appears verbatim in Gascoigne, i.111.—Bush, 327.

234,*3. bezolas manos,* i.e. *beso las manos*, Sp. 'I kiss your [*lit.* the] hands': a respectful salutation. 'The dialogue of the old [Elizabethan] drama is full of Spanish phrases of convenience like *bezo los manos, paucas palabras*, etc., which were evidently quite as well understood by the audience as was later the colloquial French—*savoir faire, coup de grâce*, etc.—which began to come in with Dryden, and has been coming ever since.'—Beers, *Eng. Romanticism, XIX Century*, 240. The phrase appears several times, for example, in Gascoigne and Nashe.

235,*19–21. Florinda . . . Amadour.* An allusion to the story, of the same name, in Painter, i.53 (source and origin in the *Heptameron*, x).

236,*10–11. mala mens, malus animus: an evil disposition breedeth an evil suspicion.* (Smith, 217, s.v. *ill doers*, cites Pettie.)

237,*6–7. Every peck of pleasure shall cost him a quarter of care.* Cf.106,*31–2.* (Tilley, No.166.)

237,*7–8. For every pint of honey he shall taste a gallon of gall.* Cf.106,*31–2* and the foregoing. (Tilley, No.166.)

—,*21–5. The fly playeth so long with the flame that he is scorched therewith . . . men dally so long with dainty dames that at length they are scorched in the flames of fancy . . .* Cf. Erasmus, *Similia*: '*Uti pyralis ultro advolans lucernis, adustis alis collabitur ac perit.*' The same analogy appears in Gascoigne, Guazzo, *Euphues* (49,395), etc. (Tilley, No.251.)

238,*25–6. Mount Aetna . . . the hill Caucasus.* Cf. Ovid, *Rem. Amoris*, 491–2. The double simile reappears in *Euphues* (105).

239,*25. eyesse*, BCDE *niesse*, F *Novice.* = *nyas*, a young, untrained hawk. *Niasse* in Guazzo; *eyas* in *Euphues* (95), in a passage appropriated by Lyly from Pettie.

240,*13–16. And as the Humblebee . . . in a cow's foul shard.* Same figure (of the scarab) appears in *Euphues* (221), Gosson, Greene, Shakespeare, etc. Unidentified earlier. (Tilley, No.26; Apperson, 317.)

—,*21–2. oil to cool their furious flames.* Cf. Erasmus, *Adagia*: '*Oleo incendium restinguere*'; also Horace, *Satires*, ii.3,21: '*Oleum adde camino.*' Versions in Guazzo, *Euphues* (97), Shakespeare, Chapman, etc. (Tilley, No.234; Apperson, 463.)

241,*25–7. [Women are] made of God only for a plague and woe unto men, as their name importeth.* An instance of commonly mistaken etymology; cf. *N.E.D.* Variants in Guazzo, Heywood, *Euphues* (49,84), Shakespeare, etc. (Tilley, No.703.)

242,*14–15. to conclude with Scripture . . .* I Corinthians, vii.1. Cf.68,*12–13*.

—,*29–30. He which toucheth pitch shall be defiled therewith.* Ecclesiasticus, xiii.1. Appears variously in Chaucer, Lydgate, Wyclif, Guazzo, Wilson's *Rhetorique*, *Euphues* (98,180), *I Henry IV*, etc. (Tilley, No.490; Apperson, 498; Smith, 172.)

243,*9. What shall be, shall be.* Heywood, *Proverbs*, II.i, and *Epigrams*, No.78. Appears from Chaucer onward, and current on the continent. Versions in Peele, Nashe, Marlowe, Shakespeare, etc. (Apperson, 560; Smith, 569.)

—,*23–4. Love first entereth in at the eyes.* Cf.221,*4–5*. Erasmus, *Adagia*: '*Ex adspectu nascitur amor.*' Also Pub. Syrus: '*Amor ut lacrima ab oculo oritur in pectus cadit.*' Variants in Castiglione, Lyly, Greene, Shakespeare, etc. (Tilley, No.408; Smith, 277.)

244,*3. Like agree best with their like.* Cf.223,*5*.

244,6. as Ovid reporteth . . . *Met.*, i.395ff.

—,*15–16. Everyone is lightly in love with that which is his own.* Cf. Erasmus, *Adagia*: '*Suum cuique pulchrum.*' Similar reflections found in Lyly, Shakespeare, etc. (Tilley, No.471.)

245,34–246,1. All is not gold which glistereth. Heywood, *Proverbs*, I.x. Early polyglot versions. Cf. Alanus de Insulis (d.1294), *Parabolae*: '*Non teneas aurum totum quod splendet ut aurum.*' Variants in Chaucer, Cervantes, Lydgate, Googe, Udall, *Euphues* (51,303), Greene, *M. of V.*, II.vii.65, etc. (Tilley, No.290; Apperson, 6; Smith, 37.)

246,4. Change is seldom made for the better. Heywood, *Proverbs*, I.iv, and *Epigrams*, No.III: 'Seldom cometh the better.' This 'common saying' appears in many forms in the early collections of proverbs: also Shakespeare. (Tilley, No.543; Smith, 383, s.v. *seldom*.)

—,*20–2. True friends . . . are rather like the stone of Scilicia, which the more it is beaten the harder it is.* Origin unknown; but cf. Croll, 38, n.4, on a probable source in Albertus Magnus and Isidore of Seville. Lyly used the simile (of women's hearts) almost verbatim in *Euphues* (38–39), and refers to it again in *Sapho and Phao*. Versions appear also in Fenton's Bandello and Greene. (Cf. camomile figure, 29,*12–14*.) (Tilley, No.559.)

—,*20–5. True friends are not like new garments which will be the worse for wearing; they are rather . . . like many wines, which the older they are the better they are.* Early polyglot versions of both figures. The double proverb is closely imitated in *Euphues* (74). (Tilley, No.274; Smith, 336, cites Pettie.)

—,*23–4. The more [spices] are pounded, the sweeter they are.* Cf.29,*11–12.*

247,6. Faustine. Cf.98,*16.*

—,*7. Blanch Maria* (i.e. the Countess of Celant). An allusion to the story in Painter, ii.24 (source and origin in Bandello, tr.Belleforest).

248. ALEXIUS. The Legend or Life of St. Alexius appears in four versions (from six MSS.), ed. Furnivall, *E.E.T.S.* (1878): Bodleian Laud MSS. 108, 463,622; Vernon MS., and Cotton, Titus A xxvi; also Trin. Coll. MS. Oxf. 57. In outline the legend is as follows: A wealthy, charitable Roman, Eufemian, is married to a barren wife, Agloes. Finally she conceives a son, Alexius, who learns, prays, and fights well. His father chooses a wife for Alexius, who marries against his will, and exhorts his wife to live a virgin. Later he resolves to leave her, and starts on a pilgrimage, having given away all his goods. He lives in poverty, in Syria, begs, is unknown to his friends and mourned by his parents. His friends seek him, but he remains lost in poverty seventeen years. Then the Virgin's image points him out; he is found and honoured by Syrians, but flees to Galicia, whence he is driven back to Rome by storm. Disguised, he begs alms of his father, is treated as a beggar and bullied by the servants. He writes his life story, but hides the book. His death is foretold from Heaven; and his spirit ascends to God. His father finds his body, the book is read to the populace, and the family lament over his corpse. He is buried in St. Boniface, where his corpse, which exudes a sweet smell, works miracles.

> 'he forsook confort of al his kynde,
> Richesse he lete al bihynde,
> To god al he hym took:
> Alexius is his name in storie,
> writen of whom is made memorie
> In many holy book.' —Laud MS. 622.

There is also an Italian version of the Legend of St. Alexius: *La Rapresentatione di Santo Alexo*, Firenze, 1554 (another ed., 1570).

248,*21*. *So many veins, so many vanities.* Cf.196,*4–5*.

—,*28*. *Kingdoms, they say, are but cares.* Cf.78,*1–2*.

249,*15–16*. *It is not possible well to go forward in anything, Invita Minerva, nature not consenting thereto.* Cf.210, 26–8. Erasmus, *Adagia*: 'Invita Minerva ("pro eo quod est refragante ingenio, repugnante natura, non favente coelo").' The phrase occurs also in Cicero, *De Off.*, i.31.110, and Horace, *Ars Poetica*, 385.

—,*27–8*. *the pilgrimage of this short life.* Cf.63,*17*.

250,*9*. *Every excess is turned into vice.* Unidentified in this form. (Tilley, No.33.)

—,*14–15*. *live . . . by the sweet of other men's sweat.* (Apperson, 614, s.v. *sweet* (3), cites Pettie.)

251,*26–8*. *A good thing cannot be too much used . . . the more common it is, the more commendable it is.* Cf.69,*13–14*.

254,*15*. *qui cunctando restituit rem.* Cf. *Aeneid*, vi.845–6: '*tu Maximus ille es, unus qui nobis cunctando restituis rem?*'

—,*16–17*. *as it did in Alexander, toward the wife and daughters of Darius.* An allusion, originating in Plutarch, found also in *Euphues* (97).

256,*14*. *out of God's blessing into a warm sun.* Cf. Erasmus, *Adagia*: '*Ex umbra in solem.*' Appears variously in Cervantes, Heywood, *Proverbs*, II.v,

Euphues (181,303), *Lear*, II.ii.168, etc. (Tilley, No.287; Apperson, 476; Smith, 350, cites Pettie.)

256,28–257,6. Massagetes . . . Pompeius , . . Seemingly a paraphrase of the anecdote in Guevara's *Diall*, 1557 ed., fol.103.—Bush, 165, n.5. (Cf. Tilley, pp.402–3.)

257,17–18. Aesop's cock. An allusion to Fable XCVIII, 'Gallus et Gemma' (Pettie's only direct reference to Aesop). A common reference, found in Guazzo, Lyly, Marlowe, Nashe, Greene, Shakespeare, etc. (Tilley, No.15.)

258,10. Best wits are soonest caught by Cupid. An unidentified epigram appearing several times in Pettie, in less pointed form. (Tilley, No.34.)

—,14–15. The greatest clerks are not the wisest men. Heywood, *Proverbs*, II.v, and *Epigrams*, No.206. Cf. Erasmus, *Adagia*: '*Magis magni clerici non sunt magis sapientes.*' Appears verbatim in Chaucer, Caxton, *Euphues* (217), Greene, etc. (Tilley, No.91; Apperson, 273; Smith, 441.)

260,18–19. It somewhat easeth the afflicted to utter their annoy. Cf. Pub. Syrus: '*Poena allevatur ubi relaxatur dolor.*' Early German and French versions. Similar sentiments in Shakespeare, Webster, etc. (Tilley, No.622.)

261,26–7. What [a] marvel is it to see a good tree bring forth good fruit. Matthew, vii.17. (Cf. Apperson, 263, s.v. *good tree*.)

262,28–9. Things most excellent are ever most envied. Cf.78,3.

263,1. Who is so bold as blind bayard? Heywood, *Proverbs*, I.viii, and *Epigrams*, No.101. The phrase appears also in *Cleanness* (c.1350), Caxton, Lydgate, Chaucer, Greene, etc. (Tilley, No.47; Apperson, 28; Smith, 46.)

264,15. Women are never without an excuse. This 'common saying amongst us' appears in Greene as 'the old proverb'—'*Tis as hard to find a hare without a muse, as a woman without a scuse.* (Apperson, 704, s.v. *woman* (14); Smith, 31,106; Stevenson cites Pettie.)

—,33–265,1. They only are fit to govern other[s] who can well guide themselves. Pettie's attribution of this remark to Solon is probably based upon Painter, i.7, 'Croesus and Solon.' Cf. Erasmus: '*Non bene imperat, nisi qui paruerit imperio*'; Pub. Syrus: '*Stultum imperare reliquis, qui nescit sibi*'; Ovid, *Heroides*, iii.85: '*Vince animos, iramque tuam, qui cetera vincis.*' Also Guazzo, *Civ.Con.*, ii.98: 'Those onlye knowe well how to commaund, which know well howe to obaye.' Versions in Cervantes, Lyly, etc. (Tilley, No.298; cf. Smith, 145, s.v. *he is not fit*.)

266,7–10. Debora . . . Sysara (= Sisera). Cf. Judges, iv.

267,*19*. *Zenobia*. An allusion to Painter, ii.80 (origin in Guevara's *Epistolas*).

268,*26–7*. *Fine marble . . . needeth no painting*. Cf. Guazzo, *Civ.Con.*, i.4: 'Corrall needeth no colouring, neither the fine Marble painting.' Ultimate source probably Pliny, xxxvi.1–7. *Euphues* (6) uses the figure verbatim. (Tilley, No.427.)

269,*10–12*. *Honey itself, if one have too much of it, seemeth nothing sweet unto him*. Cf. Proverbs, xxv.16. The paradox appears variously in Chaucer, *Euphues* (417, etc.), Shakespeare, etc. (Tilley, No.342.)

—,*29–30*. *Women [are] the way to wrack and ruin*. Unidentified. For the familiar phrase *wrack and ruin* the *N.E.D.* lists no earlier example than *Gorboduc* (1561).

270,*4–5*. *redire ad vomitem*. Proverbs, xxvi.11; also II Peter, ii.22. The phrase recurs in Erasmus, *Euphues* (301,313), Lodge, Shakespeare, etc. (Tilley, No.161; Smith, 432.)

—,*27–8*. *Wives or women [are] necessary evils*. Cf. Erasmus, *Adagia*: 'Necessarium malum . . . Nec tecum possumus vivere, nec sine te.' The Latin proverb '*Malum est Mulier, sed necessarium malum*' appears to be a translation from Menander. The sentiment appears in *Euphues* (292), Greene, Lodge, etc. (Tilley, No.705; Apperson, 706, s.v. *women* (45) lists also Melbancke's *Philotinus* (1583) and Florio; Smith, 595, cites Pettie.)

ADDITIONAL NOTES

Index to Proverbs, Maxims, and Sententiae

A foul *adulterer* is ever worse than the adultery itself. 26,*20–1*.*

Adversity is ever most bitter to him who hath long time lived in prosperity. 23,*30–2*.

Trouble and *adversity* makes quiet and prosperity far more pleasant. 141,*23–5*.

It somewhat easeth the *afflicted* to utter their annoy. 260,*18–19*.

Agree s.v. *like*.

It is too late to cast *anchor* when the ship is shaken to pieces against the rocks. 207,*33*–208,*1*.*

Annoy s.v. *afflicted, joy*.

Ascend s.v. *love*.

Athens s.v. *salt*.

Under enticing *baits* [lie] entangling hooks. 148,*23–4*.

Bald s.v. *occasion*.

Bane s.v. *body, mind*.

Bargains s.v. *speed*.

The more doubtful the *battle*, the more doughty the victory. 21,*17–18*.*

The event of *battle* is always doubtful. 30,*1–2*.

Who is so bold as blind *bayard*? 263,*1*.

Beauty hath some divinity or godhead in it. 166,*11–12*.

Set a *beggar* on horseback and he will never alight. 221,*30–1*.

Better s.v. *change*.

Blessing s.v. *God's*.

Whelps are ever *blind* that dogs in haste do get. 192,*19–20*.

Vengeance asketh vengeance; and *blood*, blood. 36,*10–11*.

Body s.v. *death, mind*.

Bold s.v. *bayard*.

Bones s.v. *sepulchres*.

We are *born* to die . . . even in our swathe-clouts death may ask his due. 49,*27–8*.

The greatest felicity is never to be *born*; and the second, soon to die. 122,*31–3*.

They that are *bound* must obey. 181,*2*.

Those that feign to be valiant, *brag* most gloriously. 157,*33*–158,*1*.*

It booteth not to stop the *breach* when the town is overflown. 131, *1–2*.*

Break s.v. *metals*.

That which is *bred* in the bone will not out of the flesh. 204,*4–5*;210, *28–9*.

Briars s.v. *rose*.

Brook s.v. *leapeth*.

Bushel s.v. *salt*.

Calm continueth not long without a storm. 215,*15–16*.

The more [the herb *cammomile*] is trodden down, the more it spreadeth abroad. 29,*12–14*.

Those which worst may, are driven to hold the *candle*. 187,*8–9*.

Canker s.v. *rose.*

The *canker* commonly breedeth in the fairest rose. 23,*14–15.*

Care s.v. *pleasure, rich.*

Cares s.v. *charge, life.*

They that cast not off *cares* before they come, cannot cast them off when they do come. 207,*32–3.**

Carrion s.v. *hawk.*

The *caterpillar* . . . cleaveth only to good fruit. 23,*12–13.**

Such as the *cause* of everything is, such will be the effect. 57,*14–15.*

Change is seldom made for the better. 246,*4.*

In greatest *charge* are greatest cares. 78,*1–2.*

Chastity s.v. *women.*

Clerk s.v. *priest.*

The greatest *clerks* are not the wisest men. 258,*14–15.*

No *cloth* [is] so fine but moths will eat it. 188,*5–6.*

Clouds s.v. *sun.*

Cocks unequally matched make no good battle in the pit. 211,*6–7.**

Coin s.v. *counterfeit.*

What wound so deadly which *coin* cannot cure? 90,*20–1.*

Cold s.v. *soon.*

Colour s.v. *wool.*

Freshest *colours* soonest fade. 80,*2–3;* 148,*13–14.*

The harder [a wild *colt*] is reined, the hotter he is. 204,*11–12.*

Every *commodity* hath a discommodity annexed unto it. 59,*27–8.*

Of good things I think the more *common* the more commendable. 69,*13–14.*

Comparisons are odious. 4,*12.*

Constancy s.v. *women.*

May one gather grapes of thorns, sugar of thistles, or *constancy* of women? 231,*23–5.*

Constitution s.v. *mind.*

The *contented* mind is the only riches, the only quietness, the only happiness. 212,*17.*

Counterfeit coin showeth more goodly than the good. 246,*1–2.**

I count any place my *country* where I may live well and wealthily. 32, *9–10.*

Courage, God knoweth, is little worth abroad unless there be good counsel at home. 252,*24–5.**

Cries s.v. *life.*

Many things . . . happen between the *cup* and the lip. 179,*19–20.*

Cupid s.v. *wits.*

Danger s.v. *delay, glory.*

Dead s.v. *live.*

Is not an honourable *death* to be preferred before an infamous life? 29, *2–3.*

We are born to die . . . even in our swathe-clouts *death* may ask his due. 49,*27–8.*

Death of the body is to be counted a less evil than destruction of body and soul. 123,*12–14.**

Death is but a fleeting from one life into another. 144,*4–5.*

Defiled s.v. *pitch.*

Delay [breeds] danger. 62,*13–14.*

Every dram of *delight* hath a pound of spite. 106,*31–2.*

Men determine, but the *destinies* do. 243,*8.*

Destiny s.v. *marriages.*

Destruction s.v. *slaughter.*

The greatest felicity is never to be born; and the second, soon to *die.* 122,*31–3.*

Discommodity s.v. *commodity.*

Disease s.v. *money, ease.*

Disposition s.v. *mind, evil.*

He which knoweth not how to *dissemble*, knoweth not how to live. 88,*28–9.*

Dogs s.v. *blind.*

Old *dogs* ever bite sorest. 124,*19.*

Doubtful s.v. *battle.*

Dreams are doubtful, and visions are altogether vain. 45,*28–9.**

Dropsy patients *drink*, and still be dry. 96,*14–15.*

Small *drops* of rain engender great floods. 127,*25.**

He careth not for *ease* who was never troubled with any disease. 141, *27–8.*

Envy always shooteth at high marks. 78,*3.*

In all degrees of friendship *equality* is chiefly considered. 21,*26–7.*

Use of *evil* maketh us think it no abuse. 124,*24.*

An *evil* disposition breedeth an evil suspicion. 236,*11.*

Of *evils* the least is to be chosen. 27, *21*;67,*13*;68,*18*;123,*11–12.*

Wives or women [are] necessary *evils.* 270,*27–8.*

Can one be *exalted* without another's wrack? 163,*2–3.*

Every *excess* is turned into vice. 250,*9.*

Excuse s.v. *women.*

Experience s.v. *learning.*

Extremities s.v. *women.*

That which the *eye* seeth, the heart grieveth. 177,*17–18.*

Eyes s.v. *love.*

Fade s.v. *colours.*

Fall s.v. *higher.*

Falsehood s.v. *speech, words.*

Fame [is] a tattling goddess. 42,*25.**

Familiarity had bred . . . contempt. 216,*9–10.*

Familiarity s.v. *salt.*

Fancy s.v. *love.*

Feign s.v. *valiant.*

The greatest *felicity* is never to be born; and the second, soon to die. 122,*31–3.*

The more hard the *fight* is, the more haughty is the conquest. 21,*16–17.*

Fire s.v. *gold, malt, metal, smoke.*

The more [*fire*] is kept down, the more it flameth up. 62,*15–16.*

The sea hath *fish* for every man. 27, *26.**

Fish bred up in dirty pools will taste of mud. 221,*28–9.*

Flesh s.v. *bred.*

Flow s.v. *streams.*

Flowers s.v. *ground, spider, thorns.*

Folly s.v. *hill, stream.*

A little thing pleaseth a *fool.* 171,*11.*

Fortune s.v. *get.*

Fortune ever favoureth the valiant. 61,*28.*

Fortune . . . favoureth not the faint-hearted. 113,*26–7.*

True *friends* are . . . like many wines, which the older they are, the better they are. 246,*20–5.*

In all degrees of *friendship* equality is chiefly considered. 21,*26–7.*

Fruit s.v. *caterpillar.*

He that would gather *fruit* should plant trees. 13,*31–2.*

Ripest *fruit* are rifest rotten. 80,*3.*

Fruits full soon do rot which gathered are too soon. 192,*20–1.**

Gall s.v. *honey.*

Generally s.v. *particularity.*

To *get* is the gift of fortune, but to keep is the power of prudence and wisdom. 78,*4–6.*

The gods themselves are pleased with *gifts*. 151,*1*.

Glory must be gotten through depth of danger. 107,*17*.*

God s.v. *man*.

God and Nature do nothing vainly or vilely. 65,*4–5*.

Out of *God's* blessing into a warm sun. 256,*14*.

Fine *gold* must be purified in the flaming fire. 107,*15–16*.

What good doth *gold* to him that careth not for it? 196,*15*.

All is not *gold* which glistereth. 245, *34–246,1*.

The *good* is ever to be used, and the ill refused. 65,*29–30*.*

Is not the loss of goods less than of one's *good name*? 29,*1–2*.

What life so loathesome which *goods* cannot make gladsome? 90,*21–2*.*

They only are fit to *govern* other[s] who can well guide themselves. 264,*33–265,1*.

Grapes s.v. *constancy*.

Under most green *grass* lie most great snakes. 148,*22–3*.

Greyhound s.v. *mastiff*.

No *ground* [is] so good but that it bringeth forth weeds as well as flowers. 142,*3–4*.

Grow s.v. *trees*.

'*Had* I wist' s.v. *wist*.

Hair s.v. *occasion*.

Those that be in *happiness* themselves weigh not the heaviness of other[s]. 94,*29–30*.*

Things the more *hard*, the more haughty, high, and heavenly. 61, *29–31*.

Haste maketh waste. 192,*14–15*.

Whelps are ever blind that dogs in *haste* do get. 192,*19–20*.

Have s.v. *nothing*.

The haughty *hawk* will not prey on carrion; neither will courtly silks practice country sluts. 21,*29–31*.

No *hawk* soareth so high but she will stoop to some prey. 113,*30–1*.

Heal s.v. *medicines*.

Heart s.v. *eye*.

The *higher* the place is, the sooner and sorer is the fall. 77,*32*.

To hop against the *hill* and strive against the stream has ever been counted extreme folly. 23,*7–8*.

Home s.v. *courage*.

For every pint of *honey* he shall taste a gallon of gall. 237,*7–8*.

Honey itself, if one have too much of it, seemeth nothing sweet unto him. 269,*10–12*.

Honour ever is the reward of virtue. 29,*15–16*.

Honours change manners. 79,*21*.

Under enticing baits [lie] entangling hooks. 148,*23–4*.

Hop s.v. *hill*.

Horseback s.v. *beggar*.

Hot s.v. *soon, strike*.

He takes no delight in meat who is never *hungry*. 141,*26–7*.*

The *husbandman* tilleth the ground, though not certain to save his seed. 91,*26–7*.

It is better to be *idle* than ill employed. 63,*13–14*.

Ill s.v. *good*.

Inconstancy s.v. *women*.

Iron s.v. *strike*.

No *iron* [is] so hard but rust will fret it. 188,*6*.

Jealousy is a pill of hard digestion. 125,*8*.*

Every inch of *joy* [hath] an ell of annoy. 106,*32*.

Keep s.v. *get*.

A *kingdom* is more easily gotten than kept. 78,*3–4*.

Law s.v. *love*.

He that *leapeth* before he look may hap to leap into the brook. 192, *22–3*.

In respect of experience, *learning* is little to be accounted of. 258,*15–16*.

Leisure s.v. *speed*.

Life s.v. *death*.

If we consider the whole course of our *life*, we begin with cries and end with cares. 40,*28*–41,*1*.*

Life is sweet to everyone. 180,*27*.

A toy *lightly* taken [is] lightly left again. 106,*9–10*.*

Like purpose, like proof; like man, like matter. 18,*30–1*.*

Every man is not of *like* mind in like matters. 196,*4–5*.

Like agree best with their like. 244,*3*.

Lip s.v. *cup*.

A *little* thing pleaseth a fool. 171,*11*.*

We must *live* by the living, not by the dead. 83,*29–30*.

You must as well love to *live* as live to love. 101,*7–8*.

Look s.v. *leapeth*.

Love hath no respect of persons. 140, *11–12*.

Those that *love* most speak least. 168,*27–8*.*

Love [is] lost when fancy is once fully fed. 197,*4*.*

Love is grounded upon the similitude of manners. 103,*27–8*.

Love [has] no law (if *love* had law). 131,*25*.

Love first entereth in at the eyes. 243, *23–4*.

Lust s.v. *marriage*.

Malt is never sweet unless the fire be soft. 192,*21–2*.

Man purposeth and God disposeth. 179,*22*;243,*7–8*.

Manners s.v. *love*.

Like purpose, like proof; like *man*, like matter. 18,*30–1*.*

Honours change *manners*. 79,*21*.

Fine *marble* . . . needeth no painting. 268,*26–7*.

Marriage is but a means to medicine the burning in concupiscence and lust. 68,*16–17*.*

Marriages are guided by destiny. 94, *2*;126,*12*.

The *mastiff* never loveth the greyhound. 211,*4–5*.

Mean s.v. *women*.

Meat s.v. *sauce*.

He takes no delight in *meat* who is never hungry. 141,*26–7*.*

Those *medicines* ever soonest heal which most grieve us. 163,*12–13*.*

Men determine, but the destinies do. 243,*8*.

No *metal* [is] so coarse but fire will purify it. 188,*7–8*.*

The finest *metals* soonest break. 148, *14–15*.

Mind s.v. *contented, like*.

The disposition of the *mind* followeth the constitution of the body. 93, *7–8*.

Nothing breedeth bane to the body sooner than trouble of *mind*. 128, *3–4*.

What disease is so desperate which *money* may not medicine? 90,*19–20*.

Moths s.v. *cloth*.

Mud s.v. *fish.*

Name s.v. *good.*

God and *Nature* do nothing vainly or vilely. 65,*4–5.*

That which *nature* hath given cannot be taken away. 210,*27–8.**

[Make] a virtue of *necessity.* 100,*3;* 216,*17;*232,*28–9.*

Nothing s.v. *willing.*

Nothing venture, nothing have. 91, *30.*

Obey s.v. *bound.*

Occasion . . . is bald behind: it cannot be pulled back again by the hair. 184,*19–21.*

Unequal *oxen* draw not well together in one yoke. 211,*5–6.**

Pain s.v. *pleasure.*

Painting s.v. *marble.*

One *particularity* concludeth no generality. 104,*13–14.*

Penury s.v. *plenty.*

People s.v. *speak.*

Peril s.v. *remembrance.*

Permanent s.v. *violent.*

Persons s.v. *love.*

It booteth not to send for a *physician* when the sick party is already departed. 208,*1–2.**

Pill s.v. *jealousy.*

Pitch s.v. *silver.*

He which toucheth *pitch* shall be defiled therewith. 242,*29–30.*

Place s.v. *higher.*

Plasters s.v. *wounds.*

Pleasure must be purchased with the price of pain. 107,*18.*

Every peck of *pleasure* shall cost . . . a quarter of care. 237,*6–7.*

He knoweth not the pleasure of *plenty* who hath not felt the pain of penury. 141,*25–6.** (Cf. Tilley, p.367,n.7.)

Poison s.v. *spider.*

In fair painted *pots* poison oft is put. 206,*22–3.*

Prey s.v. *hawk.*

A pleasant *prey* soon enticeth a simple thief. 216,*33–217,1.**

The parish *priest* forgetteth that ever he was clerk. 94,*28–9.*

Prohibited s.v. *vices.*

Prosperity s.v. *adversity.*

Pure s.v. *sow.*

Purify s.v. *metal.*

Like *purpose,* like proof; like man, like matter. 18,*30–1.**

Rain s.v. *drops.*

A rusty *rapier* is no trusty rampier to defend a man, though the scabbard be of fine velvet. 211,*26–7.*

He which would *reap* should sow. 13, *30–1.*

Rein s.v. *colt.*

The *remembrance* of the peril past delighteth. 61,*22–3.*

Reward s.v. *honour.*

The thoughtful care of the *rich* man causeth the thief the sooner to seek spoil of him. 208,*26–8.** (Cf. Tilley, p.372,n.11a.)

Rose s.v. *canker, thorns.*

He that would reach the sweet *rose* should now and then be scratched with the sharp briars. 13,*32–14,1.*

In the fairest *rose* is soonest found a canker. 88,*22–3.*

Rotten s.v. *fruit.*

Ruin s.v. *slaughter, women.*

Rust s.v. *iron.*

Rather be fed at Athens with *salt* than live with him in all delicacy. 18,*2–3.*

Eat a bushel of *salt* with a man before [you] enter into strict familiarity with him. 192,*27–9.*

Salves seldom help an overlong suffered sore. 130,*31–2.*

Sharp *sauce* gives a good taste to sweet meat. 141,*22–3.*

Scabbard s.v. *rapier.*

The *sea* hath fish for every man. 27, *26.**

In largest *seas* are sorest tempests. 78,*2.**

Seed s.v. *husbandman.*

The increase is small of *seed* too timely sowed. 192,*18–19.**

Of little *seeds* grow great trees. 127, *26.*

In goodly sumptuous *sepulchres* rotten bones are rife. 206,*23–4.*

The *she-wolf* always chooseth that wolf for her mate who is made most lean and foul by following her. 17,*5–7.*

Ship s.v. *anchor.*

Sick s.v. *physician.*

The haughty hawk will not prey on carrion; neither will courtly *silks* practice country sluts. 21,*29–31.*

White *silver* is wrought in black pitch. 107,*16–17.**

Sins oft essayed are thought to be no sin. 7,*7;*124,*24–5.*

They that sow *slaughter* shall be sure to reap ruin and destruction. 36, *11–12.**

We see *sleeping* that which we wish for waking. 109,*19–20.*

Smarting s.v. *wounds.*

There is no *smoke* but where there is some fire. 30,*15–16.*

Snakes s.v. *grass.*

Soon hot, soon cold. 193,*6.*

Sore s.v. *salves.*

Soul s.v. *death.*

Sow s.v. *reap.*

Sow that which is sound, seek that which is sure, buy that which is pure. 193,*23–4.**

Speak s.v. *love.*

People are ever prone to *speak* the worst. 30,*4–5.**

In fairest *speech* is falsehood and feigning rifest. 88,*23–4.*

Bargains made in *speed* are commonly repented at leisure. 192,*15–16.*

The more [*spices*] are beaten, the sweeter scent they send forth. 29, *11–12.*

The more [*spices*] are pounded, the sweeter they are. 246,*23–4.*

The *spider* out of most sweet flowers sucketh poison. 203,*21–2.*

It is too late to shut the *stable door* when the steed is stolen. 130,*32–*131,*1.*

Stoop s.v. *hawk.*

Storm s.v. *calm.*

To hop against the hill and strive against the *stream* has ever been counted extreme folly. 23,*7–8.*

The more you stop [*streams*], the higher they flow. 29,*9–10.*

Streams cannot be made to run against their course. 94,*6–7.*

I think it wisdom to *strike* while the iron is hot. 219,*23–4.*

No *sun* shineth so bright but that clouds may overcast it. 142,*2–3.**

Sugar s.v. *constancy.*

Sun s.v. *God's.*

One *swallow* makes not summer. 104, *13.*

Sweet s.v. *honey, life, malt, sauce, spices.*

He is not worthy to suck the *sweet* who hath not first savoured the sour. 61,*14–15.*

In largest seas are sorest *tempests*. 78,*2*.*

Thief s.v. *rich*.

A pleasant prey soon enticeth a simple *thief*. 216,*33*–217,*1*.*

Things s.v. *common, hard*.

Thistles s.v. *constancy*.

Thorns s.v. *constancy*.

From most sharp *thorns*, to wit, the rose tree, spring most sweet flowers. 91,*20*–*1*.

Towers s.v. *winds*.

A *toy* lightly taken [is] lightly left again. 106,*9*–*10*.*

Travellers' words are not much trusted, neither great matters soon believed. 199,*1*–*2*.

The *tree* is ever weakest towards the top. 78,*1*.*

Trees s.v. *fruit, seeds*.

The more you lop [*trees*], the higher they grow. 29,*10*–*11*.*

Nothing breedeth bane to the body sooner than *trouble* of mind. 128, *3*–*4*.

Trouble s.v. *adversity*.

Two wits s.v. *wits*.

Unequal s.v. *oxen*.

Vainly s.v. *God, Nature*.

Fortune ever favoureth the *valiant*. 61,*28*.

Those that feign to be *valiant*, brag most gloriously. 157,*33*–158,*1*.*

Velvet s.v. *rapier*.

Vengeance asketh vengeance; and blood, blood. 36,*10*–*11*.

Nothing *venture*, nothing have. 91, *30*.

Vices the more prohibited, the more provoked. 204,*11*.

Victory s.v. *battle*.

Nothing *violent* is permanent. 193,*7*.

Virtue s.v. *necessity*.

Honour ever is the reward of *virtue*. 29,*15*–*16*.

Dreams are doubtful, and *visions* are altogether vain. 45,*28*–*9*.*

Waking s.v. *sleeping*.

Waste s.v. *haste*.

Weeds s.v. *ground*.

What shall be, shall be. 243,*9*.

White s.v. *silver*.

Rather weigh the *will* of the speaker than the worth of the words. 102, *27*–*8*.

Nothing can be uneasy or hard unto a *willing* heart. 145,*1*–*2*.

Wills s.v. *women*.

Boistrous *winds* do most of all shake the highest towers. 77,*30*–*1*.

Wines s.v. *friends*.

Wisest s.v. *clerks*.

'Had I *wist*' is ever had at the worst. 207,*31*.

Their *wisdom* is nothing worth which are not wise for themselves. 163, *16*–*17*.

Two *wits* are better than one. 110, *33*.

Best *wits* are soonest caught by Cupid. 258,*10*.*

Wolf s.v. *she-wolf*.

Wolves never prey upon wolves. 207, *21*–*2*.

Women always live chastely enough, so that they live charily enough. 26,*13*–*14*.

It is naturally incident to *women* to enter into extremities. 37,*29*–*30*.

The mean, *women* always meanly account of. 38,*1*–*2*.

God hath endued *women* with this property, to be wedded to their wills. 94,*2*–*4*.

Women s.v. *constancy, evils*.

[*Women*] are constant only in inconstancy. 97,*23*.

Women are never without an excuse. 264,*15*.

Women [are] the way to wrack and ruin. 269,*29–30*.

No *wood* [is] so sound but worms will putrefy it. 188,*6–7*.

No *wool* [is] so coarse but it will take some colour. 198,*9–10*.

Words s.v. *travellers, will*.

Fairest *words* are ever fullest of falsehood. 206,*24–5*.

Worms s.v. *wood*.

Worst s.v. *candle, speak, wist*.

Wound s.v. *coin*.

Grievous *wounds* must have smarting plasters. 163,*11–12*.

Yoke s.v. *oxen*.

Index to Proper Names

Abel, 33.
Achilles, 155.
Adalesia, 61,79,155.
Adam, 98,241,262.
ADMETUS & ALCESTIS, 126–146.
Adonis, 94,155.
Adrastus, 95.
Aeneas, 51,155,265.
Aesop, 257.
Aetna, Mount, 238.
Agamemnon, 253.
Agave, 53.
Agesilaus, 254.
Agrippa, 56.
Agrippina, 52.
AGRIPPINA, GERMANICUS &, 56–84.
Ajax, 253.
Albania, 166,167,179,180,181,183.
Alcathoe, 147,148.
ALCESTIS, ADMETUS &, 126–146.
Alcibiades, 253.
Alcmena, 200.
Alcyone, 34.
Alerane, 61,79,155.
Alexander, 21,80,134,253,254.
Alexius, 6,7.
ALEXIUS, 248–271.
Alphonsus, 253.
Althea, 53.
Amadour, 235.
Aminius, 67.
AMPHIARAUS & ERIPHYLE, 85–102.
Amphitryon, 200.

Amulius, 78.
Anaxarete, 93,184.
Andromeda, 174.
Angelica, 93.
Antiochus, 47.
Antonius, Marcus, 146,174,253.
Apollo, 142,144.
Archimedes, 250.
Argives, 85,86,95.
Argus, 204.
Ariadne, 52,163.
Aristomacha, 99.
Aristotle, 64,97,234,258,263,264,266.
Ascanius, 266.
Aspasia, 267.
Assur, 126,127.
Assyrians, 267.
Athenians, 255.
Athens, 18,40,42,47,110,267.
Atlas, 144.
Atropos, 95.
Atys, 126,127,138,140.
Aurelius, Marcus, 98,253.

Babylon, 252.
Bacchus, 53,54.
Baucis, 142.
Bersabe, 32,98.
Bito, 144.
Blanch maria (Blanca Maris), 247.
Briseis, 155.
Brutus, 253.

Caesar, 21,253.
Cain, 33.
Caligula, 79.
Calisthenes, 253.

Callicratidas, 255.
Camma, 6,227.
CAMMA, SINORIX &, 11–39.
Candaules, 98.
Carthage, 252.
Cato, 109,252.
Caucasus, 238.
(Celant, Countess of) = Blanca Maris, 247.
Ceny, 263.
CEPHALUS & PROCRIS, 185–209.
Ceres, 145,266.
Ceyx, 34.
Charybdis, 213.
Christ, 98,271.
Cicero, 248.
Circe, 97.
Claudius, Appius, 103,118,119,120, 121,122,124.
Claudius, Marcus, 103,118,119,120, 121,122.
Cleobis, 144.
Cleopatra, 146,174.
Corinna, 98.
Craterus, 17.
Cressida, 93,200,231.
Crete, 210,211.
Croesus, 134.
Cupid, 56,70,94,133,136,153,168,236, 258,261.
Curiatii, the, 181.
CURIATIUS & HORATIA, 166–184.
Cyllarus, 146.
Cyrus, 267.

Daedalus, 210,225.
Damarathus, 253.
Damon, 111.
Danae, 86,98,200.
Danaus, 98.
Daniel, 51.
Daphne, 110,184.

Darcillidas, 251.
Darius, 252,254.
David, 32,98,253.
Deborah, 266.
Deianira, 98,206.
Delilah, 98.
Demophoon, 52.
Deucalion, 244.
Diana, 36,135.
Dido, 51,155.
Diogenes, 17.
Diomedes, 257.
Dion, 253.
Dionysus, 52,99.
Dis, 145.

Edward, King, 27.
Egypt, 174,227.
Endymion, 109.
England, 27.
Ennius, 78.
Epaminondas, 253.
ERIPHILE, AMPHIARAUS &, 85–102.
Eteocles, 78.
Ethiopia, 104.
Euripides, 78.
Eve, 68,98,241.

Fabius, 254.
Fabritius, 86.
Faustina, 98,247.
Flanders, 264.
Florinda, 235.
France, 264.
Fulvius Torquatus, 227.

Ganymede, 68,136.
GERMANICUS & AGRIPPINA, 56–84.
Glaucus, 257.
Greece, 26,86.
Gyges, 99.
Gysippus, 47,111.

Hadrian, 253.
Hannibal, 79,253.
Hasdrubal, 78.
Hebe, 68.
Helen, 26,28,93,134,200.
Hercules, 98,206.
Hero, 61.
Hippodamia, 164.
Hippolytus, 155.
Holland, 264.
Homer, 63,253.
Horace, 248.
HORATIA, CURIATIUS &, 166–184.
Horatii, the, 181.
Horatius, 166.
Hyempsal, 78.
Hylonome, 146.
Hyrcania, 119.

Icarus, 84.
ICILIUS & VIRGINIA, 103–125.
Iliad, 253.
India, 174.
Infortunio, 85,90,99,102.
Iphis, 93,147,148,152,153,164.
Israelites, 266.
Italy, 11,27,110,166,265.
Itys, 40,53,54.

Jason, 51,164.
Jove, 200.
Judas, 51,119.
Jugurtha, 78.
Julietta, 34,125.
Julius Caesar, 21,253.
Juno, 66,134,174,204.
Jupiter, 68,85,136.

Lacedaemonians, 251,255.
Latins, 267.
Lavinia, 265.
Leander, 61.

Libya, 126,127,140.
Luciano, 228,229,232.
Lucrece, 38,227.
Lycabas, 126,127,129,133,141.
Lycurgus, 251,257.
Lytae, 256.

Mahomet, 68.
Mantuan, 263.
Marcellus, 250.
Marcus Aurelius, 98,253.
Marius, 254.
Mars, 95,133,256.
Mary, the Virgin, 263.
Massagetae, 256,257.
Medea, 52,164.
Medusa, 182.
Meleager, 53.
Mendoza (Don John di), 155.
Menelaus, 26,93.
Mercury, 136.
Midas, 86.
Minerva, 105,249,256,258.
MINOS & PASIPHAE, 210–227.
MINOS, SCILLA &, 147–165.
Minotaur, 52.
Mithridates, 253.
Muses, the, 258,267.

Neptune, 264.
Nero, 52,79.
Nessus, 206.
Nestor, 253.
Nicostrata, 267.
Nisus, 147,148,153,163.
Numitor, 78.
Numitorius, 120.

Octavian, 56,80,83.
Oenone, 155.
Omphale, 98.
Orestes, 111.
Otho, 61.
Ovid, 5,55,98,166,244,258.

Pallas, 5,134,259,261.
Pan, 110.
Pancaliar, Earl of, 27.
Pandarina, 31,147,156,158,160,161, 164.
Pandion, 40,42,43,47,49.
Paris, 26,28,93,155.
PASIPHAE, MINOS &, 210-227.
Pelias, 162.
Pelops, 164.
Penelope, 38,116,227.
Penthea, 228,230,244,245.
Pentheus, 54.
Pericles, 267.
Perseus, 174.
Peter, Saint, 98.
Phaedra, 155,162.
Phaethon, 84.
Pharaoh, 97.
Philemon, 142.
Philomela, 40,42,47,48,49,50,53,55.
Phoebus, 110.
Phyllis, 52.
Picus, 146.
Piedmont, 228,232.
Polynices, 78.
Pompeius, 257.
PROCRIS, CEPHALUS &, 185-209.
PROGNE, TEREUS &, 40-55.
Proserpina, 126,145.
Pygmalion, 6.
PYGMALION'S FRIEND AND HIS IMAGE, 228-247.
Pylades, 111.
Pyramus, 34,125.
Pyrrha, 244.
Pythias, 111.

Remus, 78.
Rhodians, 164.
Richard, Sir, 102.
Rome (Romans), 78,82,86,96,103, 104,121,166,167,179,180,181,182, 183,226,263.

Romeo, 34,125.
Romulus, 78.

Saba, 267.
Sabines, 96.
Salamis, 252.
Salisbury, Countess of, 5,27,29.
Sampson, 98.
Satan, 157.
Saul, 79.
Savoy, Duchess of, 6,27,29,155,227.
Scilicia, 246.
Scio, 267.
Scipio, 253.
Scylla, 213.
SCYLLA & MINOS, 147-165.
Semiramis, 267.
Servius, 225.
Sienna, 11,22.
Simonides, 103.
Sinnatus, 11,14,27,31,32,33,34,37.
SINORIX & CAMMA, 11-39.
Sisera, 266.
Sisyphus, 136.
Solomon, 79,97,164,253,267.
Solon, 252,264.
Susanna, Lady, 51,227.
Synger, 146.
Syracuse, 250.
Syrinx, 110.

Tantalus, 136.
Tarpeia, 96.
Tarquinius, 98.
Taurus, 225.
Terentia, 98.
TEREUS & PROGNE, 40-55.
Thais, 162.
Thebes, 85,95,99.
Themistocles, 107,252,253.
Theseus, 52,164.
Thisbe, 34,125.
Thrace, 40,42.
Tiberius, 56,81,83.

Timon, 110.
Tiresias, 200.
Titus, 47,111.
Tityus, 136.
Tomiris, 267.
Torquatus, Fulvius, 227.
Trajan, 253.
Troilus, 93.
Troy, 26,181,252,253,266.
Tullia, 98.
Tully, 98.
Turk (Turks), 190,191,195,207.

Ulysses, 97,116,181.
Urias, 32.

Valerius, 86.

Venice, Duke of, 185,186,190,195.
Venus, 94,134,148,155,174,195,206, 228,244,245,258,261.
Verecundus, 210,216,221,224.
VIRGINIA, ICILIUS &, 103–125.
Virginius, 104,112,114,119,121,122, 123.
Virle, Lord of, 22.
Vulcan, 95.

Xerxes, 253.

Zealand, 264.
Zenobia, 267.
Zilia, 22.
Zophyrus, 253.

Date Due

	PRINTED IN U. S. A.	CAT. NO. 23231			